# Darwin's Apple: The Evolutionary Biology of Religion

## Mitchell Diamond

Darwin's Apple:
The Evolutionary Biology of Religion

http://www.darwinsapple.com

First Edition

Published by
**Purple Hills Books**
San Jose, California, USA

ISBN: 978-0-9863387-2-4

Dedicated to Ginny whose infinite patience, faith, and support helped me through the endless research, writing, and rewriting.

# CONTENTS

## Contents

# Preface

When I was in elementary school, I participated in the fiction that duck and cover was a reasonable response to thermonuclear attack. On an occasional basis my school ran the drill, and we got under our desks and clasped our hands behind our heads. On at least one occasion the school even went so far as to march the entire student body of little children to a building about a half-mile away that had a large basement—practice for protecting us from an imminent strike. I don't recall at what age I figured out that this was a ludicrous exercise, but by the time I was a teenager, I was keenly aware that there was something very wrong with this whole situation.

I came of age in the 1960s when the Vietnam War was escalating. There were free speech protests on college campuses, and opposition to the war was finally reaching the mainstream media. Like some of my peers, I felt that we were watching a social revolution take place. For a time I believed that we were on the verge of creating a new order that would prevent war, stop racism, and teach people how to love one another. However, I was also cognizant that wars were an ever-present phenomenon. Only 20 or so years before America had fought in World War II, by far the most malevolent, destructive series of events in human history. Millions of people were slaughtered both on battlefields and in concentration camps. And it wasn't backwards, primitive people who did this. It was the most modern cultures that perpetrated the atrocities. It was societies that provided the most advanced educations and the most sophisticated technologies of the time including mass media in which information was available to everybody through newspapers, magazines, and radio.

My parents were agnostic Jews who chose to leave the God of Moses and Abraham behind. At the same time they identified with Jewish culture and Jewish people, which included me learning about the historical persecution of Jews. As a child I saw TV dramatizations of the unspeakable horrors perpetrated on the Jews by the Nazis; not just the gas chambers but also the so-called medical experiments that were nothing more than excuses for the most unspeakable tortures. If these modern peoples could inflict the most barbaric treatment and persecution on another group of human beings, then there was something very, very wrong about our species. No amount of education or technological progress was going to make any difference to alter human savagery.

Nevertheless, my country, the United States, taught that if you want freedom from persecution for your people, you needed to prevent persecution of any people. The way to enforce this ideal was to establish a robust set of laws that provided equal treatment regardless of race or creed through civil protections. That was America! At least that's what we learned were the guiding principles of our country. It was all too perfect. My country's ideals were my ideals. How convenient was that! And within all this was the belief in a basic set of ethical principles anchored by the Golden Rule, the most elementary of all ethical principles. To make this work, one had to have faith in people's ability to transform, an assumption I took for granted.

In the first half of the twentieth century behaviorist philosophy dominated intellectual circles. Behaviorism proposed that humans were a *tabula rasa*, a blank slate, in which all behavior developed from environmental influences as opposed to humans having any inborn predispositions. One of its leading proponents was B. F. Skinner, a Harvard psychology professor. His book *Walden Two* was an imagining of an experimental utopian community in which the behaviorist ideology was practiced. If you could control the environment, then you could culturally engineer raising the children. Since people are born without any innate propensities, with the proper training and education, the children would grow into content and productive adults. The utopian ideal could be achieved. This was and remains a very attractive idea. Many adhere to the notion of human perfectibility. Wouldn't it be grand if we could eliminate poverty and prejudice? Stopping war would end untold suffering around the world. It is certainly a noble and worthy cause, and no one who holds fast to these notions should be dissuaded from their pursuit. Whether or not this is achievable is another story altogether.

As the tragedy of Vietnam slowly seeped into the American consciousness, it became clear that the American government could carry out the same inhumane acts as the enemy, the bad guys. America doled out wanton cruelty and murder during the excruciating course of war. If we Americans, beacons of liberty, couldn't avoid falling into the same hell trap reaping misery and destruction, then what chance was there for the rest of the world?

When I was 16 I received the book, *The Territorial Imperative* by Robert Ardrey. The author's message was that humans had instinctual drives, particularly the acquisition and defense of territory. I next devoured Desmond Morris' *The Naked Ape*. I was hooked. Their ideas resonated with me. It suddenly began to make sense. If humans were born as blank slates, then there should have been societies that realized a long-term utopian vision. Beyond that, if there were no instincts, then there were no limits to what people could become. For all the external variations between cultures, it was obvious that people had far more in common than differences and that people behaved consistently and predictably. The merest review of human history showed that people are doomed to repeat history again and again and never learn from past mistakes. In order to understand the cruelty as well as the obvious goodness in people, one had to divine man's biology first. It made perfect sense to start there. Our inherited heritage must endure scrutiny before we address the nurture part of the nature-nurture debate. If the laws of life as encoded in our chromosomes apply to humans as they do to other animals, then all the ennobling about blank slates, nurture, and learning are only part of the equation and can't be understood in isolation. Certainly the transformation of man the barbarian to "can't we all get along?" man was not going to happen if we didn't deal with the ravages of our animal nature. This realization set me on a meandering path seeking to comprehend that strange and immensely complex human beast.

# Moyers, Campbell, and The Power of Myth

In 1988, American public television broadcast what was, at that time, one of its most popular and widely viewed shows, *The Power of Myth*. In the course of several segments, journalist Bill Moyers interviewed Joseph Campbell, prolific author and long-time Professor of Literature at Sarah Lawrence College. The series enthralled the public like no other PBS show had ever done, reaching as many as 30 million people. Campbell, who died before the series aired, led viewers through a multi-tonal jaunt of the mythological landscape. Weaving the stories of cultures from all over the world, Campbell connected with his audience in ways that, while difficult to understand, nevertheless drew them in fascination. These stories weren't the Hollywood blockbusters or New York Times bestsellers, but were instead the primeval, universal legends that were the basis for all literature. By engaging his audience with the cosmic tales, Campbell revealed a quiescent yearning for meaning that myths provide.

Campbell touched on many mythological concepts in the Moyers' series. Perhaps the most compelling, and that which most fascinated viewers, was that modern people have lost their veneration for mythology, and that mythology still had an important role to play. Yes, I could see that this struck a note with people, but why?

I participated in a *Power of Myth* study group with friends who were similarly taken by Campbell and his myth telling. Despite the lively discussions and camaraderie, I was struck by the fact that no one knew why they were drawn to the mythologies. Everyone enjoyed discussing the myths, but when I asked what it was about the myths that were so engaging, I heard a wide range of answers, none of which were satisfactory explanations.

For Campbell the hero story is the primary, incipient myth. The hero's journey is a metaphor for each individual's journey through life. The hero must overcome obstacles like killing the dragon to rescue the maiden and retrieve the grail. Each of us can feel the challenges we face and the depth of courage required to press on in the face of barriers. I understand the meaning of the hero's journey, but what about when Campbell says that metaphor and symbol are transcendent, beyond the concept of reality? Myths provide the symbols that enable you to connect to the mystery of being, he says. What does that mean?

The one line of Campbell's from the series that stuck with most people was "follow your bliss." The meaning was crystal clear—listen to your heart and go with your inner passions. But that doesn't tell us anything about the transcendent mysteries, does it? That these mythological stories touched people's souls was not arbitrary or coincidental. The archaic stories dipped into religious waters and represented something significant. Was this a desire for religious fulfillment? Was that the purpose of myth? I certainly knew in my own life as well as many other people's that the traditional role of religion had long since receded under the onslaught of modern, secular progress. The popularity of Campbell's myths was undoubtedly due to a spiritual hole that people felt. Did this imply a deep, innate need that drew people to the myths?

I realized that of all the behaviors of modern humans, religion was the least understood from a scientific viewpoint. Modern science including evolutionary theory had explained a great deal about human development and behavior, but religion was a glaring omission in the grand picture. As a disciple of Darwinian evolution, I believed that all of life, including us humans, could be understood as the product of biological forces. To think otherwise would be to acknowledge an exception to evolution, which would challenge the veracity of the very theory itself. If it works for the rest of the biological world, then it has to work for humans and their wacky religious observances. Yet, from what I could tell, the existing theories for the evolutionary origin of religion were woefully lacking. A few professors had examined the way the brain functioned during religious practice. Other academics had proposed organic, non-metaphysical reasons why religion existed, but those reasons were far from compelling and often veered dangerously from any biological foundation. I found it unacceptable and counterintuitive that religion and religious ritual were solely the result of behaviorist cultural transmission, that religion just appeared out of thin air in preliterate tribal cultures and was then encouraged. Religion was like a low-hanging nut waiting to be plucked, but it had a terribly hard shell that resisted being cracked. As I watched The Power of Myth, I sensed a crystallization of purpose—to investigate the innate origin of religion. This was my bliss to follow. I filed this idea away and allowed it to percolate.

# ACKNOWLEDGEMENTS

My deepest gratitude goes out to all those who suffered through early drafts and provided much needed criticism as well as other feedback and *bon mots*: Galya Raz, Shana White, Daniel Wohlfeiler, Peter Wohlfeiler, Virginia Gelczis, Mike Lueck, Stan Engel, Michael Rosenthal, David Randolph, Lisa Gelczis, Norman Boccone, Lissy Abraham, Daniel Stewart, Bill Graf, Ellen Dissanayake, Matt Rossano, J. Alan LeFevre, Walter Greenleaf, Anna Malyala, Stephen K. Sanderson, Alistair Woodman, Tucker Hiatt, Brian Broome and the Atheist Community of San Jose, and Keith Swenson of Purple Hills Books.

# INTRODUCTION

The phenomenon of human religion is both pervasive and mysterious. People have probably engaged in religious practices for at least 50,000 years, far longer than agriculture and written language. In the midst of modern society's ongoing scientific and technological revolution, religion persists and is practiced by most people in the world. Even people who claim to be agnostic or atheist engage in outwardly irrational activities such as listening to music, looking at art, or, despite their overt beliefs to the contrary, anthropomorphizing things in their lives: naming one's car, cursing a truculent computer for being disagreeable, bestowing human intentions to pets.

Despite a few thousand years of philosophical and scientific investigation into theories of religion, most of those who study the origins of religion readily admit the cause and function of religion are still unknown. The purpose of religion remains unexplained, at least for people who rely more on science than on religion itself for "truth." For people who are religious, the answer to the conundrum of religion is obvious. Their belief and worship of God or gods are ends in themselves. For the devout, using science as a method for understanding the spiritual and the sacred is useless and irrelevant, but for those who adhere to science, the reason for religion isn't so straightforward. To the detached observer (think Mr. Spock), religious behavior is a bizarre and senseless activity particularly from an evolutionary point of view. If we think in typical terms about features that contribute to an organism's evolutionary success—obtaining food, avoiding predators, finding mates—religion is an enigma. It doesn't directly do any of those things. Religion seemingly fulfills no functional or useful objective.

I propose a new hypothesis for the origin and purpose of religion and its relationship to consciousness. My hypothesis may be difficult for many people to accept because it challenges long-held assumptions about our place in the world—that both physiologically and mentally we have far more in common with other animals than differences, and that we are mostly unconscious of our everyday actions. While the science in support of this is quite overwhelming, this notion conflicts with people's belief in their own volition, control, and purpose. Because some people who normally champion science will decline to accept this possibility that humans are not so special and are, in reality, far more like other animals, this book will test their faith that science truly does explain the world including humanity's place in it.

In order to appreciate this book's hypothesis, it helps to be vested in the Darwinian theory of evolution by natural selection. It is entirely within this realm that the intricacies of the origin and meaning of religious behavior revolve. However, this book cannot be a text on evolutionary theory. If you are not acquainted with the intricacies of evolution, it behooves you to get a basic book on evolution and become familiar with it. Here I will assume you are conversant with concepts like adaptation, selection, and fitness. But even for those who are well versed in evolutionary theory, there are still misunderstandings. One evolutionary misconception I want to bury here is that humans are not subject to the laws of evolution and are not evolving. Some people think that culture deflects environmental selection pressures. To pose this is to not understand evolution. While culture may indeed alter human evolution compared to what it would be without it, evolution remains. Evolution is not any specific trend or direction. It is simply the change in the frequency of alleles (genes) over time. Humans are animals, and, despite assertions of human exceptionalism, we are, in fact, deeply and fully in the throes of a period of rather rapid evolutionary change that extends back at least several million years. While I claim that humans today are pretty much the same genetically as they were 50,000 years ago, that doesn't mean that they haven't changed, and, in fact, are changing quite briskly. It's just not always clear how much and in what ways they've changed.

If you believe that science and evolution explain the derivation of life forms on earth as evolutionary biologist Richard Dawkins does, do you also believe that humans evolved similarly? Do human characteristics including behavior derive from evolutionary adaptations as well, even religion as Richard Dawkins doesn't believe? While some claim religion supports survival strategies, it does so with non-utilitarian, evolutionarily expensive rituals. The creation of and participation in rituals of music, dance (and other forms of physical movement), visual art, mythology (narratives, fiction), and prayer are ubiquitous, yet there is no consensus if and how these rituals contribute to survival and reproductive success.

Nevertheless, the task is not to abandon evolution and glom on to alternatives like byproduct explanations (only *slightly* more credible than intelligent design). Byproducts are another misreading of evolutionary theory that are solicited to account for difficult-to-explain phenomena such as religion, ritual, and art. Ironically, some scientists well-versed in evolutionary theory invoke byproduct explanations, which have minimal empirical or scientific basis. Rather the goal is to unconditionally revisit and reconsider religion within the incontrovertible theory of evolution by natural selection. Many academics are, in fact, doing that today, but an overall cogent theory of religion remains elusive.

I try to present the scientific evidence as gently as possible, and I cite all research I reference. As is the case in all aspects of science, there are always more questions than answers. Controversy is found in every facet of this discussion, and is only worse because we're dealing with the human animal. Biology is not the only discipline used to study humanity, which complicates matters further. Although I invoke a good amount of speculation from the fields of psychology, neuroscience, and certainly religious studies, I indicate when I make anecdotal or colloquial points that are not supported by evidence.

Defining religion and consciousness makes this effort particularly challenging. The very fact that religion and consciousness are so difficult to define attests to a fundamental lack of understanding about them. At the same time, everybody has strong personal preconceptions about what they mean, which erect mental barriers to possible new insights. While I give approximate definitions and provide examples to bolster my intent, the trick I beg readers to entertain is, when confronted with new and different perspectives, rather than believe them uncontested or reject them outright, hold them in your hand. Let them sit there and observe them while I explain why it's helpful and necessary to think differently about religion and consciousness. Allow yourself to consider the proposals espoused here. Then after you finish reading, critique them as appropriate. Ask if the hypothesis advanced here relies on sound evolutionary and psychological science? Does it maintain internal consistency? Does it present an explanation that addresses observed behaviors? That is the test of validity, and one I ask you to consider.

# Chapter 1

# Introduction to The Split Hypothesis of Religion

A mystic is just a man trying to think like a dog.
*Gerald Edelman*

The proposed origins and functions of religion vary widely. Anthropologist Stewart Guthrie (1980) said, "Anthropology and other humanistic studies lack an adequate theory of religion. [They] have found no single paradigm. No theory or even definition of religion is generally accepted." (p. 181) Thirty-five years after Guthrie wrote this, little has changed. There is no consensus whether religion evolved by natural selection and is in our genes or is strictly a cultural phenomenon. Does religion serve a necessary purpose or is it an accidental byproduct of habits of mind, the mental residue left over from other behaviors that are important for human survival? A theory for the purpose of religion remains as elusive as ever. Considering the importance religion has had for most people, it's quite perplexing that explanations remain wanting.

Guthrie lists several historical theories of religion including anthropomorphizing the world; attempting to explain and control the world; not explaining the world by contradicting experience; constructing an ultimately reasonable universe; forms and acts which relate man to the ultimate condition of his existence; or wish-fulfillment to name a few. (pp. 182-183) The theories that have received the most widespread attention recently are to assuage the fear of death, to answer the existential mysteries, to provide group cohesion, and the Hyperactive Agency Detection Device. I will explore them in more detail later, but even that won't help. They all describe aspects of religious behavior or belief and have legitimacy. All have serious shortcomings, and all are inadequate to comprehensively account for religious phenomena. None adequately explain how religion is adaptive and improves evolutionary fitness.

It seems as if any theory can be made to seem reasonable and describe some phenomenon, and it's certainly the case with religion. Like many aspects of the social sciences, the foundational assumptions for religion are insufficient. Anthropologist Scott Atran says, "You can find functional explanations [for religion] and their contraries, and they're all true." (Glausiusz, 2003) It's like swimming in mud. There's a lot of arm waving but not a lot of movement.

Religion is difficult to define and means many things to many people. For modern secularists religion has ugly connotations: it's a psychological crutch—the opiate of the masses—or a means of manipulation. The social form of religion is the accumulation of the combined spiritual sensibility of a group of people into a formalized and ritualized program. Collections of individuals sharing similar beliefs and doctrines constitute organized religions, which have been responsible for an astonishing amount of persecution, suffering, and death and are rightly to be distrusted or approached with caution. Here, however, religion is strictly about its effect and meaning on the individual rather than on the social group. In one sense this can be thought of as spirituality: the sensation of the sacred, transcendence, and the feeling of external powers that influence us, but whether called religion or spirituality, it begins with the individual. This book is about why humans engage in and benefit from *experiential* religion. As both a practicing Catholic and Hindu monk, Wayne Teasdale (2001) says religion arises from a deep, personal wellspring. Hormone

For thousands of years before the dawn of the world religions as social organisms working their way through history, the mystical life thrived. This mystical tradition, which underpins all genuine faith, is the living source of religion itself. It is the attempt to possess the inner reality of the spiritual life, with its mystical, or direct, access to the divine. (pp. 10-11)

People in all cultures witness or experience this sense of religious rapture to varying degrees. In these chapters, religion refers to ritual religious practices and their effects on the person. It is in this context that we look at how religion evolved. Once confident that we understand how religion is adaptive and why it exists (which certainly isn't the case yet), then we can investigate its social nature. That, however, is not within the scope of this work.

What's needed is to take a step back and consider an idea that looks beyond the above-mentioned proposals and wraps a theoretical umbrella around all intrinsic religion, the personal feeling of the spiritual. I propose The Split Hypothesis of religion. Succinctly, intrinsic religion is a compensating mechanism for higher-order consciousness. Early in human evolution as Homo brains enlarged, developing human cognition divided into two paths: higher-order consciousness took one path, and religious behaviors evolved as a different path to suppress or allay higher-order consciousness, but they were essentially two projections from the same source.

Support for The Split Hypothesis requires three legs of a stool to stand. The first leg is consciousness, or more exactly what consciousness is not. While our understanding of consciousness is still sketchy, much brain biology over the last several decades has shown that consciousness—self-awareness and volition—is not the controlling executive that many believe it to be. By far most of our behavior is driven by unconscious automatic systems. The following three chapters deal with various aspects of human consciousness. Chapter 4 in particular examines the pitfalls of consciousness and why it needs to be subdued.

The second leg of the stool is the role of emotion. In their paper *The Neural Substrates of Religious Experience*, UCLA physicians Jeffrey

Saver and John Rabin (1997) propose a unifying hypothesis: emotions are the one constant of all religious experience. They aren't the first to understand that emotions are the integrating thread and physiological manifestation of religion. People have long recognized the role of emotions in religious behavior. Indeed, a quick review of theory of religion books and articles reveals that emotion underlies all the theories. Recent studies suggest that some ritual behaviors—making or listening to music for example—stimulate the brain's reward centers deep in the limbic system, the seat of emotions. (Blood and Zatorre, 2001; Panksepp, 1995) Emotions are evolved systems that ensure our survival. Religion stimulates our emotions and suppresses self-aware or narrative consciousness. This is to say religion evolved biologically, is adaptive, and the propensity for religion is inherited and in our genes. Chapters 5, 6, and 7 explore shortcomings of the existing origin of religion theories, the biological purpose of emotions, and the relationship between emotions, ritual, and religion.

The third leg of the stool is the five ritual behaviors: music, dance, art, mythology, and prayer. Rituals are the behaviors of religion and have several aspects in common: they are seemingly non-utilitarian, are first observed historically in ancient tribal religions, are ubiquitous in all cultures, and all elicit emotions. Religious rituals are behavioral adaptations that inhibit consciousness and prompt emotions. The last part of the book looks at each of these ritual behaviors to show how they each act to reduce the conscious cacophony and enhance evolutionary fitness and success.

The first part of The Split Hypothesis focuses on the problem of consciousness as it is critical to my argument. The scientific evidence is plentiful and compelling, but won't convince those who believe with a religious-like ferver that consciousness has only a beneficial contribution to Homo sapiens. The studies of many neuroscientists and other academics are cited to substantiate all claims, but in this introductory chapter, The Split Hypothesis of religion is fleshed out with allegory, metaphor, and only a little science.

Does a frog have higher-order consciousness? Does it have self-awareness and can it access a vast array of short- and long-term memories for complex cognitive evaluation? Does it have any of the characteristics associated with higher-order consciousness such as the ability to use symbols or imagine what someone else is thinking—a theory of mind? No, a frog doesn't have that kind of consciousness. So what is it like to be a frog, to be without self-awareness? It's hard to imagine. Since we all have consciousness, how do we envision the absence of it? It's like asking someone not to think about holding a pen. Consider that the lack of consciousness is like your consciousness before you were born, even before you were conceived. Remember that? Unless you can recall previous lives, you don't remember anything; it's a big, black blank. It's not void, as that implies an empty space. It simply doesn't exist at all. In the computer programming world, it's called null, meaning the absence of anything. That's what the consciousness of a frog is like. The frog is completely capable of surviving and reproducing, driven by its genetics and its telencephalon forebrain that gives it its learning potential. The frog brain is wired to be capable of a limited amount of learning, but consciousness doesn't enter into how a frog learns. When the frog's ecosystem changes beyond a certain range, the frog is toast. Its ability to migrate to better climes is limited. It can't dig for underground water in a drought. It can't modify its environment within its own lifetime. For most of the animal kingdom, this lack of consciousness is the standard. Although some birds and mammals might have glimmers of consciousness, the vast majority of animal species are null for higher-order or awareness consciousness.

On the other hand, what is it about human consciousness that makes us so special? Despite the once common assertion that humans were the only animals to have language, to make and use tools, and have a vast memory capacity including remembering a personal past, it is now clear many mammals and birds are capable of at least some of these capabilities. Nothing about humans is strictly unique. While the overall accumulation of these features contributes to (purported) human exceptionalism, there is a more germane way of identifying what makes humans different, and that is the ability to decouple information and to create metarepresentations. Simply, this means humans can generate and retain conditional information.

Humans can adapt their behavior based on local conditions and pass those behaviors to their offspring through learning. This is the basis of culture. Longtime collaborators Leda Cosmides and John Tooby (2000a) at the University of California, Santa Barbara, describe it this way. "Arguably, one central and distinguishing innovation in human evolution has been the dramatic increase in the use of contingent information for the regulation of improvised behavior that is successfully tailored to local conditions." (p. 53)

To a degree humans are freed or decoupled from their reliance and dependence on the instructions in their genome — instincts — to survive. This new human cognitive niche that I refer to under the umbrella term of higher-order consciousness provides mechanisms that enable metarepresentations — the ability, for example, to hold for evaluation both true and false ideas and to simultaneously weigh various factors such as another person's reliability and reputation when integrating messages or the likelihood of being within an arrow's reach of striking prey. Contrast that to the hunting strategy of a big cat who slowly stalks its prey until a critical point when it makes the decision to pounce or sprint. It is unlikely that the cat considers other options beyond the perceived distance to its prey into its decision-making such as type of terrain or availability of the prey's escape route. Cosmides and Tooby call this limited mental scope of other animals naive realism.

> For the naive realist, the world as it is mentally represented is taken for the world as it really is, and no distinction is drawn between the two...From our external perspective, we can say of such basic architectures that all information found inside the system is assumed to be true, or is treated as true. However, from the point of view of the architecture itself, that would not be correct, for it would imply that the system is capable of drawing the distinction between true and false, and is categorizing the information as true. Instead, mechanisms in the architecture simply use the information found inside the system to regulate behavior and to carry out further computations. Whatever information is present in

the system simply is "reality" for the architecture. Instead of tagging information as true or false—as seems so obvious to us—such basic architectures would not be designed to store false information. When new information is produced that renders old information obsolete, the old information is updated, overwritten, forgotten, or discarded...For this reason, there is no need in such an architecture to be able to represent that some information is true: Its presence, or the decision to store it or remember it, is the cue to its reliability. In such a design, true equals accessible. (p. 60)

This is the frog mind in which perceptions are handled in an essentially automatic way, and there are no alternative options for behavioral outcomes. The true-false dichotomy simply doesn't exist for the frog, so in this null condition, there can be no evaluation or judgment. The frog is hard-wired unlike humans where choices exist. This is the *gift* of higher-order consciousness.

## Fall From Grace

First God made heaven and earth the Bible starts out. The earth was without form and void (null?), and darkness was upon the face of the deep. In only a page or two, God created the rest of the world, including animals and humans. He put the first people in Eden, the paradise where everything was in perfect harmony. The Garden of Eden was described as a place of purity where there was no judgment, no right or wrong. Adam and Eve, who were naked, were not ashamed because they had no knowledge of shame. Theirs was a state of innocence because, like other animals, they were without knowledge or consciousness.

Just as some people rationalize the six days of creation as a metaphor for the evolution of the cosmos including life on earth, the Garden represents a metaphorical, closed-eyed, nonconscious unity, a oneness representing the state of animal existence without consciousness. Think of the Garden as symbolizing the state of instinct or frog preconsciousness. The serpent told Eve that eating the fruit would open her eyes, and she would be like God knowing good and evil. Eating from the tree of knowledge and getting cast out of the Garden is the evolutionary transition from the preconscious to dichotomous consciousness in which there exists the tension of opposites—in and out, good and evil, heaven and hell. Essentially the rest of Bible, and religions in general, are attempts to reconcile the opposites. It may be thought of as the desire to return to the blissful state of unawareness or nonconsciousness, or at least to ameliorate the strain created by consciousness to solve the problems of survival that originally belonged exclusively to instinct.

Psychologist Carl Jung (1933) was keenly aware of this psychic conflict. In *Modern Man in Search of a Soul*, he summed up the human condition.

> It is the growth of consciousness which we must thank for the existence of problems; they are the dubious gift of civilization. It is just man's turning away from instinct— his opposing himself to instinct—that creates consciousness...As long as we are still submerged in nature we are unconscious, and we live in the security of instinct that knows no problems. Everything in us that still belongs to nature shrinks away from a problem; for its name is doubt, and wherever doubt holds sway, there is uncertainty and the possibility of divergent ways. And where several ways seem possible, there we have turned away from the certain guidance of instinct and handed over to fear. For consciousness is now called upon to do that which nature has always done for her children—namely, to give a certain, unquestionable and unequivocal decision. And here we are beset by an all-too-human fear that consciousness—our Promethean conquest—may in the end not be able to serve us in the place of nature. (p. 110)

The original sin was the human acquisition of awareness consciousness, which separated us from frog nonconscious unity and gave us the capabilities of God-like knowledge. Consciousness also gave humans the angst of contradictions inherent in the awareness of opposites. Before consciousness, animals lived without the ability to hold complex concepts and thoughts. They did not have the capacity to consider more than one or two conflicting scenarios; any decisions that had to be made were essentially automatic choices. For an animal there was no good and bad. There was only the singular constant of nonconscious existence without judgment.

Professor of Religious History Mircea Eliade (1975) took a similar approach towards the religious connection to human origins. Eliade understood that religion developed at the beginning of human time, or as he referred to it, *in illo tempore*, literally "at that time," meaning the specific event, but indeterminate time in the past, when people fell from grace. He also used the less than politically correct term of "savages" for pre-literate peoples but understood that they, too, shared the same mental experiences as us moderns.

> The savages, for their own part, were also aware of having lost a primitive paradise. In the modern jargon, we may say that the savages regarded themselves, neither more nor less than if they had been Western Christians, as beings in a "fallen" condition, by contrast with a fabulously happy situation in the past. Their actual condition was not their original one: it had been brought about by a catastrophe that had occurred *in illo tempore*. Before that disaster, man had enjoyed a life which was not dissimilar from that of Adam before he sinned. (p. 43)

Present time, which Eliade called profane time, was of little consequence compared to what he called sacred time when humanity was born. It was the religious act through ritual that was the universal requirement all humans must perform to symbolically return to the beginning time. People have the drive to return to the sacred time, which they do through ritual religious practices.

> Among all these paleo-agricultural peoples, the essential duty is the periodic invocation of the primordial event which inaugurated the present condition of humanity. All their religious life is a commemoration, a re-memorising. The Remembrance, reenacted

9

> ritually—therefore, by the repetition of the primordial
> assassination—plays the decisive part: one must take the
> greatest care not to forget what happened *in illo tempore*.
> (p. 45)

People cannot disdain their past as the need to remember is part of their genetic heritage. What the religious ritual attempts to do is metaphorically recall or relive the original condition of humanity, the primordial Split or fall from grace, to connect us to a time incipient to consciousness where the innocence of perfect oneness resides in frog blank blackness, and instinct is the arbiter of behavior.

From this interpretation of the expulsion from the Garden of Eden, one might get the notion that consciousness is a bad thing. Optimistically, the best I can say is that consciousness is a mixed bag. The study of mental consciousness has turned out to be very daunting. There is no consciousness center of the brain, so besides the challenge of identifying the neurophysiology of consciousness, scientists struggle to agree what the function and purpose of consciousness are. A definition or understanding of consciousness remains elusive, and although I examine some theories and proposed functions of consciousness, I'm not providing a strict definition. Rather, in order to evaluate the interrelationship between consciousness and religion, I examine various behaviors that tend to be associated with consciousness. Topics include choice and decision-making, logic or rational thought, memory, attention and awareness, and volitional intention—free will.

Even though the scientific knowledge of how consciousness works remains fragmentary, brain researchers are discovering that what we do know about consciousness is not what most of us think it is. People have the sense that they are in control of their lives and moment to moment decide intentionally what to do next. It isn't quite so straightforward. Our perception and feeling of consciousness is very different from the actual conscious and cognitive processes themselves and is to a degree illusory. Because it smacks directly into people's most fervent beliefs and desires about themselves, it's very difficult for many to accept. The evidence that our conscious volition is not what motivates us is actually quite com-

pelling and comes from several areas of study. People who suffer localized brain damage lose specific functionality, which often reveals
how neural operations work independently of rational or thinking
tasks. Also, direct stimulation of brain structures reveals how pathways carry information that doesn't reach awareness consciousness
yet still has impact. Cognitive psychologists are able to design experiments that isolate factors influencing behavior. What they find
is that it's quite easy to manipulate people unconsciously through
various subtle and not so subtle cues. It happens every day, for example, when someone's emotions affect another's emotions. *what Are*
*we doing Now?*

Our behavior is not subject to real-time conscious introspection or
control. Neuroscientist V. S. Ramachandran (2004) says on the first
page of *A Brief Tour of Human Consciousness*, "Your conscious life, in
short, is nothing but an elaborate post-hoc rationalization of things
you do for other reasons." (p. 1) By far most human behavior is
like the behavior of other animals, driven by unconscious emotions,
out of sight and out of our conscious mind. Most of consciousness
is like the TV sports announcer describing the play you've already
seen. It's nice to have the analysis of what's already taken place, but
it doesn't change what happened. Consciousness is trailing behind,
watching the activity of the emotional unconscious and pestering,
"Don't forget me; listen, I have something to say here." We are aware
of the sustained chatter, the internal discussion that goes on in our
heads. That's consciousness doing its job, checking in, monitoring
events, always observing and commenting. Consciousness evolved
to constantly query and offer assistance, but the brain chatter can be
annoying and, in some cases, even misguided. The next chapters
explore the inconsistent role of consciousness in human activity.

In *Philosophy in the Flesh*, George Lakoff and Mark Johnson (1999)
begin with the premise that our mental processes are almost wholly
unconscious. After listing several unconscious behaviors necessary to hold a conversation, they say, "Cognitive scientists have
shown experimentally that to understand even the simplest utter-
ance, we must perform these and other incredibly complex forms
of thought automatically and without effort below the level of consciousness. It is not merely that we occasionally do not notice theses
processes; rather, they are inaccessible to conscious awareness and

*Evolution has no goal*

control." (p. 11) Instead of the common belief that the unconscious exists in relation to consciousness, it is innate unconscious neural processes that are incipient, and consciousness is a Johnny-come-lately, both evolutionarily as well as contemporaneously.

Evolutionary changes to the human brain dictate that instinctual behaviors relinquish some control of the organism to learning—functions that are flexible and can modify behavior in an individual's lifetime. However, this capacity that humans excel in did not evolve to replace pre-existing cognition, only to complement it. The seemingly limitless choices humans are capable of, if not curbed, are sources of grief according to anthropologist Roy Rappaport (1971).

> The very intelligence that makes it possible for men to learn and behave according to any set of conventions makes them understand that the particular set of conventions by which they do live, and which often inconveniences them or even subjects them to hardship, is arbitrary. Since this is the case, they may be aware that there are, at least logically, alternatives. But no society, if it is to avoid chaos, can allow all alternatives to be practiced. For each context or situation, all but one or a few must be proscribed and the proscriptions must somehow be made effective. Thus human societies are faced with containing what Bergson called the "dissolving power" of their intelligence. (p. 32)

Endless choice is not a good thing. People find it very difficult to function if they have to make conscious decisions about every aspect of their lives and can easily get overwhelmed. Humans simply aren't designed to have to frequently weigh options. No animal is. A little bit of consciousness is a nice-to-have, but too much is a burden. You don't want to consider your options when the bear is coming after you. That's when the evolutionarily ancient fight or flight response, an emotional reaction, kicks in and overrides any conscious ruminations. The Homo sapiens who thought about his predicament too long didn't leave offspring.

The problem of having contingent or conditional information is that we humans are freed to consider infinite possibilities. With our higher-order consciousness, we are able to perceive and consider any alternative that we could imagine, but that potentially results in immense numbers of options. Cosmides and Tooby (2000a) elaborate.

> The costs and difficulties of the [human] cognitive niche are so stringent that only the one lineage, in four billion years, has wandered into the preconditions that favored the evolution of this form of intelligence...One of the greatest problems faced by natural computational systems is...combinatorial explosion, [which] is the term for the fact that alternatives multiply with devastating rapidity in computational systems, and the less constrained the representational and procedural possibilities, the faster this process mushrooms. When this happens, the system is choked with too many possibilities to search among or too many processing steps to perform. (p. 56)

There is an ongoing tension between our innate drives and the persistence of our consciousness. While we have freedom to consider alternatives, we also have to shoulder the burden that consciousness has no absolute answers to offer. At least some of the anxiety and alienation of modern times are the result of having too much choice and no essential knowledge with which to make decisions. There is no fundamental truth or reality accessible solely to consciousness, no pure objectivity or rationality. It remains within the purview of unconscious emotions to make the decisions. Everything good about our species that we believe derives from consciousness—our superior memory and thinking, our taming of the land, our rich culture and technology—comes at a cost. We are afraid of dying, we question our purpose in life, we agonize over our decisions. We have gnawing existential anxiety because we have consciousness. In a world without consciousness, ignorance is bliss.

# The Split

Now it's a funny thing about Darwinian evolution. We tend to think of it as a one-way street in which organisms progress and improve as natural selection whittles away the less fit. Rather, evolution should be thought of as a series of compromises. Competition for survival and reproductive success is a never-ending struggle, and evolution continually rolls the dice, experimenting with different combinations of genes (genotypes) and characteristics (phenotypes). Whoever survives and reproduces has won the short-term evolutionary battle. In no way, however, should that suggest that any one of those winning organisms is ideally adapted to its environment. It just happens to be good enough at that moment to pass its genes to the next generation.

A classic example is the compromise between upright walking and childbirth. Anthropologists Karen Rosenberg and Wenda Trevathan (2003) state, "The complex twists and turns that human babies make as they travel through the birth canal have troubled humans and their ancestors for at least 100,000 years." (p. 82) This is because bipedalism required significant changes to the pelvis. Instead of being designed to support just the rear portion of the body like in chimps, the pelvis now supports the entire weight of the head and torso. On top of that, the selection pressure for a great oversized brain pushes the cranium to grow larger in utero. This makes childbirth riskier in humans than in other mammals. This evolutionary compromise is like Newton's third law of motion: for every action there is an equal and opposite reaction. The evolutionary pressures to select upright gait and brain size come at the expense of facile childbirth. "It's the price we pay for our large brains and intelligence." (p. 82) To endanger both the fetus and mother through the increased risk of childbirth for the benefits of a larger brain and upright locomotion mean that bipedalism and large brains are extremely important to human evolutionary success.

The fallen condition of humanity is the strain between our newly acquired consciousness and the nonconscious emotional systems that served our ancestors for hundreds of millions of years. Again, Cosmides and Tooby (2000a) weigh in.

When hominids evolved or elaborated adaptations that could use information based on relationships that were only "true" temporarily, locally, or contingently rather than universally and stably, this opened up a new and far larger world of potential information than was available previously. Context-dependent information could now be used to guide behavior to a far greater extent than had been possible formerly. This advance, however, was purchased at a cost: The exploitation of this exploding universe of potentially representable information creates a vastly expanded risk of possible misapplications, in which information that may be usefully descriptive in a narrow arena of conditions is false, misleading, or harmful outside the scope of those conditions...Expanding the body of information used to make decisions is harmful or dangerous if the architecture does not and cannot detect and keep track of which information is applicable where, and how the boundaries of applicability shift. (pp. 57-58)

Cosmides and Tooby identify a number of adaptations that evolved in response to this cognitive conflict to limit potentially runaway consciousness, which they label with names such as attitude slot, source tag, credal value, and restricted scope of inferences. An equally valid way of looking at these adaptations is as examples of evolved compensating mechanisms. This is what makes us uniquely human: the decoupled brain capable of metarepresentations, what amounts to higher-order consciousness, and limitations to corral this mental capacity. The evolution of our great brain brought as much risk as benefit.

However, an adaptation they didn't identify that developed as a compensating mechanism to offset the downside of consciousness was intrinsic religion. At a critical juncture in human evolution, a cognitive Split occurred in which religion arose to offset the brain's decoupling from strict instinctual dictates. The early decoupled mind began to flounder due to newfound powers that it couldn't handle and control. Aspects of this new mode of cognition based on contingent information, the ability to form metarepresentations, gave humans great new advantages to manipulate their environment, but the way in which evolution implemented this solution was messy and problematic. Religion confined or retarded this wild child brain and caused humans to reconnect with the prevailing innate prescriptions that had worked for animals since nervous systems first evolved. It's the equal and opposite reaction of Newton's Third Law again. Religion evolved because those who, through their religious behaviors, reined in consciousness and maintained reliance on their emotional instincts—or at least kept a balance between the two—survived and reproduced preferentially. In chapter 4 we'll look at specific drawbacks from a consciousness perpective rather than a decoupling and metarepresentation perspective.

The word religion derives from the Latin *religio*, which some interpret to mean that which attaches, retains, or binds, perhaps a moral bond. For many atheists and secularists, the bondage concept is apt as they find organized religion burdensome and manipulative. But Jung (1990) interpreted the etymology of religion in a different way. "This original form of *religio* ('linking back') is the essence, the working basis of all religious life even today, and always will be." (p. 160) Linking back is revisiting instinctual emotions *in illo tempore*. Consciousness must be restrained and brought face-to-face with our primordial nature. Inner religious behavior is an attempt to honor one's innate emotional spirit.

Our animal nature remains foremost despite our obscenely big craniums, and this explains why religion is a biological, evolved adaptation. Our biology makes us who we are, and anything that dissuades or confounds our innate guidance is a potential threat to our well-being and survival. Consciousness has immense value, but it also has the tendency to interfere with our instinctual nature and throw us off track. It can only secondarily provide the guidance for continued evolutionary success. Our emotional genetic inheritance is the first line of defense.

# Splitori

The expression of religious fervor takes many forms, but there are conspicuous consistencies in the way in which people practice intense spiritual passion. Whether from the faiths of the East like Hinduism and Buddhism, the self-help books filling libraries and bookstores, or the Jewish Kabbalists, the Muslim Sufis, or the Christian mystics, the language of deep religion is strikingly similar. In all traditions, the spiritual journey describes a process for reaching a sacred union, oneness, the absolute, the infinite, nirvana. One achieves this state by extinguishing ego consciousness—losing the self, one's boundaries, or material craving. The passage to the spirit world means letting go of the tangible world. The mystical mind achieves a state of perfect understanding, clarity, and rapture devoid of the perception of time and space. Reaching the sacred bestows a sense of immortality and connection. Lluis Oviedo (2009), Theological Anthropologist at the Pontifical University Antonianum in Italy, throws a unifying definition around it. He says religious experience,

> Means a perception, feeling, and communication with a sphere beyond the actual empirical reality (transcendence). This is distinct from what is fully present in the empirical world (immanence). Religious experience proclaims the existence of a reality distinct from the empirical reality that can constrain or inspire specific human behaviors. (p. 1)

This is not dissimilar to how Eliade structured his philosophy of religion for whom there are two primary components: the sacred and the profane. This dichotomy of sacred or transcendent versus immanent or profane is akin to The Split between higher-order consciousness and religious behavior. All religious traditions have exercises that result in the mitigation of consciousness. Besides the five ritual behaviors that will be discussed in later chapters—music, dance, visual art, mythology, and prayer—there are various forms of trances and ecstasies used to enter rapturous altered states. To attain these states people endure deprivations such as fasting, rites of passage, self-mutilation or flagellation, and other forms of penance. In some cultures sex is used formally to achieve a spiritual experience. Meditation and yoga are popular exercises to step away from the conscious-heavy, hectic rat race through a refocus away from consciousness. All these methods are means to conceal or repress higher-order consciousness and mollify the tension of opposites. These religious experiences express the same thing— by silencing consciousness, self-awareness, and the knowledge of opposites, one can achieve the sense of the sacred, the state before human time when we lived in frog null blankness and unconscious instincts ruled. Without consciousness there is no I, no thou, no top or bottom, no life or death. Without consciousness there is only the all-encompassing unity that is without form. Psychologist and author Robert Ornstein (1997) says,

> This is why some of the techniques of the spiritual efforts are described as "not for your mind," or are held by others to be "anti-rational." The aim is in the simulation of a new kind of mental configuration...Even the very different forms of meditation serve this purpose: They are nonverbal, or they use music, or they are movement oriented. The meditation method most often used consists of silently repeating or chanting a phrase over and over, or of concentrating on one object not only to become relaxed but also to turn off the normal internal talk, lessening the hold of the verbal mode. (p. 164)

Transcendence, the catch-all term for deep religious experience, is popularly considered to be an effort to achieve higher consciousness, but with only a little imagination, we can reinterpret this aspiration quite differently: as obfuscating an excessively busy, overreaching consciousness. Andrew Newberg (2002), a neuroscientist who scans and studies the brains of people praying or meditating and is the author of several books about religion and belief, says, "No matter what specific methods any given tradition of mysticism might employ, the purpose of these methods is almost always the same: to silence the conscious mind and free the mind's awareness from the limiting grip of the ego." (p. 117) The perfect mystical union, the bliss of enlightenment, is not available to our mortal comprehension, for to think is to wallow in the light of consciousness, which means judging through the filter of polarities. Consciousness delivers us to the profane and obscures the sacred. The ultimate mystical union of Eastern religious philosophy is the elimination of suffering through the dissolution of dichotomies. Zen Buddhists say the barrier to satori (enlightenment) is the conscious or rational mind. In Zen religious philosophy, one cannot train to achieve satori because that requires conscious effort. Rather, Zen masters use riddles called koans that are supposed to show the fruitlessness of such mental effort. In one example, the new monk is asked to discard everything. "But I have nothing," the monk replies. "Discard that, too!" demands his master. Another koan says if sitting in meditation leads to enlightenment, then frogs must be enlightened—the null blankness of all mystical achievement.

Religion is the mechanism for returning to the original unity of mind before The Split, but after a few million years of hominid brain evolution, we humans are far beyond the actual return to the unity of pre-consciousness. The best we can do is frequently visit through religious ritual. While homage to *in illo tempore*, the beginning of human time, is still the goal for the mystic seeker, the reality for the typical religious person is more about integrating The Split rather than the journey to achieve the Absolute. We live in the rational world and embrace our consciousness. At the same time we are attracted to and enjoy ritual behaviors that suppress consciousness and evoke emotions. We engage in religious rituals because we are hard-wired to do them, and we get emotional pleasure or satisfaction from them. We learn specific religious traditions just like the specific language we acquire, but the desire and ability to receive both language and religion are genetically driven.

The interplay between consciousness, religious ritual, and emotion is a constant negotiation. The feelings engendered by religious acts and observances range from negligible to overwhelming, as when someone attains the elation of the unified state. How do emotions change as a result of religious behavior? Does ritual behavior—the actions of religion—spark specific emotional content or does the ritual have a generic effect on suppressing consciousness, which opens emotions to whatever the organism's needs are at the moment? The interaction of the human emotional system and religious behavior is an area ripe for examination.

There are many challenges to explaining how and why religion biologically evolved. Why do people create supernatural agents (gods), the mostly human-like entities that people invoke to populate their elaborate religious doctrines? If religion has a biological basis, does the imagining of gods as well? Do religious behaviors improve people's well being, and if so, how? The Split Hypothesis provides a framework with which to approach and answer these questions. This proposition offers a method for understanding the roots of religion, this most befuddling aspect of human nature, and can be used as the basis to further investigate its evolutionary origins.

# CHAPTER 2

## WHAT CONSCIOUSNESS IS NOT

> Consciousness thinks it's running the shop. But it's a secondary organ of a total human being, and it must not put itself in control. It must submit and serve the humanity of the body. When it does put itself in control, you get a man like Darth Vader in *Star Wars*, the man who goes over to the consciously intentional side. ⇀ *Not So*
>
> *Joseph Campbell*

This first chapter on consciousness begins exploring the function of consciousness and the problem of people's perception of and belief in its primacy. I describe brain defects that reveal how consciousness interacts with other brain functions, which indicates that it is not solely or even mostly the controller of human behavior. Successive chapters delve into the ways consciousness functions in people without brain defects—how it works in normal people. These sections have barely any mention of religion, but because a premise of this book is that religion is a compensating mechanism for higher-order consciousness, we need to try to understand it—a very challenging proposition. By no means do I presume to solve or explain the riddle of consciousness, but enough evidence exists to indicate what it is not. That is enough to guide us through consciousness on the way to its relationship to religion.

# Paddling Into a Headwind

Two hurdles must be overcome in order to embrace The Split Hypothesis of religion. The first requires us to accept that consciousness is just another brain function among thousands and doesn't have any precedence in the control of the human organism. In fact consciousness is a feature of the brain, which, while it evolved to successfully solve some specific environmental challenges, is also fallible and misleading, and brings with it dubious baggage. Consciousness is so errant that it actually creates problems for us, its owners. Consciousness is a classic case of an evolutionary development that is a compromise between competing forces. The last fifty years of brain science and psychology reveals that consciousness is an adaptive accommodation just like the trade-off between childbirth and bipedal walking that I described in the previous chapter.

The second hurdle to The Split Hypothesis, of course, is that religion evolved as a compensating mechanism for the problems raised by the evolution of consciousness. The evidence for the first challenge is far more plentiful. The Split Hypothesis, however, breaks new ground, so the case for it hangs on circumstance and correlation rather than substantiation. This is not to say that it can't be confirmed by science, but the road starts with the hypothesis followed by experiments designed to test it. More about this later when we switch from consciousness focus to religion and ritual focus. Nevertheless, there is research to indicate that religious rituals have the effect of suppressing aspects of consciousness while promoting emotions, the innate behavioral constructs that ensure evolutionary fitness. It's just that researchers haven't designed their experiments within such a framework. They don't know that their work has this consequence that reveals the relationship between consciousness, emotion, and religious ritual.

For most people to consider, let alone accept, what I'm proposing is formidable. When people ponder the components of consciousness, they cite the human capacity for language, our extensive memory—the ability to recall past events and imagine future options—and the ability to process multiple scenarios and make reasoned choices from among them. In addition, self-awareness gives us the ability to imagine what others might be thinking—the theory of mind. Taken together, our sense of our own consciousness is that this wonderfully evolved toolkit gives us our humanity, and it does. But what flies under the radar is that we are animals first, and we take for granted all the unconscious, automatic functions that constantly go on inside us, precisely because they are unconscious. The incessant, undetected signals zipping around happen without our knowledge and awareness and are thus invisible. Because of this they are deemed insignificant and even non-existent by some.

The modern theory of the unconscious, first popularized by Freud, is over one hundred years old. Despite a century of knowledge and awareness of the unconscious, people find it difficult to accommodate its role, and scientists are people, too. I say this because, when confronted with evidence that nonconscious processes have far greater impact, many academics ignore or reject this position for the same reason that non-academics do. It contradicts conscious experience. It's like the theory of relativity. The behavior of matter moving near the speed of light is completely counterintuitive to our everyday experience. Most people cannot comprehend what matter and energy are like at 186,000 miles per second. It's beyond our mortal imagination. It takes sophisticated machines and experiments to reveal the true nature of matter and energy. Yet the atomic bomb and nuclear power have convinced people of its reality even if they don't know how it works. The consequences of splitting atoms make a convincing case for $E = mc^2$ despite the fact that very few people actually understand what this really means. Similarly, people can't place a mirror in their brains and watch their own neural activity. It isn't until scientists create tools to measure brain activity or design experiments that manipulate human subjects' unconscious that self-introspection becomes inconsequential. Brain function is now recorded by machines removing the need for people to use their consciousness to analyze their own consciousness. (The blind leading the blind? A conflict of interest?) It's time to bring the evidence for how the unconscious brain works to the fore. It's not as high-profile as nukes, perhaps, but it's just as evident.

# Consciousness's Downsides

For those who haven't studied the psychobiological consciousness research from the last half-century, the conclusions can be startling and disconcerting. What the cognitive and brain scientists have found flips our understanding of consciousness on its head. "The critiques and contrary evidence [against the role of consciousness] have been so thoroughly devastating that some have begun to wonder openly whether conscious thought has any usefulness at all," Baumeister and Masicampo (2010, p. 947) state in *Conscious Thought Is for Facilitating Social and Cultural Interactions: How Mental Simulations Serve the Animal-Culture Interface*. In their paper in support of the role of consciousness, they nevertheless admit that consciousness doesn't function at all as most people believe.

> We are prepared to concede the correctness of much (not all) of the negative evidence against [consciousness]...Many theories have assumed that conscious thought is for perceiving the environment and for directly controlling action, but the detractors have revealed its inadequacies for those functions...The naïve view that the conscious self knows all about what the person is doing and can direct behavior at will has come under fire from several well thought out and *empirically supported* perspectives. [emphasis added] (pp. 947-948)

The authors summarize five pitfalls of consciousness. First, conscious introspection of one's own behavior is often wrong or false. People tend to borrow from group beliefs [ed. note: often, but not solely, religion] to justify actions, and those beliefs may have little to do with actual events. People easily convince themselves of the truth of untrue causes. Second, the authors distinguish conscious introspection from conscious explanations of external events and state that people misinterpret the world around them. Consciousness is undermined by false conclusions, which suggests a kind of dereliction of conscious duty. Third, consciousness is latent or tardy in the flow of time. It is incapable of real-time interaction and is always slightly behind the moment, and thus unable to dictate behavior in close-to-synchronous fashion. Fourth, consciousness is not the initiator of action. Studies show brain activation for an action starts significantly before conscious awareness of the intent to act. Fifth, consciousness assigns itself the role of activator when it is not. Our sense of our volition is a trick of consciousness, and we are mistaken about the self intentionally inciting actions. We falsely believe our own conscious volition when, in fact, our consciousness is not the initiator. *of My Atheism it is.*

We have at best limited introspective means to know what causes a particular decision or action, whether consciousness influences the actor or if action is the result of unconscious forces or some combination. "The implication is that consciousness does not know what goes on inside the psyche to produce behavior, and it will invent false explanations (borrowed from the collective stockpile of group beliefs) to cover its ignorance, then passing them off as if true. What's worse it often ends up believing its own false explanations." (p. 949)

The evidence for the impotency of consciousness is compelling and pervasive, but it contradicts how we believe our quotidian consciousness performs. Consciousness is a trickster and fools us into believing in its intelligence and perspicacity. We have an egomaniac sitting on our shoulder, whispering in our ear, telling us that we're running our own show. Meanwhile, there's no advocate for the unconscious brain processes. They go about their jobs without raising the merest peep. Since the beginning of our species, consciousness has propagandized its own importance despite not being the all-powerful executive.

Lakoff and Johnson (1999), whom I quoted in the last chapter, state that at least 95 percent of our thought processes are unconscious and that's probably a low estimate. (p. 19) Michael Gazzaniga (1998a), a neuroscientist whose work we'll look at shortly, claims that the unconscious is responsible for 98 percent of our mental function—that only two percent of our mental function comes from consciousness. (p. 21) John Bargh, a Yale social psychologist, posits the least role for consciousness: 99.44% automatic, a not so subtle nod to an old Ivory soap commercial. (Wyer, 1997, p. 243) These numbers are estimates, of course, but they all indicate a very minimal influence for conscious awareness of intention in everyday activity. Before we begin to look at the science behind these estimates, Bargh provides an intuitive way to understand the logic behind these numbers.

> If one is scrupulously honest about the number of times per day that one actually takes more than a half-second to make a decision (one signature of a control or nonautomatic process), the number could be counted on one's fingers. This is a very small percentage (0.56%?) of all perceptions, behaviors, judgments, evaluations and intentions one constantly makes each day. When it does happen—when we do override the automatic process—these occasions are memorable and salient precisely because they are effortful and unusual. As a consequence, we are misled by the greater availability of the occasions in memory into hugely overestimating how often we really do engage in acts of deliberate control. (p. 244)

In the next few chapters I will flesh out the evidence that consciousness lacks the skills we attribute to it, but first I give a very brief and evasive description of consciousness followed by the first studies that clued scientists to its infirmity. If you already accept or acknowledge the relative incompetence of consciousness, you may want to skip to Chapter 4, The Problem of Consciousness, dedicated to exploring its specific pitfalls and problems.

## The Consciousness Swamp

For thousands of years philosophers have debated the essence and meaning of consciousness and human nature. They did so with a tool called consciousness, which (theoretically) included a rationality or logic brain engine. One of those well-known philosophers, Plato, wrote that the philosopher was most suitable to be king. (I'm sure it was only coincidence that he was a philosopher.)

This self-reflecting bias is the nature of consciousness as well. Like Plato's partiality to be philosopher-king, consciousness tells us that our thinking and awareness is evidence of our superior competency and skill, which is, we believe, due to facets of consciousness itself. For eons people have accepted this as reality. Consciousness constantly reminds us of this inviolable fact.

Plato also wrote the allegory of the cave in which he asked, what if people lived their entire lives in a cave and the shadows cast by a fire were perceived as real because it was the only thing the cave dwellers saw besides themselves and the fire. I remember not being terribly impressed by this proposition when I read it in college, but life has a funny way of coming full circle. What if our consciousness, this function that we think informs us in real time about events taking place and directing us how to act in the next moment, isn't actually doing those things? What if our self-awareness is constantly telling us that "I'm in control," except it isn't so? Is it possible that consciousness is not the principal driver of our motivations and volitions but fools us into believing that it is, like Plato's suggestion that cave shadows are reality?

Before continuing, I'm obliged to scope the meaning of consciousness, a nasty undertaking as it remains a treacherous subject to pin down. The experts are far from agreement as to what consciousness is. However, as I am discussing it at length, omitting this imperative will only lead to confusion and complaints. Ned Block (1995), Professor of Philosophy and Psychology at NYU and one of the leading academics studying consciousness, bemoans the consciousness swamp and highlights the difficulty of defining consciousness. "The concept of consciousness is a hybrid, or better, a mongrel concept: the word 'consciousness' connotes a number of different concepts and denotes a number of different phenomena." (p. 227) For some, consciousness is simply subjective states of awareness or sentience while awake or not sleeping. Block disagrees and instead identifies four modes: phenomenal consciousness or P-consciousness, access consciousness or A-consciousness, monitoring consciousness, and self-consciousness. P-conscious states are experiential, *what something is like*. Block includes sensations, feelings, and perceptions, thoughts, desires, and emotions in P-consciousness. A-consciousness is content derived from P-consciousness that is poised for use in reasoning, rational control of action, or for rational control of speech. Self-consciousness is intuitively as it sounds—

having a concept of the self and the ability to use this concept in thinking about oneself. Also like it sounds, monitoring consciousness is the perception or awareness of internal states. It is its own category because it can observe the activities of any and all of the other consciousness states.

There are many more interpretations of consciousness. I like neuroscientists Antonio Damasio (2000) and Gerald Edelman's (2004) definitions, in part because they are similar and have only two components. Damasio's core consciousness and Edelman's primary consciousness equate roughly to the capacity of animals to interact with their environments but with limited ability to recall the past, to weigh future actions, and a minimal concept of self. Damasio and Edelman describe extended consciousness and higher-order consciousness respectively as pertaining to the self-awareness that humans and perhaps some other animals have. "Higher-order consciousness involves the ability to be conscious of being conscious," Edelman says. (p. 134)

Damasio's extended consciousness derives from the sense of self, part of most animals' core consciousness that is extensively accessed and reiterated in the form of acquired autobiographical memories.

> Extended consciousness is the precious consequence of two enabling contributions: First, the ability to learn and thus retain records of myriad experiences, previously known by the power of core consciousness. Second, the ability to reactivate those records in such a way that, as objects, they, too, can generate a "sense of self knowing," and thus be known. (p. 196)

Because no single definition of consciousness prevails, the use of the term consciousness is difficult to maintain consistently. Note that core or primary consciousness applies to virtually all animals with nervous systems, but this is not what I mean when I refer to consciousness. For our purposes consciousness means those characteristics that make humans cognitively different from other animals; what makes us special. Many people believe non-human animals are conscious, and clearly many animals have sophisticated learning and memory skills, even self-awareness, but it is the combination of these cognitive features that makes Homo sapiens remarkable. The consciousness intended here refers to the ingredients that truly makes us unique and gives us our singular capabilities. Higher-order consciousness is specific to humanity and involves the internal narrator, the voice in our head that we sense as our mind reflecting our thoughts in mostly language form. From this we have the perception of introspection, of looking inwards, of being aware of being aware. That this inner dialog reveals itself as self-awareness explicitly unmasks a sense of self and, therefore, a corollary concept of non-self. This is the source and beginning of the awareness of opposites, which enables a theory of mind — the knowledge that another person can have their own thoughts different from yours.

Included in this description of consciousness is the novel recombination of knowledge with past experiences — creativity — and projecting possible scenarios into the future. These capacities give humans the vast power to learn and to modify their environment within their lifetime — culture — which is a huge achievement and permits humans to pass incredible amounts of proficiency and information to their progeny and tribe. Without a doubt, human culture, buttressed by consciousness, has enabled humans to settle in almost every part of the globe and altered every aspect of the natural world. Consciousness is the label I use to identify the idiomatic skill set that humans possess that makes us remarkable on earth.

I want to emphasize, though, that higher-order consciousness does *not* mean higher consciousness, the new-age spirituality that borrows heavily from Eastern mystical traditions like Hinduism and Buddhism. This form of thought and belief belongs specifically within religion's domain.

Having offered a bare-bones definition of consciousness, I have the additional task of clarifying what it means to inhibit or suppress it. Given that the idea of consciousness even needing modulation is new and that we can't pinpoint exactly what consciousness is anyway, this is a difficult job. Having elevated the self-aware internal narrator as best representing consciousness, I want to propose an anecdotal way of thinking about what it means to suppress consciousness. The gift of self-awareness comes in the form of the internal reporter. This inner private discussion manifests as a constant background noise, which much of the time seems to work just fine, but at other times, such as under stress, illustrates the disadvantages of consciousness. In any given situation each of us has the opportunity to assign values (that inform decisions) to the span of possible outcomes. Where in the range of good and bad does a situation fall? The problem is that having consciousness primarily means having awareness, but it doesn't inherently also provide answers or solutions to the options provided by the environment. What we will see shortly is that, for the most part, the internal conversation we have with ourselves is mostly reporting to us what we already know and offers little in the way of true knowledge or useful advice. It is the nature of consciousness to tout its own importance, to whisper in our inner ear that it is in control, watching, observing, and formulating the next plan of action. For the most part, it is not doing these things and actually gets in the way at least as much as or even more than it contributes.

The easiest way, if not the best way, to think about what it means to inhibit consciousness is to describe it by its conventional characteristics like we did for consciousness itself. For instance, in the first chapter, I cited Newberg saying that mysticism silences the conscious mind and frees the mind's awareness from the limiting grip of the ego. Quieting the conscious mind is one example of inhibiting consciousness. When we get to the chapter on ritual, we will look at a paper that finds that religious rituals swamp working memory. Working memory is closely tied to awareness of our immediate environment, sense of recent activity, and ability to apply rational thinking. Religious rituals seem to scramble aspects of what we think of as consciousness. As we explore the manifestations of religious behavior later in the book, we will see more descriptions that suggest an interference with awareness consciousness, our sense of self, and serial thinking processes.

# The Split Brain

An early indication of the surprising effects on consciousness of alterations to the brain came from attempts to curb the deleterious effects of epilepsy. In severe forms of epilepsy the seizure began as a storm of neural activity localized in a specific brain region but then spread throughout the brain leading to the acute seizure symptoms associated with the disease. Preventing the migration of this neural storm throughout the brain was achieved in the 1960s by a procedure called a commissurotomy that severed the corpus callosum, a thick band of nerves that connects the brain's left and right hemispheres. (Drugs are now preferred to control epilepsy.)

Roger Sperry and his student Michael Gazzaniga at Caltech (whose quote we saw about the minimal influence of consciousness) set up formal experiments to test if these patients suffered any consequences from the surgery. They discovered a startling result in these split-brain people, who superficially looked and acted as normal as a non-split-brain person. When presented with pictures or printed words to either the left or right visual field, a split-brain patient had the peculiar inability to verbally identify the visual image reaching her right hemisphere but didn't have that problem for the visual image reaching her left hemisphere. The researchers found that, since the language center of the brain is in the left hemisphere, the visual cues from the right visual field, which were processed in the left hemisphere, could be passed to the language center and therefore verbally represented—spoken. Cues from the left visual field processed by the right hemisphere were cut off from the language center on the left and therefore were unable to be verbalized. In other words, when the word or object *hammer* was presented to the left hemisphere, the subject said, "hammer," but when presented to the right hemisphere, the subject didn't know or couldn't report seeing the word. (Gazzaniga, 2000)

As a check on his conclusions, Gazzaniga put several items next to the subject, but the objects were screened so the subject couldn't see them. A picture of one of the objects was presented to the left visual field (the right hemisphere visual cortex), the one that would not result in speaking the name of the object. The subjects were asked to feel with their left hand (controlled by the right hemisphere motor cortex) and find the physical object that was seen on the card from among the several items. The subjects performed this task successfully and consistently.

To review these results: a picture or word presented to the left visual field could not be acknowledged and spoken by the subject, but the subject could tactilely select that same object from among several other objects. Additional observations showed that in some cases the right hand literally did not know what the left hand was doing. One hand might be pulling up the subject's pants while the other hand was trying to pull them down. In another experiment, the split-brain subjects could not verbalize the names of Adolph Hitler and Johnny Carson from photos shown to the left visual field. However, with their left hands (right hemisphere) they signaled a vigorous "thumbs down" for the dictator and "thumbs up" for the comedian. (Schiffer, 2000, p. 88)

Brenda Milner, also a researcher in Sperry's lab, described showing a "sexy" picture to a split-brain woman's left visual field. The woman claimed she saw nothing unusual, but showed the emotional signs of embarrassment: flushing in the face and giggling. Her right brain registered an emotion, but her left brain could not understand it or at least indicate the proper integration of the experience. There was a disconnect between the visual experience and the signal to the language centers. Milner interpreted the woman's awkwardness by saying,

> This young woman—NG—she blushed a little. Of course, emotion can get transmitted by lower centers that are not separated [by the commissurotomy surgery], you see. So, this patient probably felt a bit uncomfortable. And the left hemisphere said, "Oh, Dr. Sperry, what a strange machine you have there," or made some comment about the machine, or what Sperry was doing. Because she obviously had no idea of what actually had happened—did not have access—but had access to the emotion and was rationalizing, trying to understand the way she was feeling, I suppose. (Campbell, 2008, p. 18)

In another experiment, Gazzaniga (1998b), working with Alan Kingstone at the University of Alberta, asked subjects to draw images of the words presented. The researchers showed the word *bow* to one hemisphere and *arrow* to the other, then asked the split-brain subject to draw what was seen.

> To our surprise, our patient drew a bow and arrow! It appeared as though he had internally integrated the information in one hemisphere; that hemisphere had, in turn, directed the drawn response.
>
> We were wrong. We finally determined that integration had actually taken place on the paper, not in the brain. One hemisphere had drawn its item—the bow—and then the other hemisphere had gained control of the writing hand, drawing its stimulus—the arrow—on top of the bow. The image merely looked coordinated. We discovered this chimera by giving less easily integrated word pairs like "sky" and "scraper." The subject did not draw a tall building; instead he drew the sky over a picture of a scraper...Finally, we tested to see whether each hemisphere could, on its own, integrate words. We flashed "fire" and then "arm" to the right hemisphere. The left hand drew a rifle rather than an arm on fire, so it was clear that each hemisphere was capable of synthesis.
> (p. 52)

Each brain hemisphere controlled the graphic representation of the written word through its opposite hand, but only one hemisphere, the left, was capable of verbally expressing what was observed. Knowledge of the written word or image existed intact regardless of the ability to communicate this knowledge through language.

What about other brain lesion examples that aren't derived from the split-brain subjects? Ramachandran (2004) describes a condition called blindsight discovered by British psychologist Lawrence Weiskrantz. Damage to the visual cortex on one side of the brain results in the experience of blindness in the opposite side eye. (Recall that the left hemisphere of the brain controls the right side of the body and vice versa.) A blindsight patient whose right visual cortex is damaged perceives she is blind to everything to the left of her nose when looking straight ahead.

> [Weiskrantz] showed the patient a little spot of light in the blind region and asked what he saw. The patient said "nothing" as would be expected. But then [Weiskrantz] asked the patient to reach out and touch the light, even though he couldn't see it. "But I can't see it," said the patient. "How do you expect me to point to it?" Weiskrantz said to try anyway; take a guess. To the researcher's surprise, the patient reached out and pointed accurately to the dot that he could not apparently consciously perceive. After hundreds of trials it became obvious that he could point with 99 percent accuracy, even though he claimed on each trial that he was just guessing. (p. 28)

Again, there is a disconnect between the conscious perception—what the person consciously senses or knows—and the person's actual ability or functioning separate from consciousness. This disconnect manifests repeatedly in various ways. Some of this is due to the multiple pathways that information travels in the brain. There are both higher level (neocortical) pathways and lower level pathways—the limbic system where emotions are managed, for example—that handle incoming sensory messages.

Joseph LeDoux (1996), a Professor of Neuroscience and Psychology at NYU, uncovered such a situation in rats. LeDoux conditioned the animals to associate a sound with a mild electric shock. Eventually the sound by itself would cause an elevated heart rate in the animals indicative of a stress reaction. Next LeDoux lesioned the pathway to the auditory cortex in the higher neocortex. Now the animal was theoretically deaf, but when the conditioned sound was played, the animal still showed signs of stress and elevated heart rate. LeDoux knew the sound caused this response because when a different sound, not associated with shock, was played, no fear response occurred. Conversely, when only a lower region was lesioned—the thalamus in this case—the animal showed no emotional response to the conditioned sound. LeDoux showed that normally the auditory input arrives at the thalamus, which then forwards the auditory signal to several areas including the higher auditory cortex as well as the amygdala in the limbic system where emotional responses are regulated. The pathway to the limbic system generated a quick, emotional, and unconscious response to the sound stimulus while the pathway to the neocortex made the sound input available for further integration and interaction with additional brain centers. (p. 152)

Similarly in the case of blindsight, Ramachandran explains that the patient is blind due to damage to what he calls the new pathway of the visual cortex, but the patient still has the other old pathway going through his brain stem and superior colliculus. The visual message doesn't reach the visual cortex through the damaged pathway that would make the person consciously aware of it, but takes a separate route, which allows the patient to locate the object in space. The visual message is relayed from the occipital to the parietal lobe, which guides the hand to point to the (seemingly) invisible object. The separate brain modules interact rather independently. Ramachandran interprets the blindsight sufferer as not conscious of the light because the subject verbalizes that he can't see it.

So is the patient truly blind or is this better attributed to consciousness blindness? The blindsight person's eyes perceive the spot of light. The visual information reaches the visual cortex in the occipital (rear) region of the brain where it registers its position in space and is then shunted off to other parts of the brain including the motor cortex where muscle and motion control occurs. However, pathways necessary to inform the consciousness areas are damaged, so short circuits the visual message to awareness. Alternatively, the visual signal from the light may reach awareness consciousness, but then doesn't reach the language centers of the brain and cannot be reported.

Can someone be conscious of an external or internal event if they are unable to verbalize it? We've already noted that the split-brain patients communicated nonverbally by manually selecting or drawing an object or indicating thumbs up or thumbs down. The subjects showed clearly that they could identify an object based on a visual cue without the involvement of verbal language. Does this show a deficiency in consciousness or solely with language?  Does consciousness require language?

# Brain of Non-Requirement

Blindsight and other brain lesion defects confirm similar multiple pathway patterns in humans as LeDoux showed in rats. This gives credence to the conclusion that some older pathways work completely outside the purview of consciousness, while other pathways, more recently evolved, feed the newer neocortex where they contribute to higher-level cognition. This means that much brain activity can take place before consciousness has a chance to collect and process input. This raises a thorny issue: how can we know if consciousness is achieved or involved if it can't be communicated?

Ornstein (1997) described an example of a visual defect in right-brain-damaged people (not as a result of commissuratomy). Patients were presented with two simple line drawings of houses, one to each visual field. The drawings were identical except for fire coming out of a window on the right house.

> When right-hemisphere-damaged patients look at these, they say, amazingly, that they're the same, but when asked which might be a nicer place to be, they all say they'd like to live in the left house (without the fire). If you ask them why, they say, "No idea," or "I always pick the one on the left," or "It just looks nicer." (p. 77)

It's not that language doesn't exist but that the intrinsic knowledge was not available to the language centers and could not be verbally expressed. The integration of information (house on fire) took place without the involvement of language. Verbal speech, of course, isn't the only form of human dialog. Nonverbal communication—facial expression, prosody (patterns of rhythm, stress, and intonation in speech), gesture and body language—all indicate meaning and intention. Examples were given previously that clearly showed a form of cognition outside spoken language.

Alternatively, can thinking be the basis of measuring or determining consciousness since it doesn't require spoken language to operate? While we sense that we think in language, we also think in non-language symbols, often visual symbols, but all senses contribute. Sounds, smells, and tastes all stimulate emotions, encode and evoke memories, and are retrieved in their own notation and lexicon into thinking. Thinking is another huge topic for discussion that draws on areas such as memory, attention, and so-called reasoning. We will evaluate choice and decision-making in a succeeding chapter, but for now, the short answer is no; thinking is not consciousness and, like other cognitive processes, is generally opaque to self-reflection, although on occasion, it can become available for self-analysis. In general, conscious attention to the thinking process is the exception, not the rule. Recall that at the beginning of this chapter I quoted Lakoff and Johnson who said that at least 95 percent of our *thought* processes are unconscious.

Jonathan Cole (1995) wrote about a very different kind of nerve damage in *Pride and a Daily Marathon* about the pitiable plight of Ian Waterman. At the age of 19 Waterman suffered a degeneration of his sensory nerves that sent information from his body to his brain. He lost his sense of proprioception, the ability to know where his body was in space, something we all do effortlessly and unconsciously. As his symptoms worsened at the onset of the disease, Waterman tried to get out of bed, and "he fell in a heap by the radiator like a pile of wet clothes. What was terrifying was that the reason he fell was not that he had tripped, or that he was weak or faint, but that he could not control and coordinate himself." (p. 11)

Despite Waterman's debilitating condition, he was able to regain a certain amount of self-control. It took not only tremendous will and courage but more importantly he needed to be able to see himself. Rather than his limbs sending his brain position signals, he determined where parts of his body were by observation. He trained himself to be able to control his movements visually. In the dark he was helpless. He overcame, to a degree, his handicap utilizing a different sensory system, his vision, to achieve a modicum of normalcy. This unusual condition shows how much unconscious processes are constantly at work and taken for granted. Mr. Waterman was able to consciously control his body to a certain extent, but it took every ounce of mental energy to do so, and this was solely for controlling his movement. He had to call on higher-order mental processes to compensate for his lack of sensory input, and it was a laborious task. Consider the challenge of controlling all the other functions necessary to prosper while attending to movement. We rely on automatic internal processes for our literal survival.

Proprioception, the sense of one's body in space, is considered a reflex activity that is normally handled below consciousness. It requires not just the innervation of neurons from the peripheral nervous system outside the skull and spinal column, but specific brain regions to receive and process those signals. Many people assume that most mental activity, however, is not reflexive and is controlled by conscious processes. How do they know that? Because consciousness tells them that this is so, but in reality, people have no insight into how they move neural impulses through their brains. The brain's cognitive systems, no differently than the peripheral nervous system, function beyond awareness access. Sometimes sensations and the results of mentality reach our awareness, but that is incidental more than integral. Consciousness is a news reporter who tells you he is fair and balanced yet is anything but.

All these instances of lesions or other nerve damage—and there are many more types with similarly bizarre consequences—highlight the ways in which specific brain areas are responsible for specific functions. Normal people don't think twice about their cognitive abilities and struggle to imagine what it would be like to suffer from one of these conditions. The extremely complex interplay of neurons, neurotransmitters, blood flow, and other biochemical processes must work precisely in order for us to survive. Humans have amazing capabilities, but it all has to start with brain biomechanics, which are taken as given until something goes wrong. The integration of the brain's many functional modules is so seamless that we are completely unaware of the rapid, dynamic neural interactions constantly taking place. Because awareness consciousness and language are perceived to be closely tied in normal behavior, people assume they are closely connected or even part of the same functional system, if indeed, consciousness is even found to be a specific module, which hasn't yet been established. While consciousness and language may closely interact, they are separate and functionally distinct.

It happens that consciousness informs us that our ability to make choices and ultimately, to have culture, is free from the constraints of our nature, our instinct. Because of this, many people want to believe that our biology does not determine our behavior. People invest a great deal of psychic energy in the conviction that human nurture is independent and superior to human nature. That is wishful thinking, and the evidence doesn't bear this out. Nurture and its offspring, culture, are not separate from nature. They are not only a part of it, but are deeply rooted in it. Compare learning a new language right now compared to how you learned language as a 3-year old. How much is consciousness involved in each scenario? You will never have the capacity to learn language as easily as you did as a toddler. That is due to limitations of brain development and is just one more example of how biology circumscribes what is possible.

Humans are programmed to be capable of learning a tremendous amount, but the underlying mechanism for learning is no different than in other animals. On the spectrum of blank slate learning at one end and determinism at the other, humans are slightly farther from determinism and closer to pure learning than other animals, but that distance separating us from other animals is small. We humans see everything that makes us special in that narrow gap from our animal brethren, but its importance is far oversold. We have a wider range of behavioral choices, but it is not limitless. In fact, as we will see in the next chapter, too much choice is a problem. On the learning-determinism scale we're still much closer to determinism. However, it is that slight extra distance farther away from determinism than other animals that gives us our humanity but also causes psychological problems and gives rise to mechanisms such as religion necessary to pull us back closer to our instincts.

We're in a revolutionary time in that our grasp of our own cognition is being upended by neuroscience, and it flies in the face of everyday experience as well as inflaming historical debates about human nature. People have complete and utter faith that they control their own volition and will based on the constant input and feedback of consciousness. However, what is continuously reported by consciousness is not equivalent or contemporaneous with actual events, and the role and function of consciousness is completely different from what it is perceived or sensed to be. It's practically heresy to propose this. Consciousness has important and critical functions, which contribute mightily to the evolutionary success of Homo sapiens, but this doesn't mean that consciousness is solely a boon to the development of culture and society. Humans evolved this wonderful feature called consciousness, which gives us the sense of our own omnipotence, but, to a great degree, it's a cruel ruse. Consciousness creates a mind-cave, convinces us that shadows are reality, and comes with costs and downsides.

In the next chapter I discuss aspects of human cognition that most people attribute to consciousness—choice, decision-making, and logic or rational thought, which reveal the ambiguous nature of consciousness in brain-intact people and underscore the importance of unconscious processes. What we find is that the various so-called benefits of consciousness are inconsistently or marginally present and, as often, delude us or lead us astray creating survival problems that religion (and other mechanisms) evolved to mitigate.

# CHAPTER 3

## CAGE MATCH: THE CONSCIOUS VS. THE UNCONSCIOUS THINKER

Common sense is nothing more than a deposit of prejudices laid down by the mind before you reach eighteen.
*Albert Einstein*

In the last chapter, I described how some kinds of brain lesions or brain damage revealed behaviors that undermine traditional views of consciousness. In this chapter I examine various characteristics attributed to consciousness in non-compromised people: rationality and decision-making, learning, attention, and awareness. Because consciousness remains an ill-defined feature, it's difficult to target any specific cognitive characteristic of consciousness in order to make the case that religion and consciousness are inexorably linked. What rises to the top, however, is consciousness's relatively insignificant role in any cognitive facet of human affairs. Any aspect of consciousness that can be identified turns out to have far less influence in conventional human activity than supposed. Instead, unconscious processes do the heavy lifting. Because they don't reach awareness consciousness, these processes are misunderstood and underappreciated.

Why, then, do atheist exist?

For those who already accept the reality or even possibility of the subservience of consciousness to unconscious mechanisms, this chapter may be unnecessary. The next chapter addresses the specific pitfalls of consciousness, which is a crucial leg of The Split Hypothesis stool. After that, we'll look at religious rituals and their relationship to emotions.

## Overview of Unconscious Influences

Bargh, Chen, and Burrows (1996) studied the role of automaticity: behaviors that bypass consciousness and are unconscious reactions to environmental or internal stimuli. Bargh, who posited that 99.44% of human behaviors are automatic and below consciousness, found that any behavior that can be attributed to conscious motivations can alternatively be found to be triggered by automatic mechanisms that bypass consciousness.

Testing conscious versus unconscious contributions is frequently done by means of subliminal priming. In a typical study, researchers ask the subjects to perform a language task such as a word puzzle or word association. The words, unknown to the subjects, however, are weighted for a particular bias such as generosity. In a second, presumably separate, follow-up experiment, the researchers test the effect of the priming. For example, priming words related to aggression would be tested to see if the subjects would be more likely to give longer shocks to collaborators for giving "wrong" responses, or, in the case of the generosity prime, would subjects be more likely to perceive others as altruistic.

Bargh described a set of experiments in which subjects, college students in an introductory psychology class, were asked to construct a sentence from a series of words. Unbeknownst to the subjects, one group received elderly priming words like old, grey, bingo, and retired that were based on a previous study of the elderly stereotype. A control group received neutral words. After completing the task, the subjects were instructed to go to another room and inform the experimenter that they had finished. The true test of the experiment was to measure the time it took the subject to walk to where the experimenter was. The hypothesis was that the group who had the elderly words would take longer to walk the corridor to the experimenter. Indeed this is what was found. Bargh concluded that "exposing individuals to a series of words linked to a particular stereotype influences behavior nonconsciously." (p. 237)

In another study (p. 238), Bargh gave subjects a tedious and repetitive computer task. As the subjects, all non-African Americans, performed the task, subliminal pictures of either African-American or Caucasian male faces were flashed on the screen. When a subject reached the 130th task, the computer put up a failure message that instructed the subject to begin the task from the beginning. The reactions of the subjects to this bad news were recorded on video. Reviewers, who had no knowledge of the purpose of the experiment or which of the two face groups the subjects had seen, rated the subjects reactions on a hostility scale. The results indicated that those who had been shown the African-American faces displayed more hostility than those who saw the Caucasian faces. As a check, the experimenters gave the participants two questionnaires to evaluate racial feelings. Racial attitudes were found not to be correlated to the hostility measures. Also, the subjects were interviewed afterwards to see if any of them were aware of the faces that were flashed. Only two of the 41 subjects stated that they saw the faces, but these two were unable to identify the race of the faces. None of the participants perceived the experiment was about race.

Overall, experimental priming results in consistent and significant behavioral changes. When subjects are debriefed and told about the priming, they invariably report that they are unaware of any priming taking place. In fact subjects often suggest that, while others are probably vulnerable to the modulating effects of priming, they themselves are not. It's identical to people who proclaim that they are immune to advertising even though they realize that others are susceptible to the media onslaught of promotions we encounter daily.

Studies show that virtually any behavioral modality is susceptible to priming effects. Social norms, emotions, goals and motivation, social behavior, and knowledge structures (stereotypes and trait constructs for use in comprehension and encoding of information) all re-

*consciously rejecting them?*

spond to priming. "Such effects are ubiquitous and pervasive across the major forms of psychological phenomena," Bargh says. (2006, p. 148) Not only that, but any one particular priming stimulus has multiple effects: changing goals, judgments, affective response, and more. Priming produces a range of altered behavioral outcomes compared to non-primed controls. Even the concept of achievement as a motivational goal was shown to lead primed subjects to overcome difficult tasks, obstacles, and interruptions. Subjects who were achievement primed were more likely to continue working longer at tasks than non-primed controls. *Not Me*

Another area of human cognition that responded to unconscious priming was the environment-perception-behavior sequence: external stimuli can lead directly to behavioral responses, bypassing conscious intervention. Behavioral coordination is the phenomenon in which people unconsciously mimic others' body movements or facial expressions and is an example of how small environmental signals can trigger prosocial behaviors. In experiments confederates who purposefully, but subtly, copied subjects' movements were judged more positively by the subjects. Behavioral coordination in general has been shown to increase liking or rapport between people within social groups.

On the other hand, threats to self-esteem caused immediate and reflexive self-defense responses. When people were confronted with negative information about themselves, they automatically and unconsciously worked to restore their self-esteem. They resorted to stereotyping behaviors, drawing upon negative impressions about other people to boost their own self-image. The goal to correct and improve self-worth is a ubiquitous human response.

Bargh points out that many behaviors, which initially require conscious learning, are practiced over time and require less conscious control as skill increases. With repetition behaviors become more automatic. As activities require less conscious observance, they are handed over to unconscious processes and can be triggered or manifested automatically, which frees up limited consciousness resources (see next chapter). The process of automation itself is automatic. As we become adept at a skill such as playing an instrument, we are aware that our proficiency increases, but we are not aware of how the skills required to play the instrument are passed to unconscious mechanisms and require less mental oversight. Practice just makes it happen. While we think of goals as something that we decide to do after thoughtful consideration, that's mostly not the case. People are generally unaware of their goals as well as their efforts to pursue them. Academic degRees?

Consider when a child first begins to learn to speak as a toddler. Every child has the desire to learn to speak, but the child is not conscious of having that desire. We don't think of language acquisition as a goal, but it is, and the goal to learn language is innate — hardwired.

Similarly, adult desires derive from innate and environmentally-driven unconscious forces with conscious aspects layered on top like icing. We see the icing, but not the cake underneath, so we attribute the superficial icing to be the causes of goals. The clearest example of this is sexual behavior. The forces underlying the urge to reproduce are powerful and drive people to behave extremely irrationally. Music and literature are filled with stories of human sexual misadventure. (We'll revisit this theme in the chapters on religious behavior.) In any given culture, the actual modes of courtship vary widely, and people give a great deal of introspective thought to objects of lust and desire. Nevertheless, the underlying drive is instinctual and powered by a genetically built and managed neuroendocrine complex. People presume that many of their other goal-oriented behaviors derive from conscious self-reflection, but goals emanate primarily from unseen lower brain regions. pRiMed?

If any explicit, consciously-intended behavioral outcome is elicited by unconscious mechanisms, the question arises as to whether the ultimate cause is truly conscious reflection. The brain processes that modulate these outcomes look the same regardless if the motivation is conscious or unconscious. If any behavior can be generated from unconscious triggers, what indication is there that so-called conscious intention is responsible for an action rather than by prior unconscious processes? The primary justification for believing we consciously own our own causes is because consciousness says so. People assume that consciousness is the norm, and subliminal messages are an unwelcome or unintentional invasion. Instead, consider that our unconscious sensory apparatus is the norm. Our bodies are attuned to picking up environmental information without our awareness, and subliminal messaging is simply our sensory system doing its job while our focus of attention might be elsewhere. This is a clear-cut benefit for avoiding surprises, some of which could be lethal. These sensory triggers began evolving in the very earliest organisms—the single-cell creatures, and we retain this most important inheritance albeit in a more complex form. Reaching consciousness is an optional component of integrating sensory information, and as we saw with brain-damaged people, unconscious functioning through unacknowledged sensory input occurs properly and fittingly. But all things being equal, shouldn't important sensory input reach consciousness?

## Limits of Attention and Awareness

Attention and awareness are characteristics often associated with consciousness, but how much do they support or contribute to conscious processes? Simons and Chabris (1999) performed the well-known gorilla-basketball study evaluating the role of attention and awareness. The subjects' task was to watch a video of three white-shirt people passing a basketball back and forth and count the number of passes, while at the same time, three black-shirt people were also passing a basketball. Into the midst of this video, a person dressed in a gorilla costume walked into the scene, and, in the middle of the ball passers, faced the camera, pounded its chest, and walked out of frame. The gorilla was completely visible for nine seconds. About 50% of the subjects were so engrossed in counting the passes by the white shirts, they were unaware of the presence of the gorilla. This effect is opposite to that of subliminal messaging. Here there is no attempt to evade conscious attention with millisecond picture flashes or inserting surreptitious words. The presence of the gorilla is explicit but reveals a perceptual failure that scientists call <u>inattentional blindness</u>. Some subjects are so focused on their task that they miss the gorilla's presence.

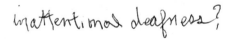 inattentional deafness?

Intuitively we know that far more information is processed by our senses than we can be aware of, and our senses and our brain actively filter input in order to reduce noise and seek relevance. The inability to attend to or be aware of the gorilla is not evidence of not seeing the gorilla. The visual system sees it, but the visual stimulus does not get reported by downstream brain processes. If people can be motivated by subliminal messages flashed at them for fractions of a second that don't rise to awareness consciousness, it's also assuredly the case that the visual system—the eyes and the primary visual cortex in the occipital lobe—receive the image of the gorilla who is just as apparent as any person in the video, but somewhere in the post-processing the gorilla image doesn't make it past a cortical gatekeeper.

Victor Lamme (2003), a Professor of Cognitive Neuroscience at the University of Amsterdam who studies visual consciousness, delineates the differences between attention and awareness and explains why the two are often confabulated. In his article, *Why Visual Attention and Awareness Are Different*, Lamme says that in order for a stimulus to reach awareness, it has to reach a "privileged status" in the brain. Sensory stimuli reach the brain and, via the process of selective attention, some of these reach a conscious state, which enables us to report about them. He says that selective attention is a "process where some inputs are processed faster, better, or deeper than others, so that they have a better chance of producing or influencing a behavioral response or of being memorized." (p. 14) Note that behavioral responses don't always require awareness. "Fully attended stimuli are occasionally not perceived, suggesting that sensory processing does not necessarily always complete to a perceptual stage." (p. 12)

Lamme lists several instances of invisible stimuli or "unconscious" inputs that have cryptic names such as anti-correlated disparity or the non-dominant patterns during perceptual rivalry. More importantly, though, Lamme explains subliminal priming neurologically. "The processing of a stimulus will leave a trace of activated and inhibited neurons that can last for a variable amount of time. The processing of subsequent stimuli might benefit from this trace if the two stimuli share properties (such as retinal position), resulting in attentional priming." (p. 15) Priming inputs such as the implicit meaning of words activate neurons in our brain but never reach consciousness, yet clearly have an impact on behavior. Attention is the process that selects from among all the competing sensory inputs, some of which get passed on for additional handling. This selection process feeds awareness, but is not because of it. A few of these attended inputs can reach the privileged status of awareness, particularly by reaching working memory. Focal attention can also be acquired by conscious intention as in the gorilla ball-passing experiment, but such intentional attention is the exception.

What does this mean about the role of consciousness? When conscious intention grabs the reins, there is likely a converse sacrifice of cognition elsewhere. Some subjects attending to a task, purposively concentrating on counting basketball passes, don't see the gorilla. Conscious focus can blind the person to obvious stimuli while, alternatively, subliminal stimuli can unconsciously change behavioral outputs. It's always a give and take.

Access to the workings of the brain are beyond self-reflection. Neuroscientists can look at the brain in action, but no person can turn their sights inward and perceive the dynamic interactions taking place. And, in fact, those tacit interactions are invisible to self-reflection, and they don't operate in ways that are intuitive. In *Strangers to Ourselves, Discovering the Adaptive Unconscious*, Professor of Psychology Timothy Wilson (2002) points out humans have inherited the nonconscious brains of our animal ancestors.

> It is difficult to know ourselves because there is no direct access to the adaptive unconscious, no matter how hard we try. Because our minds have evolved to operate largely outside of consciousness, and nonconscious processing is part of the architecture of the brain, it may not be possible to gain direct access to nonconscious processes. (p. 16)

# Implicit and Explicit Learning

Explicit learning is another capability associated with human consciousness. Wilson describes explicit learning as focusing conscious intention on a task like learning a foreign language versus implicit learning, which occurs outside conscious intention. He cites a study by Lewicki, Hill, and Bizot (1988) that was performed on psychology professors rather than psychology students, who are the usual guinea pigs. The professors were told that the study was about nonconscious learning, which was true. The subjects of the study, the professors, were asked to indicate in which of four quadrants an X appeared on the computer screen by clicking one of four buttons. Unbeknownst to the subjects, the researchers had programmed some rules into the computer that controlled in which square the X would appear. For example, the X never appeared in the same square twice in a row, and it never returned to a previous square until it had appeared in two other squares. There were several of these different patterns, and some were complex, but the subjects seemed to learn the patterns as their performance on selecting the squares improved over time. At a certain point the sequence rules changed. The subjects made more mistakes, and their response time plummeted.

When interviewed afterwards as to why their performances changed, the psych professors revealed they did not consciously perceive the shift in rules. They acknowledged the change in their task performance but claimed their fingers "suddenly lost their rhythm" or that the experimenters had flashed subliminal pictures on the screen to distract or fool them, which was not the case. The researchers concluded that the initial increase in task performance was due to training occurring as the subjects unconsciously learned the patterns. When the patterns changed, their abilities faltered, and they had no idea that the learning they had achieved was being undermined by the nefarious researchers.

When we have to learn the skeletal system in class or memorize the Gettysburg Address, we are keenly aware of the tedious nature of necessary repetition. As we succeed at a learning task, our aptitude becomes more effortless. We manage to store information in the corners of our brain, but we have no idea how the neurons did it, and how we are able to retrieve the data. At the same time, we take implicit learning for granted because it requires no conscious effort as when we learn to talk as toddlers. Small children effortlessly learn many words a day simply by listening and practicing. Even in adults, unconscious learning is far more common than we might imagine. Implicit learning may slow into adulthood, but it never ceases as the above experiment indicates.

Most behavior is performed without self-awareness consciousness. The flip side of this is when consciousness is intentionally invoked but fails to provide the intended result. While taking a test, you stumble on a question that you know you know the answer to, but can't arrive to it. Similarly, you can picture that actor from that movie but can't remember her name. Later you spontaneously remember the answer or name. You did, indeed, really know the answer, but you couldn't access it in the moment. These are instances in which intentional volition was unsuccessful. Your marvelous brain was unable to reach into that neural storage area and pull out the requisite information. We really don't understand how to make our brains function. Our bulbous cortex just does, sometimes well, sometimes less well.

This is one of those cases that highlights the differences between brains and computers. When a computer searches its memory for stored information, it does so using memory addresses that it keeps and manages. Without maintaining an index of memory addresses, the stored information is inaccessible. If humans have the equivalent of an index of memory addresses, we are unconscious of it. The brain has the equivalent of a database of memories, but we have no idea how it works, at least from an awareness point of view. I may instruct myself to retrieve the capital of Nepal and verbalize it, but I'm not saying, "go to brain sector 47B in the hippocampus and return its contents." Opaque, unconscious processes in our brains make it happen.

In *On Being Certain: Believing You Are Right Even When You're Not*, Robert Burton (2008) promotes the premise that people's beliefs, attitudes, and even intelligence are based, not on conscious rational thought, but on the feeling of knowing.

We know the nature and quality of our thought via feelings, not reason. Feelings such as certainty, conviction, rightness and wrongness, clarity, and faith arise out of involuntary mental sensory systems that are integral and inseparable components of the thoughts that they qualify. (p. 139)

Burton feels it unequivocally when he states,

There is no isolated circuitry within the brain that can engage itself in thought free from involuntary and undetectable [unconscious] influences. Without this ability, certainty is not a biologically justifiable state of mind...But abandoning or even qualifying the idea of the self-examining mind flies in the face of every fact of contemporary thought. (p. 141)

Scientists and non-scientists alike have a devil of a time relinquishing their belief in objectivity and free will. In one example, Burton takes umbrage with Malcolm Gladwell, author of bestseller *Blink: The Power of Thinking Without Thinking*. Gladwell, who said Timothy Wilson's "*Strangers to Ourselves* is probably the most influential book I've ever read," isn't completely ready to jump on the inaccessible unconscious bandwagon. Burton quotes Gladwell who said,

When our powers of rapid [unconscious] cognition go awry, they go awry for a very specific and consistent set of reasons, and those reasons can be identified and understood. It is possible to learn when to listen to that powerful onboard computer, and when to be wary of it.

Just as we can teach ourselves to think logically and deliberately, we can also teach ourselves to make better snap judgments. (p. 147)

What part of us can teach ourselves to think logically and deliberately? After lauding *Strangers to Ourselves*, which virtually rules out conscious access to the unconscious mind, Gladwell proposes using some higher aptitudes available to us. It's wishful thinking, and Gladwell is certainly not alone in preserving this hope.

Burton also disputes the late Harvard biologist, Stephen Jay Gould, who said, "Objectivity resides in recognizing your preferences and then subjecting them to especially harsh scrutiny." (p. 157) Gould adheres to the typical optimism that we have a way out of our unconscious bind and that we must have self-control and free will. If we can recognize and scrutinize our preferences and biases, we can moderate or redirect our cognitive processes. The rational mind must be maintained, yet it is not to be. "Introspection will, at best, only result in a partial view of our minds at work," Burton writes. "Complete objectivity is not an option." (p. 159) It isn't that we humans have no conscious control or ability to intercede in our unconscious processes; we're just very limited. And such efforts are the exception rather than the rule.

## The Logic of the Decider

So you want to get a new smart phone or TV or car? There are fifty models available in the store for any of these items. But then there's several other stores carrying more options. And the Internet gives you access to all the rest—literally hundreds of choices. Which one is right for you? Can you find the combination of features you're looking for? Do you need all the features offered or even know what you want? Do you even understand what all the features do? How much do people even know about the products they already own? Most people don't know more than the basics about the functions in their digital cameras, options in their DVD players, or even the settings in their microwave. How do people determine what they want? A common assumption is that decision-making is the result of higher cognitive processes, the rational brain sifting all the evidence and arriving at the most logical outcome. In reality, nothing is further from the truth.

A study by Sheena Iyengar of Columbia University and Mark Lepper of Stanford (2000) looked at how available choices had an inverse affect on buying. They set up a jam tasting table in a busy upscale

California grocery store. In one test they presented six jam choices and on a separate day presented 24 jam choices. The shoppers could taste as many or as few of the available jams as they wished. The researchers found that 30% of the six-jam table tasters bought jam compared to only 3% of 24-jam table tasters. Too many choices overwhelmed and disincentivized consumers.

Humans' cognitive ability is finite and one way this shows up is in decision-making capacity. Swarthmore College Professor of Psychology Barry Schwartz (2000) explains that despite the noble notion that freedom of choice is a good thing, too much choice swamps our mental apparatus. In our modern consumer society we are bombarded with purchasing choices as well as mate choices, career choices, and lifestyle choices. Schwartz suggests that this plethora of choices can actually result in discontent, even unhappiness and dysfunction. He points to a 2003 *Journal of the American Medical Association* study suggesting that too much choice has led to a 300% increase in clinical depression over the last 25 years of the twentieth century. "Some estimates are that depression is ten times more likely to afflict someone now than at the turn of the [twentieth] century." (p. 85)

People believe that unlimited choice is preferred and even beneficial. After all, we live in a free society, and what exemplifies freedom more than unlimited choice? But Schwartz says this belief is misplaced and downright sinister. "This aspiration to self-determination, presumably through processes resembling those of rational choice, is a mistake both as an empirical description of how people act and as a normative ideal." (p. 80)

Consider that for the first few million years of human existence people lived in societies that offered minimal choices. Early humans passed on cultural mores and customs such as toolmaking and religious ritual from generation to generation that changed little over thousands of years. For over 99% of human existence people lived in tribal societies in which long-standing traditions dictated the way in which people lived. This is not accidental. People, or other animals for that matter, are not designed by evolution to be able to choose among myriad options. Between the way the senses filter and refine input and the way the central nervous system preferentially processes information, humans are predisposed to interpret and react to the world in ways that obviate most conscious options. Despite humans having the greatest flexibility of any animal to learn, imagine, and consider alternatives, such conscious behavior still comprises a minimal amount of our activity.

Nevertheless, the adherence to and unquestioning of traditional social codes have slowly waned. In the last hundred years, societies have undergone radical changes in which traditions have fallen away to be replaced by lifestyles. There suddenly exists a multitude of choices that humans have never had to face before whether we want them or not. People are ill-prepared to obtain and study all the aspects and consequences required to make a truly informed decision. And that assumes that people have the mental equipment to even make rational decisions—a bad assumption.

It's a deeply-held conviction that we have the consciousness-enabled freedom to determine our future. The cognitive development we call consciousness evolved in parallel with religion for at least the last hundred thousand years. Consciousness makes humans perceive that they have a modicum of self-control, but that is mostly an illusion created by consciousness. The human ability to choose and decide derives from so-called cognitive biases that themselves evolved much earlier in our animal forebears. After briefly posing the challenge of too much choice, we now turn to specific modes of human decision-making. What are some examples of cognitive biases, and how do they impact human behavior?

## How We Decide

In a study by Christopher K. Hsee and his team at the University of Chicago (2003), college students were presented with doing a task for six minutes, which would get them a reward of vanilla ice cream. Alternatively, those who worked at the task for seven minutes got pistachio ice cream. Three-quarters of the students chose vanilla, partly because they preferred vanilla, but also for the shorter task-time. A separate group of students were given the same choices except that the six minute group received 60 points, which earned them vanilla versus 100 points for the seven minute group, which earned them pistachio. Over half of the second group chose pistachio because of the perceived higher point value despite the same actual compensation of ice cream as the first group. A rational chooser seemingly would have seen that the real reward was based purely on ice cream preference or on willingness to save an extra minute of work.

One could argue that college students are generally highly motivated and responsive to virtual or intangible rewards like points. While they are conditioned to correspond points to grades, this doesn't diminish the problem of choosing. What constitutes the best goal or result? Even in retrospect the best choice may not be obvious or rationally obtained. Certainly each person has her own basis for valuing the available choices. Is there an intuitive highest desired end that scientists agree is optimum?

In his popular book, *Predictably Irrational*, Professor of Behavioral Economics Dan Ariely (2008) asserts,

> We are pawns in a game whose forces we largely fail to comprehend. We usually think of ourselves as sitting in the driver's seat, with ultimate control over the decisions we make and the direction our life takes; but, alas, this perception has more to do with our desires—with how we want to view ourselves—than with reality. (p. 243)

Ariely reviews a number of studies that illustrate how decisions result from unconscious compunctions. A simple experiment he performed looked at people's ordering behavior in restaurants. Ariely compared what people ordered when dictating to a waitperson compared to what they ordered if they wrote their order on paper without consulting their companions. When subjects didn't know what their friends ordered, they presumably requested exactly what they wanted. However, when verbalizing their orders, patrons tended to opt for items that their companions hadn't ordered or that they thought would impress them. Ariely noted that uniqueness can be seen as a desirable trait in some cultures, so he also looked at cultures where conformity is important and found that, indeed, in conformity-valuing cultures, people changed their orders to be the same as others. In both instances, however, some people ordered differently based on their companions' preferences rather than what they would have otherwise chosen. In both cases this resulted in some people not enjoying their food and drink as much as if they had gotten what they had originally or tacitly wanted. (pp. 233-238) This is not meant to criticize people's motivations, but only to emphasize different inclinations at work and that people are mostly unaware of these forces.

> While these [motivational] influences exert a lot of power over our behavior, our natural tendency is to vastly underestimate or completely ignore this power. These influences have an effect on us not because we lack knowledge, lack practice, or are weak-minded. On the contrary, they repeatedly affect experts as well as novices in systematic and predictable ways. The resulting mistakes are simply how we go about our lives, how we "do business." They are a part of us.

> Our visual and decision environments are filtered to us courtesy of our eyes, our ears, our senses of smell and touch, and the master of it all, our brain. By the time we comprehend and digest information, it is not necessarily a true reflection of reality. Instead, it is our representation of reality, and this is the input we base our decisions on. In essence we are limited to the tools nature has given us, and the natural way in which we make decisions is limited by the quality and accuracy of these tools. (p. 243)

Psychologists Amos Tversky and Daniel Kahneman (1981) are the godfathers of the study of human choice. They have closely examined if people are rational or logical in their decision-making processes. In a typical experiment they begin by proposing a situation to their subjects. (The percentage of subjects who chose each option are in brackets.)

> Imagine that the U.S. is preparing for the outbreak of an unusual Asian disease, which is expected to kill 600

people. Two alternative programs to combat the disease have been proposed. Assume that the exact scientific estimate of the consequences of the programs are as follows: If Program A is adopted, 200 people will be saved. [72%] If Program B is adopted, there is 1/3 probability that 600 people will be saved, and 2/3 probability that no people will be saved. [28%] (p. 453)

Statistically, these are identical outcomes, but despite that, the majority selects Program A because of the certainty of saving 200 people. This is called a risk averse preference.

The researchers then reframe the question to a different group of subjects: "If Program C is adopted 400 people will die. [22%] If Program D is adopted there is 1/3 probability that nobody will die, and 2/3 probability that 600 people will die. [78%]" In this case the majority selects the second option, which is the risk taking option. In both instances, the choices were set up for an equal result, but were framed differently. The subjects' decisions were not made based on a cold, logical mathematical analysis. We might expect closer to a 50-50 response if that were the case. *some are math challenged*

Obviously most people don't have a masterful grasp of statistics, but it still begs the question of what constitutes decision-making criteria. Tversky and Kahneman state that people make judgments based on heuristic or common sense principles: intuitions, so-called educated guesses, and rules of thumb. (Tversky and Kahneman, 1974, p. 1124) Their research undermines attributing logic or rationality as a primary component of human decision-making. This isn't to say that there's no conscious, rational aspect to decision-making or that deductive reasoning doesn't exist; only that it's extremely limited in scope. What then are these heuristic principles and how do they guide us? *what about us (AOF)*

# Our Biased Nature

The predilections and prejudices we inherit through evolution are collectively called cognitive biases. What the work of Tversky, Kahneman, and others show is that the various human cognitive capacities such as judgment, memory, belief, and motivation, are imbued with cognitive biases. There are many observed and described cognitive biases, which each render behavioral results that have been adaptively favored by evolution. An example is representativeness, which is a fancy way of saying stereotyping. We imagine an introvert would not be a salesman, for example. Humans have a long history of enlisting representativeness or stereotyping in sociopolitical posturing, and it is deeply embedded in our psyches.

Both pareidolia and subjective validation are cognitive biases that describe types of wishful thinking and often permeate religious beliefs. Pareidolia is when something innocuous or random is instilled with special significance like seeing the Virgin Mary in a tree trunk or in a rock formation. Subjective validation is the habit of seeing coincidences in unrelated events. Many of us are guilty of thinking that some behavior or item of clothing affects our favorite sports team and as long as the team is winning, we continue to wear the item or repeat the behavioral charms. We do this despite knowing full well deep down that these are just superstitions (or do we?), but that doesn't stop us.

Another bias is availability, the tendency to focus on what's common, familiar, and easily brought to mind. In one experiment, subjects listened to a list of well-known people. At the end, the subjects were asked to guess if the list contained more men or women. "In each of the lists, the subjects erroneously judged that the class (sex) that had the more famous personalities was the more numerous." (Tversky and Kahneman, 1974, p. 1127) The more the subjects recognized the names, the more often they were retained in memory and counted, which caused subjects to deviate from an accurate assessment.

A version of the availability bias is the availability cascade, which occurs in social settings. It "is a self-reinforcing process of collective belief formation by which an expressed perception triggers a

*Religion*

chain reaction that gives the perception of increasing plausibility through its rising availability in public discourse." (Kuran and Sunstein, 1999) In other words, if you repeat something over and over again, it becomes true. This is a common technique used in the political sphere to rally the masses. Availability cascade is an essential component of propaganda and works all too well. *Religion*

A different bias also has implications for politics. Miller and Krosnick (1998) study how the order of candidates on a ballot affects voters' preferences. They find a consistent two percent benefit to the candidate listed first on the ballot, and in the United States, this takes into account the number of registered Democrats and Republicans in any particular precinct. Krosnick attributes this to the primacy affect, a type of cognitive bias in which the first instance or event is preferred. While two percent may seem small, that difference could have changed the outcome of many elections including the 2000 U.S. presidential election.

The belief that conscious choice and decision-making are based on considered objective judgment is pervasive. We sense and feel it. Indeed, the radiant light of our consciousness is like a jealous lover or ensconced bureaucrat. "I will not be ignored. I have the power and control. You can't turn your back on me. You need me. You can't live without me." From the beginning of the written word, philosophers have adhered to and succumbed to consciousness's plaintive entreaties, but the relentless goddess of science is telling us we've got it all wrong. The evidence indicates that there is no pure rationality and that heuristics, a combination of inherited and learned biases, primarily determine choices and judgment. The prevalence of cognitive biases and active sensory filtering indicates that consciousness is not first in line to provide decisions and motivation. Consciousness is just another component of broader forces at work.

The Split Hypothesis purports that consciousness and religion co-evolved because, as the neocortex grew and programmed an enormous capacity for memory and learning, humanity was (somewhat) freed from the strictures of instinct. The cognitive flexibility to think outside the box of instinct enabled human creativity and inventiveness while deviating from innate, genetically-driven directives. Behavior once dictated primarily through genes was amended by a cognitive versatility that, through the tools of consciousness, allowed for a wider behavioral repertoire while imbuing people with self-awareness of their own thinking, reasoning, and the perception of volitional attention and intention. Consciousness gave humans culture, the ability to modify their environment within their own lifetime, and the capacity to pass cultural knowledge forward through generations.

We feel that our consciousness dominates or overrides instincts, but this is not the case at all. Instincts are evolved adaptations that ensure evolutionary success and remain the primary motivators despite our conscious sense of self. Consciousness evolved because it occasionally contributed beneficial insights, but recent investigations reveal that consciousness also misinterprets input and misdirects output based on sketchy decision-making processes. Too much choice is not only overwhelming, but is, in a sense, the burden humans inherited with the advent of consciousness—the punishment acquired with the expulsion from the Garden of Eden. "Unconstrained freedom leads to paralysis and becomes a kind of self-defeating tyranny," Schwartz says. (2000, p. 81)

In this chapter, I describe many ways in which the unconscious contributes to behavior. The hope here is to plant a seed of doubt in the prevailing dogma that humans are in control of their own behavior, and that consciousness is the executor of that control. In the next chapter, we focus specifically on the downsides of consciousness, which is crucial to The Split Hypothesis. By accepting the possibility that consciousness is not all good, one can entertain the idea that the behaviors of religion function to suppress its emanations, which benefits human evolutionary fitness. *How!?*

*Religion*

# CHAPTER 4

## CONSCIOUSNESS: A PROBLEM THAT NEEDED FIXING

The unconscious self is the real genius.
Your breathing goes wrong the moment
your conscious self meddles with it.
*George Bernard Shaw*

Because this castigation of consciousness has been non-intuitive and even distressing for many to contemplate, I spent a couple sections looking at various ways consciousness fails or fools. By looking at split brain and other neurally-compromised patients, I hoped to open the possibility to readers that consciousness didn't function as they believed. I continued to beat this drum by showing how rationality and logic were primarily apparitions of consciousness, and cognitive biases have far more to do with the business of life than so-called conscious reason. If you've made it this far then you've likely not rejected outright the notion that consciousness isn't the executive in charge, and that the majority of human processes, including behavior, function from frog-like null nonconsciousness. Of course the difference between humans and creatures with smaller brains is enormous, but perhaps not quite as enormous as presumed.

*is conscious* [handwritten]

The impediments of consciousness were severe enough during its evolution that, despite its simultaneous advantages, compensating mechanisms, including religion, developed to offset it. This chapter closes out the prolonged discussion of consciousness by addressing its specific drawbacks. After this we begin looking at religion expressly, the main topic of this screed.

In the first section on consciousness, I listed its five problems or drawbacks. First, explanations about one's own behavior are often wrong or false. Second, people draw false conclusions about external events based on conscious introspection. Third, consciousness is latent or tardy in the flow of time. Fourth, consciousness is not the initiator of action. Fifth, consciousness assigns itself the role of initiator when it is not. (Baumeister and Masicampo, 2010, p. 947) Here we dig in and look at these in more detail.

*Brought me to ROF meeting* [handwritten]

## Behind the Times

Benjamin Libet at the University of California upended the consciousness status quo when he determined that conscious awareness always followed after the intention to act was set in motion; consciousness did not precede or start intentional action. Libet set out to determine the relationship between neural signals and willed action—what happens in the brain when it directs a "conscious" act. Using EEG electrodes attached to the scalp to measure brain activity, subjects were asked to perform simple movements like bend a finger or wrist or press a button. The subject would indicate when she was first aware of the desire to act. The researchers determined that it took 200 milliseconds—a fifth of a second—from the subject reporting or indicating the perception of conscious will to performing the physical action. When the EEG recordings of the corollary brain activity were compared to the physical action, they showed a full half second had elapsed between the initiating brain activity in the secondary motor cortex and the actual motion. It took a third of a second from the time the motor cortex initiated the instruction to act before the subject was conscious of the intention to act. In other words, the initiation of action took place significantly

*Finger movements*

before sensing the conscious intention to act. (The time lapses for reporting of the awareness to act were taken into account as were several other parameters that affected the timing.) What Libet found was that the order of brain events for an action was motor cortex > (sometimes) conscious intention > action, rather than conscious intention > motor cortex > action. The volition to act was not coming from areas of higher cognition and reasoning such as the forebrain but rather from the motor or movement control part of the brain. A full 300 milliseconds later our conscious awareness caught up. Ornstein (1997) concluded, "A 'spontaneous act'...begins before we are aware we have 'decided to act.' " (p. 147)   *Me to AOF?*

Damasio (2000) interprets Libet's experiments by saying,

> By the time you get "delivery" of consciousness for a given object, things have been ticking away in the machinery of your brain for what would seem like an eternity to a molecule...We are always hopelessly late for consciousness and because we all suffer from the same tardiness no one notices it...We are probably late for consciousness by about five hundred milliseconds [half a second]. (p. 127)

Controversy remains about the interpretation of our sense or conviction that our awareness is concurrent with initiation, the will to act. At least one reason for this reticence to accept Libet's findings is the agenda many people have to preserve faith and belief in free will. This is a social, political, and even religious preference, not a scientific one. Reject the science when it's inconvenient to one's position. This is another consequence of the human propensity towards cognitive biases. It's more important to retain belief than deal with challenges to belief.   *Atheist?*

Is there a mechanism that backfills awareness to the instigation time or is our consciousness simply fooling us into believing we are synonymous with intention? Edelman (2004) calls this phenomenon that we sense the volition to act as simultaneous with initiation of action as the *remembered present*. (p. 77) Are our self-conscious observations shifting reality backwards? As Seager (1999) notes, studying consciousness could be "akin to a camera trying to take a picture of itself; the best it can capture are reflections." (p. 252) We sincerely and honestly feel that we instigate actions with our free will, but the evidence, gleaned from neuroscience, indicates our consciousness lacks the ability to discern the source or reason for intention.

T. H. Huxley (1894) intuited the situation long before the science was available to support it.

> It seems to me that in men, as in brutes, there is no proof that any state of consciousness is the cause of change in the motion of the matter of the organism. If these positions are well based, it follows that our mental conditions are simply the symbols in consciousness of the changes which take place automatically in the organisms; and that, to take an extreme illustration, the feeling we call volition is not the cause of a voluntary act, but the symbol of that state of the brain which is the immediate cause of that act. We are conscious automata. (p. 244) *Then we would all be Religious*

Combine the significance of Libet's results with the brain lesion studies. So-called conscious volition occurs some time after the initiation of action. Split brain people are not able to name the thing they are looking at with the left half of their visual field, not even to acknowledge that they even see anything, yet select it correctly from among several other objects purely by feel. Blindsight people correctly point to a spot of light that they claim they can't see. Our ability to function depends on nonconscious brain modules that perform interactively and cooperatively with many other brain modules. Consciousness is ultimately itself a module and an adjunct, an overlay of functionality. Consciousness is an observer after the fact. We (mostly) *know* how to do the things we do without having to consciously sift through, select, retrieve, and implement mental procedures and algorithms. *How did you decide to write this?*

Libet's experiments indicate that our actions derive nonconsciously from deep within our brains while our consciousness is a latent observer, a voyeur if you will. These results have huge implications for all disciplines studying Homo sapiens including the biology of religion and have turned the free will philosophers on their heads. They gamely hold fast to their guns and invoke anti-determinist and anti-reductionist arguments to preserve their agendas. The debate is enjoined and embraced. The truth must be battled out, and everyone must have their say. The science, however, must take precedence over the conscious(!) introspections of philosophers for reasons I hope are obvious here.

## When Consciousness Doesn't Know It's Wrong

Not only is conscious thought late for the train and inaccurate assigning cause to actions, it is often just plain wrong about its judgment and conclusions. Many studies have shown that memory and decision-making are fallible and subject to faulty interpretations, some of which have been described in previous sections. Memory researchers reveal that people's recollection of events over time can change quite dramatically. When confronted with the evidence that their memories don't match their original feelings and beliefs, people will often disbelieve their original opinions preferring to adhere to the perspective of the instant.

In a fascinating experiment Goethals and Reckman (1973) surveyed American high school students about their attitudes towards various social issues including, at that time, the controversial practice of busing students to achieve racial integration. The students formed discussion groups based on their pro- or anti-busing responses. Then a student confederate of the researchers made persuasive arguments opposite to the particular group of students. Many students' opinions not only changed, but when the students were asked to recall what their original opinions had been before the discussions, they perceived them to be much closer to their new positions rather than the positions they had stated in the original survey. Of course people's memories are not always so errant, but we don't have access to know when our memories are accurate or faulty, and our assumptions are that our memories, like our consciousness in general, portray the true nature of the moment. It isn't always the case, and we rarely have the perspicacity to know when our own mental apparatus misleads us.

Alternatively, our unconscious memory may provide us with insight and knowledge despite ourselves. Damasio (2000) describes an institutionalized man who had lost his ability to preserve short-term memories, which also prevented the patient, David, from forming long-term memories. Within moments of people leaving David's presence, he would forget having met them or been with them. Damasio set up an experiment in which collaborators acted towards David as either a good guy, bad guy, or neutral guy. Then David was given pictures of four faces that included one of the three collaborators.

> David behaved in a most spectacular manner. When the individual who had been positive to him was part of the set of four, David chose the good guy over 80 percent of the time, indicating that his choice was clearly not random—chance alone would have made David pick each of the four 25 percent of the time. The neutral individual was chosen with a probability no greater than chance. And the bad guy was almost never chosen, again something that violated chance behavior. (p. 45)

In a second task, David consistently chose the good guy from pictures of the three collaborators when asked to choose which of the three was his friend, despite David's testimony that he had never met or couldn't remember any of these people. Despite David's inability to recall short-term memories—that he had met these collaborators—there still existed an emotional memory that was independent of his autobiographical memory. As we saw in previous chapters, this was likely due to the brain having multiple pathways carrying inputs to different regions. David retained working pathways to store emotionally-based memory information despite his inability to preserve conscious or long-term memories.

Many of the studies I've cited showing the impact of the unconscious brain tend to involve some kind of experimenter subterfuge: flashing subliminal content, influencing perception with laden words, or otherwise manipulating situations to test a hypothesis. But even when experimental subjects are queried in a very straightforward way, they may display startling misconceptions or misjudgments. In a study by Wilson and Kraft, (1993) college students who were dating were asked to evaluate their relationship and how happy they were with their partner. This upfront approach asked the students to self-reflect, a typical indication of conscious effort. Compared to a control group of dating students who didn't analyze their relationships, the analyzers tended to change their attitudes more toward their relationships over time. (Is there any question that people have very little understanding of their attraction to other people to begin with?)

> People brought to mind reasons that conformed to their cultural and personal theories about why people love others and that happened to be on their minds. Because there is a certain arbitrariness to these reasons, they often do not match people's prior feelings perfectly. In fact the reasons people gave bore almost no relationship to how happy they said they were with their relationship a few weeks earlier. But because people do not recognize this fact, they assume that their reasons are an accurate reflection of their feelings, leading to attitude change. In short, people construct a new story about their feelings based on the reasons that happen to come to mind. (Wilson, 2002, p. 169)

When the researchers adjusted the experiment by asking subjects to list reasons why the relationship was developing as it was, those who listed reasons (versus the control group who didn't list reasons) did a poorer job of predicting the longevity of the relationship.

> This is consistent with the notion that when people analyzed reasons, they contracted stories based on faulty data, such as which aspects of the relationship were easiest to put into words, which were on their minds or were consistent with their theories about how they should feel, leading to attitudes that were less well informed than those of people in the control group, who just gave their unanalyzed, gut feelings. (p. 171)

Emotions are the actual basis of intrinsic knowledge, not consciousness, which has little overall insight. This is exactly why consciousness is a problem, and why mechanisms are necessary to, at times, subdue consciousness.

## The Knock on Free Will

In the previous chapter I explored how decision-making and choice are driven by heuristics—rules of thumb—that generally have little to do with logic or rationality. This area of investigation treads dangerously close to one of consciousness's most sacred cows, that it is the seat of or generates our free will, our sense of volitional control. This belief in the sanctity of conscious intention is considered perhaps the greatest hallmark of humanity. Bursting this bubble, Harvard psychology professor Daniel Wegner (2002) claims free will is a fabrication of consciousness in his book, *The Illusion of Conscious Will*. Wegner says mental causation, the perception that our thoughts cause our behavior, is mostly wrong. Our experience of will is separate from the true causes of our actions. why did I Ao I?

Wegner cites a range of studies to support his thesis including Libet's work that conscious awareness is belated to the events preceding it. Much, if not most, of the initiation of behavior is generated by unconscious intentions hundreds of milliseconds before a chance subset of perceptions might rise to awareness. Wegner quotes from Libet's *The Neural Time—Factor in Perception, Volition and Free Will*.

> The initiation of the voluntary act appears to be an unconscious cerebral process. Clearly, free will or free choice of whether to act now could not be the initiating agent, contrary to one widely held view. This is of course also contrary to each individual's own introspective feeling that he/she consciously initiates such voluntary acts; this provides an important empirical example of the possibility that the subjective experience of a mental causality need not necessarily reflect the actual causative relationship between mental and brain events. (p. 54)

But Wegner also cites the other kinds of studies we've already looked at—the experiments that manipulate subjects subliminally. While we've only considered a few experiments, thousands of psychology professors have found it remarkably easy to sway people's behavior without the subjects' knowledge that they are being duped. Wegner cites Joaquim Brasil-Neto and colleagues at the NIH who magnetically stimulated the motor area of subjects' brains while asking them to choose to extend one of their index fingers. However, without the subjects' knowledge, the researchers changed which side of the brain to stimulate on the fly and found that significantly more often subjects extended the finger of the hand stimulated by the magnetism (the hemisphere opposite the finger). Crucially, though, the subjects reported that they had made their own voluntary decision to move their fingers.

> Although the stimulation led participants to have a marked preference to move the finger contralateral to the site stimulated, particularly at short response times, they continued to perceive that they were voluntarily choosing which finger to move. When asked whether they had voluntarily chosen which finger to move, participants showed no inkling that something other than their will was creating their choice. (p. 48)

Some will say that the unconscious deceptions are the exception rather than the rule. However, the accumulation of evidence suggests the opposite. For Wegner, it is not only the comparison of conscious versus unconscious control to be considered, but rather the mental apparatus itself that undermines our belief in our own force of consciousness.

> When we turn our attention to our own minds, we are faced with trying to understand an unimaginably advanced technology. We can't possibly know (let alone keep track of) the tremendous number of mechanical influences on our behavior because we inhabit an extraordinarily complicated machine. So we developed

a shorthand, a belief in the causal efficacy of our conscious thoughts. We believe in the magic of our own causal agency. (p. 27)

Alien hand syndrome is a real disease that was mimicked by Peter Sellers' character Dr. Strangelove in the eponymously-named movie. Just like the split brain patients who can have different parts of their bodies behave in contradiction, the alien hand sufferer's hand makes complex, coordinated motions completely without the knowledge or intention of the owner. This is an extreme example of unconscious motor processes at work but illustrates the range of unwilled actions our bodies and brains are capable of. The question is how much or at what point does conscious volition enter into willed action? Wegner says consciousness may have little impact at all.

It appears possible to produce a voluntary action through brain stimulation with or without an experience of conscious will. This, in turn, suggests the interesting possibility that conscious will is an add-on, an experience that has its own origins and consequences. The experience of will may not be very firmly connected to the processes that produce action, in that whatever produces the experience of will may function in a way that is only loosely coupled with the mechanisms that yield action itself. (p. 47)

How can this be? Our entire lives have been lived with the experience that we first generate intention, which is followed by willed action. Yet the experimental evidence removed from the bias of introspection suggests that conscious will is the mind making connections between thoughts and actions as if those connections were actually causal rather than just observations. "People experience conscious will," Wegner says, "when they interpret their own thought as the cause of their action. This means that people experience conscious will quite independently of any actual causal connection between their thoughts and their actions." (p. 64)

This mechanism of conscious will infers links between thoughts and actions, however those inferences provide no guarantee that people actually draw correct links between them. Far more often than we might imagine, we attribute incorrect causes to our actions. The reasons people give for their actions frequently are not the actual reasons. In their classic paper, *Telling More Than We Can Know: Verbal Reports on Mental Processes*, Nisbett and Wilson (1977) cite three indications that people are either unaware or mistaken about how thoughts lead to actions. First, people simply cannot or do not report on the stimuli that elicit action, the inferences that took place, or even the resulting actions themselves. "The accuracy of subjective reports is so poor as to suggest that any introspective access that may exist is not sufficient to produce generally correct or reliable reports." Secondly, rather than basing interpretation of action on internal cognitive processes, people "base their reports on implicit, *a priori* theories about the causal connection between stimulus and response." In other words, biases or presuppositions infiltrate the causation assertion. Thirdly, even when perception of cause is accurate, it is "not due to direct introspective awareness. Instead, it is due to the incidentally correct employment of *a priori* causal theories." (p. 233) Sometimes people get lucky when correctly attributing reasons for behavior. Got Lucky?

In just one of the many studies cited by Nisbett and Wilson, subjects were instructed to listen to a human voice in one ear, the attended ear, while tone sequences were played in the other, non-attended ear. Because the subjects were asked to focus on the human voice in the attended ear, they reported that they mostly didn't hear the tone sequences in the unattended ear. Later they listened binaurally (both ears) to both new and previously played tone sequences. While they were unable to identify which sounds were new and which they'd heard before, "subjects showed the traditional familiarity effect on liking of the tone stimuli. 'Familiar' tone sequences, that is, tone sequences previously presented to the unattended channel were preferred to novel stimuli." (p. 239) The preponderance of evidence indicates that much more stimuli is perceived, cognitively integrated, and acted on than reaches short-term memory, working memory, or awareness consciousness. Integration of stimuli directly influences our judgment and behavior, and we have little idea when and how much it does.

Note the similarities to Kahneman and Tversky's assessment of decision-making in which heuristics and biases are the real causes of behavior. Whatever consciousness is, whether conscious will, decision-making, thinking, or any of the other perceptions of self-awareness, it doesn't quite provide the executive function that humans believe motivate them.

## The Cause of Gods

One of the differences between humans and other animals without higher-order consciousness is, we believe, that animals don't run internal queries asking what are the causes of actions? Having consciousness means that people strive to link thought and action together. That doesn't mean, though, that people are good at it. Humans have only a marginally evolved conscious causal determination mechanism and are generally inaccurate estimating what generates their own actions. While the human propensity for causal attribution may be one of consciousness's key but underdeveloped features, it is good enough to enhance survival and reproduction, and in the evolutionary picture, that's all that matters.

> The experience of will, then, is the way our minds portray their operation to us, not the actual operation. Because we have thoughts of what we will do, we can develop causal theories relating those thoughts to our actions on the basis of priority, consistency, and exclusivity. We come to think of these prior thoughts as intentions, and we develop the sense that the intentions have causal force even though they are actually just previews of what we may do. Yet in an important sense, it must be the case that something in our minds plays a causal role in making interactions occur. That something is, in the theory of apparent mental causation, a set of unconscious mental processes that cause the action. At the

same time, that something is very much like the thoughts we have prior to the action. (Wegner, 2002, p. 96)

The ability to consider causes in the first place was the result of enhanced self-awareness that rode in on the consciousness train. In the course of the evolution of higher-order consciousness, proto-humans developed the sense of self as different from *the other*. In order to have knowledge of oneself, one had to, by extension, know non-self. I am a separate entity from you and from trees, rocks, and everything else. This realization of the self separate from the other was the first essential dichotomy that equipped humans with the knowledge of opposites, an essential precursor to assigning the source of causes. Because people differentiated between self and non-self and could identify discrete entities like *person*, they could attempt to assign causation to the self or external non-self entities. But that, by itself, doesn't explain why humans invented non-real agents (gods, totems, fairies) that they believed impacted their lives.

The human penchant to believe in counterintuitive forces that have the power to change human events is the result of this unrefined psychological inclination for attaching causes to actions. It is compensation for a marginally emerging causation identification skill set. The human ability to accurately assign causation is relatively weak, and this is why humans need to offload causation to non-corporeal entities like gods. It is exactly the inability to ascertain true causes that results in the mind creating non-real agents, and it isn't a conscious effort. This is a reaction to the shortcomings of how higher-order consciousness has evolved. In conjunction with humans' inability to have genuine insight into their own mental workings, they actively project causality and invent reasons for their own and others' actions. Not only do humans detect other humans, animals, and inanimate objects as having causal properties, but they create non-existent or imagined beings on which to assign or project causality. As we'll see in the chapter on mythology, the supernatural creations are not random. Rather, they are projections of aspects of the self. It's not coincidence that polytheistic gods usually take human shape and, even when they embody animal forms, gods still retain abundant human behavioral characteristics.

Even for most consciousness denigrators such as Gazzaniga, Wegner, and myself, it's beyond the pale to believe that humans are totally clueless about their own motivations and behavior. People are not completely bereft of insight into their own causes, highlighted in part, thanks to the extreme symptoms of schizophrenia. Many schizophrenics, Wegner says, have a higher than usual inability to distinguish between their own and others' thoughts. They, like the alien hand or split brain patients, are on the extreme of the bell curve for lack of consistency perceiving or linking causes and actions. Yet these cases illustrate a matter of degree, and humans display a spectrum of thought-action detection ability. Similarly, people attribute external forces such as gods as impacting human events to various extents. Belief in supernatural entities, a perception of causation, runs the gamut; some people attribute much or most of their experiences to external forces while others less so. According to Wegner,

> The appeal to hypothetical outside agents is far too common an experience in human life to be attributed to schizophrenia alone. The occurrence of spirit possession or channeling, for example, is so widespread across cultures and so highly prevalent in some cultures—affecting as much as half of the population—that it has become a major focus of the field of anthropology. Attribution of behavior to angels, spirits, entities, and the like is sufficiently common throughout the world that it is a mistake to assume it is limited to traditional cultures. Industrialized cultures have their share of channels, trance dancers, and people who "speak in tongues" or otherwise attribute their action to divine intervention as part of religious ceremonies. The common denominator for these phenomena is the attribution of what otherwise appears to be voluntary behavior to an imagined outside agency. (p. 95)

Agency is also invoked when we assign intention to cars, computers, and other inanimate objects. "My stupid computer hates me!" To what purpose are false beliefs? The Hyperactive Agency Detection Device (HADD), a popular explanation for why people believe in gods, leverages sensory perception systems that all animals have. Humans are sensitive to environmental cues like predators or enemies lurking in the brush or other things that go bump in the night. In situations where the source of an event is ambiguous or unknown, like when you think you see something out of the corner of your eye, it is natural for humans to extrapolate and assign agency to these unknown events. Humans not only have a proclivity to latch onto possible causes (Is that a leopard swaying that branch or just the wind?), but HADD proponents make an enormous leap of faith by claiming people generate imaginary entities—gods and spirits—due to hyperactive agency detection. "From an evolutionary perspective, it is better to be safe than sorry regarding the detection of agency under conditions of uncertainty. This cognitive proclivity would favor emergence of malevolent deities in all cultures." (Atran and Norenzayan, 2004, p. 719) In the view of HADD theorists, the ability to transfer causation to gods is a byproduct of the desire to establish agency in response to potential threats.

Hyperactive Agency Detection is an exquisitely insufficient answer for why people invent gods. HADD only addresses a narrow range of situations—when humans are alert for risk or danger—but the bigger problem is the claim that it should normally or naturally lead to the invention of gods. All mobile animals have agency detection devices, but as far as we know, none besides human animals invoke fictitious agents. In evolutionary terms, it's intuitive that animals that more accurately identify potential causes including threats would survive preferentially to those that weren't as accurate or (theoretically) conjured unreal reasons. It is counterintuitive to invent gods as a response to unknown causes and doing so suggests increased risk to survival. Why do people invoke non-real entities rather than latching on to explanations that at least are plausible in the tangible world? When faced with the possibility of a real predator or enemy, how is imagining a god going to help you?

No other animals have such a highly developed sense of self as humans. For that very reason one might expect that people would keenly focus on real causes rather than invent new, imaginary ones. Given just the opposite—and given the abundance of evidence that humans are very bad at establishing cause—humans invent gods because of their negligible competence to determine causation, to support their desire but relative impotence to acquire explanations. Humans can do this because they can imagine the separate *other* as a consequence of their keen awareness of self. Because people not only perceive the *other* as separate from themselves, they can also imagine others' thoughts and feelings—the theory of mind. And since the brain actively filters perception and manufactures cognition, it is capable of creating the *other* as a projection of its own psyche. The mythologies people contrive are representations of psychological predispositions, sometimes in the form of imaginary entities we call gods. In reality, humans manufacture gods and project external causation for all kinds of reasons. They anthropomorphize; they transfer human traits to non-human objects. We will look at this in more detail when discussing mythology as religious ritual.

The detached science reveals higher-order consciousness contributes only a small portion to everyday life, but people feel it is far more important. Self-aware consciousness has the ironic consequence of giving people the illusion that it sits atop a throne and sees itself as the executive in charge. People believe that they have conscious control of their actions because their consciousness tells them that they do, but consciousness is misinformed and misinforming. Despite our sense of consciousness's importance, consciousness comes with serious downsides. Introspection is more likely to lead to false or erroneous conclusions than true ones. Consciousness is an observer after the fact and rationalizes reality rather than directs it. People are lucky if they can accurately attribute actual causes to their behavior.

The way consciousness evolved was far noisier than its actual impact and effectiveness. This is another great pitfall of consciousness, its very *modus operandi*. Consciousness is intrusive and persistent. It doesn't have a specific way to know when its skillset is relevant. There is no method for calling on consciousness only when it's required, so is continuously listening, observing, polling and asking, "Can I help? Do you need me now?" The constant chatter is tolerated for the occasional nuggets it offers, but also needs to be reined in when it gets too loud, bullies its own agenda, and interferes with automatic, innate, and adaptive nonconscious activity.

Why would we have evolved this mechanism called consciousness that deceives and underachieves? Evolution is random, never clean, and always comes with compromises. It's a referee you can't argue with. Consciousness, like any evolved trait, arose because it solved or ameliorated specific environmental challenges, but it did so in a peculiar fashion—by developing a barely-good-enough cognitive feature that marginally gets the job done. The advantage of culture brought by consciousness is enormous, but the way it got there was obtrusive and indiscreet. Having acquired too much knowledge, the ability to reflect on the *why* as well as the *what*, humans developed a compensating device. During the fall from unconscious frog-like grace, *in illo tempore*, humans gained the knack for transferring causality to non-real entities, which provided the resolving relief necessary to rationalize events that couldn't be fully understood.

The derivation of supernatural agents is essentially another version of salving the existential anxieties and answering the great mysteries, but as an explanation of the origin of religion, it only addresses redirecting causality to supernatural forces and neglects all the other behaviors of religion. It is not the whole story. As we'll see in the next chapter, belief, whether in gods or anything else, is not the primary basis on which to define religion. It is related to but doesn't directly address the myriad other religious behaviors humans engage in, particularly religious ritual and its concomitant emotional legacy. In subsequent chapters, we will explore religious behaviors—actions rather than beliefs—that provide a more solid scientific grounding for establishing what religion is. In all cases we see that religiously-based phenomena offset the detrimental or dispiriting elements of consciousness.

People of all stripes have psychological investments in believing Homo sapiens is a special animal. Our consciousness is singular, but that doesn't make us superior, just different. For those who determinedly resist relinquishing their faith in the preeminence of consciousness and its contribution to self-determination, free will, and the rest, ten more chapters of consciousness science won't be sufficient. Some consciousness defenders argue that all these isolated indications of unconscious forces at work do not culminate in an overall indictment of consciousness and its provenance in human activity. Sure, they say, each of these cognitive biases and emotional predilections have their imprint, but that doesn't add up to relegating consciousness to an insignificant or secondary role. Some protest that existing research techniques are insufficient and even flawed; the results of subliminal studies are misleading or just wrong, for example. Others purport reductionism is too limited an approach to analyze human cognition, and strong emergence is the direction to pursue the essence of human nature. Whether secular humanist, religious adherent, or academic scientist, we all cling tenaciously to our biases and beliefs. Such is the nature of the species. Much more work needs to be done to flesh out consciousness's positive role as well as its pitfalls, but the extant research warrants a reevaluation of its historically-perceived role in human affairs. For those who embrace empiricism—the scientific method—the topic begs for an open and ongoing evaluation. *Show me the science.*

Despite many unresolved questions about higher-order consciousness, we humans wouldn't be who and where we are without it. Clearly, consciousness has a beneficial purpose, or it wouldn't have persevered. Despite legitimate questions about its efficacy, it contributes to sophisticated human capabilities such as reasoning and logic, plasticity and learning capacities—our flexibility and adaptability in the face of environmental challenges. Our distended frontal lobe boosts our capacities to consider and engage novel approaches to problems and effect alternative solutions. While none of consciousness's features are unique in the animal kingdom, they combine to generate the fabulous human product called culture, which is certainly unlike anything else in the natural world. This leads people to believe they have limitless adaptability to new situations, which effectively frees them to embrace all possibilities constrained only by the physical laws of nature, and even some of those we overcome. We build machines to fly like birds or go to the depths of the ocean like fish.

Humans are in the midst of a roiling, volatile brain evolution and, as is evolution's wont, there is no direction and no end. Evolution has thrown down some fascinating human mental capabilities, but as animals, we continue to rely, first and foremost, on innate directives and inherited morphology to guide us. Our corporeal bodies, like all biological life, are made of DNA-based, physiological structures and, therefore, have finite limits.

I undoubtedly overemphasize the unconscious processes, but they have fewer proponents. Those who promote the sanctity of human free will, reason, and self-control are plentiful, have an abundance of historical material, and have the intuitive sympathies of the masses. I don't need to defend them. Regardless of one's stance in the consciousness debate, who we are as human beings doesn't change one iota because of any possible acceptance or realization of the possible underwhelming role of consciousness. Humans remain the same as we've always been regardless of perspective and belief, which, upon reflective examination, is just as agog, striving, confused, and hopeful as ever.

The greatest problem for most cognitive theories of religion is their inability to account for religion's evolutionary adaptiveness. How and why does religion improve human survival and reproductive success? Some origin of religion theories consider it to be a non-adaptive byproduct that is neutral and may not aid humanity at all. Even those who offer that religion is advantageous and improves evolutionary fitness have a difficult time making a cogent case for its advent. The next chapter finally turns directly to religion, and sets up the second leg of The Split Hypothesis. Most of the traditional theories of religion study it in terms of belief systems, but from a biological point of view, analyzing actual behaviors rather than doctrine and dogma are a more salient approach. I explain why studying religion's belief systems are of secondary interest. In succeeding chapters, we will see how these ritual behaviors of religion—music, dance, myth and narrative, art, and prayer—impede the noise of consciousness and stimulate adaptive emotions.

# Chapter 5

## Some Problems With Existing Theories of Religion

> There is currently no overarching theory,
> which is able to explain all or at least
> the most important aspects of religion.
> *Detlef Fetchenhauer*

After several chapters putting human consciousness into its proper perspective, it's time to return to the topic of religion. Over the past several decades, there has been a growing interest in explaining why humans have religion, and it remains a contested and controversial topic. As is reflected at the beginning of the first chapter and Fetchenhauer's quote above, there's a lack of consensus as to why religion exists. Many people intuitively sense that theory of religion explanations are insufficient, if for no other reason than that there continue to be several possible, disparate solutions and no good definition of religion. The leading contenders accounting for religious behavior are to increase group or community cohesiveness, to answer the existential mysteries—why we die, our purpose in life—and the Hyperactive Agency Detection Device theory, which was discussed in the previous chapter. Within all these positions is the question: is religion a byproduct and strictly cultural or does it have biological, innate components? Also discussed previously was an explanation for why humans believe in gods, but a theory of religion does not and should not depend primarily on belief. Before examining the problems with existing theories of religion, I address why beliefs are a poor avenue to pursue a theory of religion.

## Belief in Belief

Generally, the study of religion depends on analyzing belief systems. Historically, a great deal of effort has been spent contrasting religious systems: East versus West, the three Abrahamic religions, or the subtle differences between various Christian denominations — Roman Catholic versus Eastern Orthodox versus various Protestant sects. Without question belief in supernatural entities such as gods is a universal component of religion. However, that's only the beginning of religious belief. From the creation of gods, religion spirals out elaborate doctrines that are histories, proscriptions, and prescriptions for living. The Bible, Torah, Upanishads, and Quran are among the most well known examples. Their study is expected in comparative analyses of religion, but in an evolutionary approach, beliefs are not the proper currency.

Launching an inquiry into a theory of religion based on religious beliefs is troublesome for two reasons. The first problem is interpreting belief and meaning in the religious context. Are there external powers and entities beyond our standard sensory experience? What do people believe God is and does? Can we reasonably interpret the religious beliefs of those who conceive a world radically different from ours? If we subscribe to theories of religion based on beliefs, we need to be pretty sure what those beliefs are and how they came to be. What exactly is it that people believe? And how are we to ascribe meaning to something that is completely without tangible substance? This turns out to be an arduous and impractical task as I'll examine shortly.

Secondly, many believe the purpose of religion is to answer the great mysteries such as what is our purpose in life or why must we die? Similarly, religion rationalizes why things happen the way they do. What's so striking, at least from a modern rationalist's point of view, is that religion does this by inventing non-real agents to account for truth. Religious belief is blatantly based on non-observable, unverifiable faith, which cannot be the basis for physical reality, only for self-generated and self-proclaimed conviction and ideology. Religious belief answers the big questions with fictitious beings, yet this is an unreasonable means for establishing the nature of the material world. If the previous chapters have done anything, it's to call into question the human capacity for self-knowledge, thought, and judgment. People are generally unaware about their own internal feelings and motivations. Even if people have a relatively accurate sense of their own goals and views, the counterintuitive, ethereal, and metaphysical nature of religious belief is completely baffling.

The point that's missing and must be addressed is, if these irrational creations provide solace for existential anxieties, why do humans need this salve in the first place? What is it about humans that they require this psychic buoy and the rest of the animal kingdom doesn't? What's different about humans that leads to belief in counterintuitive agents? If you answer that humans are different from other animals because of features of consciousness such as self-awareness, an outstanding ability to learn and remember, and a mental logic engine, that only exacerbates the problem. Why would these keen cognitive characteristics succumb to organized fantasies? Yes, religion does these things, but specific beliefs and the fact of belief are not the means with which to construct a theory of religion.

One problem is interpreting religious belief and meaning. In *Modern Man in Search of a Soul*, Jung (1933) describes how primitive man, as he called pre-literate people (or was translated from the German), perceives the world differently from modern people.

> A white man shoots a crocodile. At once a crowd of people come running from the nearest village and excitedly demand compensation. They explain that the crocodile was a certain old woman in their village who had died at the moment when the shot was fired. The crocodile was obviously her bush-soul. (p. 162)

While only obliquely religious in content, this incident highlights a different way of looking at the world, which has implications for understanding the meaning of religion to both modern and traditional cultures.

E. Richard Sorenson studied the Mbotgate people on the New Hebrides Island of Malekula in the South Pacific. The Mbotgate men said that angry spirits would steal and kill the baby pigs that were pets of the Mbotgate women if the women offended the ancestors. Sorenson witnessed a Mbotgate man take a piglet and burn it to death. Upon seeing the dead piglet, the woman who owned it became severely ill. Sorenson described her as being virtually comatose and vomiting profusely. (Breeden, 1973, p. 39) It's not clear if the woman knew that one of her tribesman killed her pig or not, but it hardly matters. We struggle to judge or comprehend what these people believe especially when we don't ourselves believe that we must appease our ancestors' spirits.

Additionally, tribespeople have no way of expressing their beliefs in a paradigm that would satisfy academic observers. In *Belief, Language, and Experience*, anthropologist Rodney Needham (1972) said he couldn't satisfactorily interpret religious meaning and belief in tribal societies. He cited the work of fellow anthropologist E. E. Evans-Pritchard who studied the Nuer people of East Africa.

> Nuer religion is ultimately an interior state. When the social and cultural features of the religion have been abstracted, we are told, what is left is a relationship that transcends all forms; but the ethnographer cannot give any clear account of what for the Nuer is the nature of this spiritual relationship. To do so is difficult, partly because Nuer religious conceptions are not concepts but imaginative constructions, and these relate to an intuitive apprehension, a spiritual experience; and, again, the anthropologist cannot say for certain what this experience is. (p. 14)

Needham elaborated on the problem of interpreting the beliefs of other cultures.

I realized that I could not confidently describe their attitude to God, whether this was belief or anything else...In
fact, as I have glumly to conclude, I just did not know
what was their psychic attitude toward the personage in
whom I assumed they believed. Clearly, it was one thing
to report the received ideas to which a people subscribed,
but it was quite another matter to say what was their inner state (belief, for instance) when they expressed or en-
tertained such ideas. If, however, an ethnographer said
that people believed something when he did not actually
know what was going on inside them, then surely his account of them must, it occurred to me, be very defective
in quite fundamental regards. (p. 2)

This is hardly an issue specific to traditional societies. Modern
people's religious beliefs and attitudes are essentially the same as
traditional people's. The names of the deities change, but the supernatural agents still persist. In *How the Mind Works*, Steven Pinker
(2009) observes,

In culture after culture, people believe that the soul lives
on after death, that rituals can change the physical world
and divine the truth, and that illness and misfortune are
caused and alleviated by spirits, ghosts, saints, fairies,
angels, demons, cherubim, djinns, devils, and gods. According to polls, more than a quarter of today's Americans believe in witches, almost half believe in ghosts, half
believe in the devil, half believe that the book of Genesis
is literally true. 69% believe in angels, 87% believe that
Jesus was raised from the dead, and 96% believe in a God
or universal spirit. (p. 554)

That's a whole lot of fabrication to solve a problem that only humans have.

Not surprisingly, even modern people's self perception about
their own religious beliefs is suspect. Most people would be willing to admit that they themselves don't really grasp a lot of their
religious canons; they just believe it in a popular way. Studies of

religious adherents show a great disconnect between their understanding of official, delivered religious doctrine and a more intuitive set of folk ideals. Psychologists Justin Barrett and Frank Keil (1996) showed that what people claimed to be their belief about God did not accurately portray their real world views. The researchers gave questionnaires to ascertain subjects' attitudes about God and then presented vignettes containing God in the story. Subjects then answered questions about the story. The researchers concluded that people's stated attitude about God changed depending on the mode in which God was presented.

> It appears that people have at least two parallel God concepts that are used in different contexts, and these concepts may be fundamentally incompatible...The concept of God used in the context of listening to and remembering stories is not the same as the concept of God that is claimed in a more abstract, theological setting...People seem to possess and use more than one concept of God in real-life activities, and these parallel concepts have some markedly different properties. (pp. 240-241)

This led Pascal Boyer (2004) to sagaciously say, "People do not believe what they believe they believe." (p. 4)

Religions themselves change (culturally evolve) over time. Doctrine is modified, and sometimes radical changes occur. The Protestant reformation gave rise to dozens, if not hundreds, of variations of Christian sects, but even before that, Greek and Russian Orthodox Churches flourished in parallel to Roman Catholicism. Christianity retains traces of pagan religion such as Santa Claus and Christmas trees, which have nothing to do with the birth of Jesus. Similarly, the Easter bunny, eggs, and other symbols are irrelevant to the Resurrection. Well, maybe not. They are symbols of fecundity and rebirth, a universal theme throughout all cultures and a symbol of Jesus resurrection as well. The church leveraged these themes to promote their own principles and teachings that attempted to divert or redirect from traditional beliefs. Modern debates rage over whether early Christians borrowed mythological motifs from pre-Christians that were adopted into Christian form such as virgin birth. Formalized ecclesiastical edicts never fully replace the old religion; they only integrate and adapt to it.

These changes to canon continue in modern times. The Catholic Church changed its tradition regarding eating fish on Fridays or holding masses in Latin. They still require priests to be male and celibate, which has led to a crisis of faith due to sexual predation and criminal coverup. The Catholic hierarchy also decries contraception, which, according to polls, is used by the vast majority of Catholic women in the United States and Europe. And many other contemporary social mores have changed, too. In the Bible God endorses or condones practices that are forbidden today by virtually any Christian: selling a daughter to pay a debt (Ex 21:7-11) and polygamy (CH 11:22, KI 11:3) to name a few.

Examples of changes in religious dogma are found in many non-Christian cultures. American Indians have undergone revitalizations and spiritual rejuvenations often based on dreams or visitation visions in which gods or prophets instruct a seer to tell the people to change in ways both sacred and profane. (Wallace, 1966, p. 31) Judiasm is well known for its scriptures, the Talmud and Torah, that are interpreted and debated in yeshivas, the schools for religious education. A certain flexibility is built into Judaic law. Even defining what it is to be Jewish remains a topic of controversy.

Belief is a popular topic for comparative religion, but it is not an explanation of why people believe in supernatural forces, or why they experience ineffable, emotional states of awe and revelation. In addition, people have beliefs about everything: social, political, even science beliefs. Belief is a characteristic of humanity and is not specific to religion, so must be understood on its own. The only truism is that people have faith and religion, and it includes people's conviction that there are external powers in the universe that may alter the course of their lives. For a theory of religion, it doesn't matter what the differences are between religions or even that people believe in gods. Belief is an important aspect of religion, but it cannot take precedence as the basis for a cognitive theory of religion.

# Belief in Science

This is an attempt to understand the human expression of religion from a scientific point of view, but not everybody buys into the notion that science is an appropriate paradigm to evaluate religion. Émile Durkheim (1994), the founder of sociology, said the problem of the origin of religion "is not a scientific one and must be dismissed out of hand." (p. 109)

The problem for those who oppose the scientific method as a means to understand the world is that there is no reasonable alternative. Religious advocates contend that they *know* God is real, but they have no way to show it. Religious belief is not based on tangibles; they only have their internal feelings. The concrete manifestations of religion are people's behaviors and the things people create as symbols to honor their religious beliefs. There is simply no external substantiation of a religious God independent of the human mind. As Gerald Edelman (2004) says of consciousness, "Principles of physics must be strictly obeyed and that the world defined by physics is causally closed. No spooky forces that contravene thermodynamics can be included." (p. 114)

The scientific method requires that we observe, hypothesize, measure, and repeat and that the same procedures get the same results. The only thing that preserves the validity of science is that the experiments that support a theory are consistent and repeatable. That's all. We only accept the science when it provides reliable and dependable experimental outcomes and that all who play by the rules of the scientific method reach the same end product. We essentially choose to agree that we partake of the same world experience, and that's as good as it gets. Newberg (2002) says,

> Science...is mythological, and like all mythological systems of belief, it is based on a foundational assumption: All that is real can be verified by scientific measurement, therefore, what can't be verified by science isn't really real. This kind of assumption, that one system is exclusive arbiter of what is true, makes [the methods of] science and religion incompatible. (p. 171)

A great deal of media is currently dedicated to the tension between religion and science, but here that struggle is not pertinent. Religion and belief are just aspects of the human animal and are ripe for scientific study. The irony here is that religion also explains the origin and nature of the world through its mythologies, but the purpose of myth and religion is very different from the purpose of science. Science attempts to generate cause and effect scenarios for tangible domains. Religion fulfills a psychological requirement. Science can show that religion performs a necessary function. However, no specific religious experience or belief system will ever be universally shared, only the overarching fact that people have spiritual feelings and encode those feelings into mythologies.

Then again, science is a human expression, and scientists are people, too. Rather than exhibiting the highest standards of reasoning, scientists, like anybody else, can let their personal biases and agendas obscure their thinking. They do it far more often than we'd like to believe. Like all human endeavors, scientific progress is fraught with stops and starts and occasional buffoonery, ego, and greed. But in the end the relentless checks and balances of the scientific method sift out the human bias and chicanery, leaving a core body of knowledge that we are confident explains the world, at least as well as we can at the moment given our abilities. The physicist Richard Feynman offered a perspective for scientists to keep in mind.

> [Physicists have] learned to realize that whether they like a theory or they don't like a theory is not the essential question. Rather, it is whether or not the theory gives predictions that agree with experiment. It is not a question of whether a theory is philosophically delightful, or easy to understand, or perfectly reasonable from the point of view of common sense. (Dennett, 2006, p. 219)

If evolution explains how life forms came to inhabit earth, then a Darwinian explanation must be pursued for all aspects of biology such as behavior, including religious behavior. If religion evolved in small tribal bands roughly 50,000 to 100,000 (or more) years ago, that's where we must focus. What's needed is a cohesive, verifiable hypothesis for the biological evolution of religion. I offer one for which scientific experiments both have been run and can be designed that either confirm or disconfirm the predictions of the hypothesis. The Split Hypothesis is an effort to fit religion into an evolutionary model and evaluates the cognitive changes to paleohumans in its discourse.

## Existing Theories of Religion

Many cognitive religion theorists take the position that religion evolved and is adaptive. They consider why and how religion improves human survival and reproductive success. A different group of academics prefers non-adaptive, religion-as-byproduct interpretations such as the Hyperactive Agency Detection Device. This school proposes that religious beliefs and behaviors accidentally arose as byproducts of other evolved characteristics as opposed to having adaptive benefit on their own. What does this mean and what is the scientific evidence for byproducts?

It's hard to say. Biological byproducts sometimes refer to vestigial structures such as the whale's pelvis, which is an example of a feature that was once adaptive but is no longer so. Since religion is a completely new phenomenon, this doesn't apply. Byproducts are also used to describe a characteristic of a feature. Bone is white due to the mineral salts comprising it, and this relationship of descriptor to an item is sometimes called a byproduct. Again, this has no significance to ritual and religion and has virtually no informational value at any level.

Another type of byproduct is exaptations. Many, if not most, new biological features result from exaptations: features that evolve for one purpose and become co-opted to perform a different function. An example is the development of feathers in dinosaurs and other reptile-like species. Feathers were originally believed to have evolved for insulation and temperature regulation. Only secondarily did they become utilized for flight some millions of years after they first appeared. In each case, however, feathers were adaptive regardless of their evolutionary origin and purpose. Nowhere in this scenario would feathers be considered non-adaptive. New features or new uses for features would not persist without being adaptive and increasing evolutionary fitness.

Finally, new features can arise that have no functional or evolutionary consequence. This is called noise or random effects and refers to characteristics that are neutral and have no impact on an organism's evolutionary success. Some of these newly evolved, non-adaptive features may arise as exaptations. If any case could be made that religion as well as art and music are non-adaptive byproducts or exaptations, it is based on the premise that these behaviors are neutral and don't affect human evolutionary fitness. Religion and the arts, however, are enormous resource expenditures. In no way can they be considered adaptively neutral.

Richard Dawkins (2006), the enforcer of evolutionary theory, says, "Darwinian selection habitually targets and eliminates waste. Nature is a miserly accountant, grudging the pennies, watching the clock, punishing the smallest extravagance." (p. 190) Any organism that squanders its efforts on activities that don't contribute to its survival and reproductive success will not be favored in the competition of natural selection. Organisms that don't waste resources will survive preferentially and pass on their genes for efficient behavior. Religious behaviors might have initially stemmed from adaptive characteristics as exaptations. Given that religious behaviors are ubiquitous in our species, are clearly evolutionarily expensive and not adaptively neutral, then religion must be adaptive and selected for—at least if you believe Dawkins when he says selection punishes the *smallest* extravagance.

The bigger problem for byproduct proponents is that scientific support for non-adaptive non-human byproducts is thin to non-existent. In any scientific area of research, there are hundreds, if not thousands, of journal articles in the scientific literature evaluating every aspect of a particular subject. The literature for non-human, non-adaptive byproducts is meager at best with only a handful of articles, but bizarrely, this doesn't seem to bother byproduct theorists. Of the few scholarly discussions about non-adaptive byproducts, some of them criticize byproduct theory and defend a religion-as-adaptation approach. Other articles propose theoretical models for how byproducts might work but offer paltry examples at best.

David Buss is lead author of *Adaptations, Exaptations, and Spandrels,* (1998) one of the few papers that rigorously examines biological byproduct theory. In it he calls for the same stringent empirical requirements to show a trait is a byproduct as for a feature claimed to be an adaptation.

> Hypotheses about functionless by-products must meet rigorous scientific standards that include a functional analysis of the original adaptations responsible for producing the functionless by-products and the existing human cognitive and motivational mechanisms responsible for the co-opting. Without this specification, the mere assertion that this or that characteristic is an exaptation encounters the same problem...leveled against adaptationists—the telling of "just-so stories." (p. 542)

Based on this criteria, Buss concludes "we could not find a single example of an empirical discovery made about humans as a result of using the concepts of exaptations or spandrels." (p. 545)

There is a dearth of hard science describing actual non-adaptive byproducts in the real world, and, for some strange reason, there is little criticism of this omission. The onus seems to be on the evolutionists who favor religion as an adaptation. In his article, *The Adaptationist-Byproduct Debate on the Evolution of Religion,* Richard Sosis (2009) defends the effort to show religion is an adaptation. "Much of the debate can be resolved by clearly defining important but ambiguous terms in the debate, such as religion, adaptation, adaptive, and trait, as well as clarifying several misunderstandings of evolutionary processes. I argue that adaptationist analyses must focus on the functional effects of the religious system." (p. 315)

Where's the same burden of proof for the byproduct crowd? The 150-year-old theory of evolution is essentially fact in the scientific community, while non-adaptive byproduct theory is anything but. This is an odd instance of the *Emperor's New Clothes* in which byproduct theory is paraded around as a valid account to explain religion when actually the byproduct emperor is naked. Stephen Sanderson, professor at the University of California at Riverside, says, "Byproduct theorists present no real evidence at all to defend their claims. It's all quite speculative." (email communication 24 Jan 2013)

Without selective advantage, without an evolutionary reason, the likelihood of new features like ritual and religion enduring universally throughout all human cultures is minuscule. I will explore the reasoning for this in more detail in the next chapter, Emotion and Evolution, but since almost all new traits can be considered byproducts or exaptations of existing traits, the concept becomes meaningless and irrelevant. It certainly doesn't justify or explain whether ritual and religion are advantageous or non-adaptive regardless of how they developed.

Religion as byproduct is a way to explain the difficult issue of why humans exhibit religious behaviors. It solves an intractable problem for some academics in the same way that mythologies solve cosmological mysteries for the religiously inclined. The urge to plug a hole in the knowledge gap is stronger than the requirement for empirical evidence. When academics deny a genetic basis for religion and promote a byproduct account for it, they are trying to rewrite evolutionary theory to fit their postulates. Byproduct proponents are forcing a concept specifically to account for unique human proclivities that have minimal significance in the rest of the animal kingdom. Regardless of the likelihood of the byproduct solution to elucidate the origin of religion, proponents must establish robust examples of non-adaptive behavioral byproducts in animals, unless they claim that behavioral byproducts only apply to humans. Making humans the sole example of non-adaptive byproducts is highly dubious and demands more thorough, demonstrable biological support.

As I've said several times, popular theories of religion suffer from the inability to pinpoint why humans need the various props of religion in the first place, and other animals don't. Other animals don't have existential anxieties about the fear of death. All animals have sensory systems to alert them to threats and already have hyperactive agency detection. Thousands of social species have existing mechanisms for group cohesion and don't require religion to improve it. Why does humanity have a yen for enjoining religion to solve problems for which other animals either already have solutions or simply don't suffer from?

Many religion theorists implicitly assume that religion solves these issues for people, but they don't ask what it is about Homo sapiens that necessitates evolving and utilizing religion in the first place. This is another example of anthropocentrism, that humans are special and different in the animal kingdom. Its historic roots can be seen in geocentrism—the earth is the center of the universe—as well as in religion—humans were made in God's image. Even as science has knocked down humans to a tiny, inconsequential speck in the incomprehensibly massive universe, this prejudice remains. To address this concern, origin of religion theorists would have to drop the assumption that they don't have to tackle why humans need additional mechanisms for social cohesion relative to other animals or why humans need to allay existential mysteries and anxieties. Because religion is exclusively a human attribute, scholars would want to look for what's different between humans and other animals for clues why elaborate religious behaviors only exist in people. If they did, they would have to focus on behavioral and cognitive differences between humans and other animals—things like intelligence, learning, memory, and self-awareness—in other words, higher-order consciousness.

We can perform a mini-thought experiment regarding whether or not religion persists purely through cultural transmission (after perhaps beginning as a byproduct) or has genetic, innate components. If a characteristic is solely or mostly cultural, it is likely to display wide variability. There will not only be many forms, but there will be cases where a feature such as religion will be non-existent and play little or no role at all. Over the tens of thousands of years that modern humans have existed, we would expect some societies to have abandoned or rejected religious practices or perhaps never have had it in the first place, but it simply isn't the case. And despite agnostics historically recent rejection of religious institutions and atheists rejection of god(s), for the vast majority of human existence religion has been an indelible part of life.

Noam Chomsky, the Massachusetts Institute of Technology linguist, showed language has an instinctual heritage even while there are thousands of different languages—the cultural aspect. And though there are thousands of languages, they all share certain characteristics in common, the inherited component, such as having grammar, syntax, symbol, and metaphor. All children, given the opportunity, rapidly learn language during a critical period as toddlers. Of course language is immensely practical and essential for transmitting information, so it makes sense that it has genetic roots. Religion, though, is ostensibly non-utilitarian and optional, which makes it even more of a mystery that it is found in every culture since the advent of modern humans. However, religion is exactly the same as language in that there are (or were) thousands of religions, and the roots of religion are in the genes. The difficulty with religion for the scientific and evolutionarily minded has been the inability to weave it into the Darwinian principles of fitness and adaptation.

The fact that, even today among atheists and agnostics, the original religious behaviors (prayer, music, art, mythology, dance and ritual movement) are omnipresent indicates a deeper primordial presence in our genome. All religion is variation on a hereditary theme. The real question is why and how religion is adaptive.

The next chapter looks in detail at emotions in humans, which helps clarify why religion could not have persisted as a byproduct. I review some basic evolutionary processes and describe how emotions are the drivers of human behavior and are adaptations that ensure our biological success. This exploration of emotion and evolution is necessary prior to jumping into the last section of the book about religious ritual behavior. Then we'll finally be ready to look at the first ritual behavior—music—to see how it stimulates emotions and quiets consciousness.

# Chapter 6

## Emotion and Evolution

> Although many of us may think of ourselves
> as thinking creatures that feel, biologically
> we are feeling creatures that think.
> *Jill Bolte Taylor*

In this chapter I discuss the function and meaning of emotion and why the emotional responses to ritual are the key to breaking down the mystery of religion—why religion explicitly benefits humanity. In succeeding chapters, I show how five ritual behaviors function to inhibit aspects of consciousness while promoting adaptive emotions resulting in improved fitness and evolutionary success.

## The Pleasure Principle

Michel Cabanac (2007) at the Université Laval in Quebec studies how pleasure and displeasure inform our actions. He posits that the "main concern of decision makers is to maximize pleasure rather than rationality in their decisions. Even when told to make a rational choice, [his study] participants' decisions were close to their hedonic [pleasure-seeking] choices." (p. 52) Cabanac proposes that the maximization of pleasure and the minimization of displeasure serve as the common currency in the tradeoffs between clashing motivations. This is just more ammunition that humans are less than rational creatures. It's rather intuitive, isn't it, that we want to do things that give us pleasure and avoid things that are not pleasant? But it happens that we're usually not aware of our internal hedonic motivations and how those forces can influence and even dictate our choices. Given the difficulty of constraining a clear understanding of motivation and judgment, we shouldn't take Cabanac's pursuits for granted.

What's pleasurable changes rapidly depending on circumstance. Sitting down to a meal when hungry and beginning to eat is satisfying, but after filling up, taking another bite can be uncomfortable. Motivation and choice, then, are transient and dependent on the status of other needs and desires. A person who is extremely cold may strive to resume a normal body temperature first rather than eat a meal even if very hungry. Sating hunger, finding warmth when cold, and having sex are pleasurable, but they also benefit a person's ability to flourish and leave offspring.

Avoiding displeasure also describes behaviors that improve an organism's success. We accept fear, anger, and mourning as normal and necessary. Lack of fear at the wrong time may mean becoming somebody else's lunch. Responses to negative stimuli are required in the appropriate circumstances and, on average, increase the likelihood of survival. For the most part achieving pleasure and avoiding displeasure translate as improving survival. In fact, there's no need to treat the pleasure and displeasure drives separately from increasing one's evolutionary fitness; they are one and the same—at least for 99.9% of human existence.

Walter Cannon, a Harvard physiology professor in the early twentieth century, made several important contributions to biology including the concept of homeostasis—maintaining physiological equilibrium. Homeostasis is almost completely under the control of hormonal and neural reflexes and is closely integrated with emotional systems. Humans, and all animals as well, strive to eat when they're hungry, sleep when they're tired, fight or flee when they're attacked, and mate when...well, that's a little more complicated. Some call this the four Fs of survival: feeding, fighting, fleeing, and reproduction. Cannon gave the name homeostasis to the intricate internal interactions that balance the various physiological mechanisms necessary for life and is an inherent, embedded characteristic of all living beings. The nature of life is cyclic, so animals are constantly shuffling the goal of the moment depending on what the most pressing need is, and humans are no different in this respect. The bottom line is that, as animals, humans strive to survive, which requires maintaining homeostasis. Without attending to this first order of business, the human dies, and leaves fewer or no offspring. Any inherited, genetic directive that compromises the ability to survive is winnowed out of the population, sometimes quickly, sometimes slowly. Emotions are the behavioral drivers and promulgators of homeostasis.

Damasio (2000) amplifies the connection between homeostasis and emotion.

> The pervasiveness of emotion in our development and subsequently in our every day experience connects virtually every object or situation in our experience, by virtue of conditioning, to the fundamental values of homeostatic regulation: reward and punishment; pleasure or pain; approach or withdrawal; personal advantage or disadvantage; and, inevitably, good (in the sense of survival) or evil (in the sense of death). Whether we like it or not, this is the *natural* human condition. (p. 58)

But like any human characteristic or feature, there is a wide range of opinions as to exactly what emotions are and how to differentiate them from other similar attributes. Are feelings the same or different from emotions? Do we have to be consciously aware of an emotion for it to be an emotion? Are emotions physiological activations—the release of hormones for example—or are they the affective results of such activity? In my typical way, I won't directly address these questions but, instead, focus on evolutionary aspects of emotion, which is more relevant to this discussion of religion. I make the point of stating that emotions have deep instinctive roots to highlight the interrelationship of emotion and religion and that they require evolutionary explanations.

Regardless of whether emotion is the physiological activity or the conscious perception of activated body states, the mechanisms that give rise to emotions are generally the same throughout the vertebrates. Emotions are driven by old brain regions, colloquially referred to as the reptilian brain. Backboned animals have hormone secreting neural areas analagous to the pituitary and hypothalamus, which are instrumental in generating fight-or-flight or courtship and mating behavior. A fish with a hook through its lip shows a strong flight reaction regardless of whether it's a response to pain or restricted movement. The apparatus for generating emotional states, which humans have inherited, have been honed for hundreds of millions of years.

Favorites Cosmides and Tooby (2000b) say emotions are superordinate programs that coordinate various subprograms to work in concert and overcome internal conflicts that might seek different goals at the same time. Emotions make sure the different homeostatic urges don't clash with each other, so, for example, either food gathering or fleeing behavior is selected depending on circumstance. Emotions begin as unconscious neural decisions that orchestrate a cascade of reactions dedicated to solving a particular problem or challenge. Cosmides and Tooby address the problem of defining emotions, whether as underlying physiology, overt behavior, or conscious perception.

> An emotion is not reducible to any one category of effects, such as effects on physiology, behavioral inclinations, cognitive appraisals, or feeling states, because it involves evolved instructions for all of them together, as well as other mechanisms distributed throughout the human mental and physical architecture. (p. 93)

Some people make the argument that only humans have feelings such as pain and suffering, which, again, is an anthropocentric conceit based on the assumption that humans are different from other animals. This particular bias tends to be proffered by those who hurt animals for various reasons such as slaughterhouses, fishermen, or researchers who use lab animals. Interestingly, many traditional people developed a somewhat religious method for dealing with the necessity to survive by killing by projecting a spirit onto the slain animal. The hunter thanks the animal for making the sacrifice to feed the people. Some cultures simply fail to empathize with the prey animals and don't anthropomorphize feelings of sadness or guilt for killing. Today some people feel the need to protect animals from pain while other don't, but their bias often establishes their attitude to the question of whether animals feel as much as people, or if animals have emotions. The point is that, despite claims to the contrary, human emotions descend from thousands of species who evolved before us. To understand human emotion, we are required to accept that it works similarly in other animals.

How does actual emotion get triggered? Damasio says the environment can cause emotional responses, which he calls emotionally competent stimuli or ECS. Such stimuli can be objects, events, or even memories (our internal environment). Memories of mom and birthdays can elicit happy, pleasant emotions. Mean bosses or romantic break-ups can bring out discordant emotions. Many emotions are faint and undetectable by conscious awareness. Looking at faces of strangers causes unconscious emotional evaluations of trustworthiness or attractiveness based on physical features including the subtle emotional cues displayed by the strangers themselves. These evaluations are the associations of sensory perceptions with emotion-laden value judgments and happen constantly. Damasio (2003) says,

> Signals related to the presence of [an emotionally competent] stimulus are made available to a number of emotion-triggering sites elsewhere in the brain. You can conceive of those sites as locks that open only if the appropriate keys fit. The emotionally competent stimuli are the keys, of course. Note that they select a preexisting lock, rather than instruct the brain on how to create one. The emotion-triggering sites subsequently activate a number of emotion-execution sites elsewhere in the brain. The latter sites are the immediate cause of the emotional state that occurs in the body and in brain regions that support the emotion-feeling process. (p. 58)

Damasio describes the emotional stimuli as keys that open preexisting locks. The locks are brain structures that expect the keys, the environmental stimuli, in order to initiate the emotional response. The ability to respond to ECS is dependent on genetic instructions that wire the brain. For example, studies have shown that infants at a very young age are capable of sophisticated emotion and cognition unlikely to be caused by learning.

> Four-month-old infants are surprised when a panel just in front of a cube somehow manages to fall back flat to the ground, right through the space that the cube should be occupying...Infants don't expect an object to pass through a barrier or through a gap that is narrower than the object is. (Pinker, 2009, p. 318)

We are innately programmed to anticipate that objects act according to the laws of Newtonian physics. Infants show surprise when objects violate cohesiveness, show spontaneous movement, or other counterintuitive behaviors. It makes sense that babies are designed to have a sense of object permanence so they don't go bashing into furniture. But people make the unwarranted assumption that other emotional behaviors follow a different trajectory and only accrue from learning and experience. Damasio's lock and key model indicates that complex behaviors are derived from existing brain wiring that only needs an environmental releaser to be expressed.

The brain is wired to perceive, interpret, and react to varieties of inputs and is predisposed to handle stimuli in predictable ways. Brain structures whose growth is controlled by inherited directives must form predictably for the inputs to be acquired and integrated meaningfully. Nevertheless, the wiring of the human brain is less determined in infancy than in other animals. We humans start life more open-ended and require more learning and experience to accomplish the development of what we are to become. However, that doesn't mean people are blank slates or even close to it. Even though humans require more nurture than other animals, our nature is still inescapably the foremost factor of who we are.

# What Dung and Religion Have in Common

As I said in the introductory chapter, if there is one thing most religion theorists agree on, it's that religious behavior elicits emotion. Saver and Rabin, in their 1997 *The Neural Substrates of Religious Experience*, coalesced that view, but almost any other theory of religion includes allusions to emotion. (Strangely, many cognitive religion theorists never pursue this fertile direction.) This is the flip side to the focus on beliefs. Rather than investigating the contents of imaginative and cognitively-biased contemplations, students of the origin of religion would be better served by exploring the universal, physiological, and emotional responses of religion. A physiological response is more easily and accurately measured, especially compared to analyzing beliefs, which as we've seen are fraught with questionable intention and interpretation problems. But why should religion stimulate affective response? Or more to the point, why would religious behaviors have evolved to leverage human emotional systems? The consistent emotional responses to religious behaviors persist because they must be adaptive, or evolution, the miserly accountant, would have eliminated them.

When discussing or researching how religion and ritual evolved in primordial humans, I frequently encounter descriptions of how dance and music began that are along the lines of "one caveman started beating on a hollow log. Others in the tribe began moving to the rhythm of the drumming, and everybody liked it. Soon it became a regular practice of the tribe, and it made everyone feel good. Then other tribes heard the drumming and saw the dancing and began doing it themselves, maybe because they liked it, or maybe they thought that they had better do it or the other tribe might have a competitive edge on them." This kind of thinking drives me crazy. There's no inherent reason why rhythm and acoustic tones should *naturally* motivate humans any more than any other animal. It raises the question I've asked several times: why don't other animals enjoy coordinated and synchronized music and dance? Well, many do, typically during courtship rituals or territorial displays, which are for very specialized, evolutionarily adaptive reasons. They didn't *just happen* to become entranced by their own rhythmic movements and sounds. What changed along the way for humans? People don't create elaborate mythologies just because it's *natural* to do so. We don't get wired to have religious ideas just because we can. Pervasive, evolutionarily expensive behaviors do not endure as accidental byproducts. Complex behaviors demand adaptation explanations. To do that, we need to examine how behavioral characteristics evolve and are selected for. What follows is an evolution thought experiment.

Consider that there are species of animals that eat feces, the dung beetle, for example. These creatures evolved to take advantage of a particular niche in the ecosystem. When eating feces, the animal doesn't have the *neural equivalent* of "This tastes like shit, but it's the only food around!" How do we know that? Hundreds of millions of years ago some insects evolved the biochemical processes necessary to digest and utilize the energy in other animals' waste. (Actually, this capability first evolved in microorganisms, but for our purposes, go with the beetle.) These beetles also developed resistance to the potentially dangerous microbes they were consuming. In parallel, and this is a crucial concept, these animals evolved to have a positive response for eating feces, acquiring the *neural reaction equivalent* of "this is good shit!" That positive emotional response is similar to the rush of pleasure humans get from eating ice cream. In the dung beetle's evolutionary journey, not all the genetics were in place at first. Sometimes the feces-eating insects evolved genes for "digest and absorb nutrients from feces" but not "resist microbial infections." The beetles having these genes didn't survive as much and make as many new beetles. Others evolved "resist microbial infection" and "digest and absorb nutrients from feces" but not the affective response "some feces smell and taste good." The beetles that evolved all the components necessary to take advantage of the energy available in feces survived and reproduced more than those who didn't have all the genetic components. The creatures that didn't evolve the complete range of biological (genetic) prerequisites for taking advantage of the abundance of animal waste were less able to thrive and, on average, left fewer offspring, hence those genes became less frequent in the beetle population.

Natural selection favors traits that increase fitness over traits less fit. Even in a situation where some organisms only lack positive feedback for a beneficial behavior, but otherwise share the same traits as others, they are at a distinct and significant disadvantage. Evolutionary geneticists have found that over the course of a relatively few generations, individuals with less fit traits will have less offspring, and on average, the genes (alleles) that code for that trait will become less frequent in a population.

The organisms we see today are the result of billions of generations of trial and error. Massive numbers of creatures perished along the way without leaving offspring, whether from bad luck (getting stepped on by a dinosaur, forest fire, volcano, flood), from the result of mutations or other genetic mistakes like incorrectly copying genes when cells divide or, more interestingly, from genes coding for traits that were less adaptive than their brethren. We don't see those failures since they didn't leave progeny, so we don't consider that they even existed. Even now genetic errors result in organisms that are missing a component necessary to prosper. They die. They don't leave any offspring. The parallel evolution of emotional neural feedback and adaptive behaviors are completely without intention. Today we only see the winners of the evolutionary lottery so it's easy for us to think that maggots and dung beetles eat excrement because it was planned. "How convenient that it worked out for the dung beetle," but the reality is, it didn't work out for the many who didn't reproduce.

People don't think in terms of the kinds of evolutionary challenges organisms face, but it's important to understand evolutionary methodology because it's significant to how we look at the evolution of religion. There has to be positive emotional feedback for a behavior that is otherwise adaptive for it to enhance survival and reproductive success. (Alternatively, negative feedback can also be adaptive by preventing organisms from eating something poisonous, getting eaten, or challenging a bigger rival.) The ability to absorb the nutrients from feces is not enough. The creature has to be neurally wired to get an emotional reward for the behavior, or it won't seek out, eat, and enjoy the benefit the food source has to offer. Keep in mind that this is a separate mechanism from the ability to actually digest other animal's excrement but both processes evolve more or less in parallel.

We take for granted that certain foods taste good and are desirable. Some of that appears to be culturally acquired, but it's mostly the case that much of what we observe to be culturally acquired has as its basis a genetic component. Ever offer a dog or cat a segment of orange? Most refuse it. Of course, they're meat-eaters, you say, but again, their ancestors didn't one day say, "Oh, I like the taste of meat, so I'll become a carnivore." I know, they don't say or think, but I beg this anthropomorphism to make the point. Your carnivorous pets don't like oranges because they evolved to mostly eat animals. In conjunction with the ability to capture, consume, and digest animal flesh, their brains' reward centers evolved to get excited by the look and smell of prey and the taste of meat, not fruit like primate brains did. It's not a choice for animals to decide what they like and don't like. It's how they evolved.

Our brains' pleasure and reward centers didn't need to learn in infancy that sugar tastes good. It's hard-wired. We like the taste of sugar because our predecessors hundreds of millions of years ago evolved to extract energy from it, specifically the sugar glucose, through a biochemical process called the citric acid or Krebs cycle. A concomitant evolutionary movement led organisms to be successful, who, through the luck of their genetics, had a *good* neural reaction to eating substances that they could also utilize nutritionally. The earliest life forms co-evolved the ability to metabolize sugar and mechanisms that provided positive feedback when they detected and consumed it. Microorganisms evolved receptors on their cell membranes that could recognize and capture sugar molecules, which, in one sense, are functionally like the taste buds in animals. Animal cells have similar receptors for glucose in order to capture it from the blood and provide fuel for cell functions. Human brain regions like the nucleus accumbens, anterior insular cortex, and orbitofrontal cortex are some of the reward centers that interact with sensory input and alert us that something is desirable. Without the positive feedback to and from these reward brain areas, any otherwise adaptive behavior, on average, becomes less frequent in a population. If organisms aren't motivated to do the adaptive behavior as often or at all, over the course of thousands of generations those individuals are outcompeted and don't reproduce as much as individuals who, by the luck of their genetics, are wired to receive encouragement through their reward systems. Evolutionary success requires both the neural reward as well as the physiological benefit.

Neural circuits develop in animals under genetic control with the expectation of receiving inputs in the form of sensory information — Damasio's lock and key analogy. Brains do not form their structures amorphously. Neurons have a certain amount of plasticity to form connections during ontogenesis — during stages of growth including later in life — but that plasticity is well within circumscribed limits of opportunity. "Anything goes" does not go in neural circuits. Animals, including people, are designed to anticipate a variety of environmental inputs or experiences. The dung beetle can't receive and evaluate internal positive reinforcement from its food sources without specific neural bundles connected to taste sensors. This first necessitates having the genetic instructions in place that direct the connection of these neural areas. Taste signals get passed to reward or displeasure modules based on how substances stimulate the taste sensors, and those connections evolved over evolutionary time but not within a lifetime. The pleasure or displeasure neural sites are the locks awaiting the sensory keys sent by the taste sensors, but the lock and key mechanisms are already in place. Emotions instigate chemical and neural changes that are "designed" by evolution to benefit an organism's survival and ultimately enhance reproductive success. Emotional reactions that increase an organism's survival, and the neural pathways underlying them, are retained while those emotional reactions that don't provide benefit or reduce survival and reproductive success disappear.

Because of the evolutionary relationship between reward systems and adaptive behaviors, anything that excites the reward system is explicitly defined to be adaptive (without a specific reason otherwise), and so it is with religion. When we say that we like music and dance, and it feels good to do it, it's because these religious behaviors are intrinsically adaptive. There is nothing inherently positive or "natural" about human ritual behaviors any more than the generic chemical structure of sugar, $C_6H_{12}O_6$, inherently tastes good. We desire and enjoy sugary food because of the Krebs cycle, which extracts energy from the sugar glucose. The crucial involvement of neural reward systems in the evolution of animals' behavioral repertoire is a key element in the effort to understand the motivation for ritual behaviors, which provides context for religious behaviors as well.

## Emotional Primacy

When humans developed their grand consciousness, they believed they broke the mold of restrictive instinct—at least that's what consciousness informed. But consciousness is a trickster whispering in our inner ear that it is the all-knowing ruler, and we would be well advised to follow its guidance. But it mostly doesn't have advantageous knowledge and is like a punch-drunk boxer swinging wildly. Once in a while it connects, and when it does can be a powerful force. Without question consciousness supports the cognitive tools that enable humans to control their environment so they can thrive in the frigid Arctic or the hottest jungles and deserts. The quotidian contribution of consciousness that results in human dominance of the Earth is small, well under five percent of human mental activity, yet it is loud and makes its presence felt far more than its true role. Most of the time it has little to offer, and it's insistence on having its say interferes with tried and true innate, adaptive, emotionally-based motivations. The ascendence of consciousness was so problematic that a parallel mechanism arose—intrinsic religion—to counterbalance consciousness's deleterious aspects. This Split in cognitive function—the coevolution of consciousness and religion—is what makes humans unique and constitutes an essential aspect of the human condition.

The brain regions active in regulating emotional behavior are well documented. The limbic system in general and the amygdala specifically are a central hub for emotion regulation, neural structures that developed far back in evolutionary history. While the neocortex—the big, modern brain—makes us uniquely human, most, if not all, sensory inputs and behavioral outputs at one point or another route through the limbic system. Whatever new roles are played by the neocortex, they are modulated, moderated, and ameliorated by the limbic system. The prefrontal cortex (PFC), that area of the brain that is unusually large in humans and is thought to give us our "superior" cognitive powers, has myriad interconnections with the limbic system. Just as the limbic system is a general region that has many specialized functional and structural areas, the PFC is also comprised of many subregions that functionally interact with other brain regions. Those connections are predictable and genetically derived. While the strength of the connections between these various regions can heighten or diminish based on experience and conditioning, the range of potential behavior is circumscribed by the established neural couplings. Like any organism, what we are or can become is limited by incipient, predetermined nerve networks.

Limbic-driven emotions affect all aspects of our physiology, which can be measured and observed. Despite being inadmissible in some courts of law, polygraphs (lie detectors) measure several emotionally-influenced traits such as blood pressure, pulse, and breathing rate. It also measures skin conductance, which is influenced by sweat on the skin, a measure of emotional arousal as well as temperature regulation. Whether or not the results of polygraph testing can determine a person's veracity is a matter of debate, but there's no question that emotions, even very subtle ones, cause measurable physiological changes. Even the perception of physiological changes can unconsciously affect one's inclinations.

In an ingenious experiment, Stuart Valins showed that emotions and judgment could be altered by manipulating heart rate. Male subjects were shown pictures of scantily clad women, while at the same time these subjects believed they were listening to their own heartbeat. They were asked to judge the attractiveness of the women in the pictures. However, unbeknownst to the men, the experimenters either provided the subjects with a false high heart beat rate or a false low rate heart beat. "The subjects judged as more attractive the pictures of women that had been associated with the high heart rate sounds, even though their actual heart rate was not high during exposure to these pictures." (LeDoux, 1996, p. 49)

The perception of the manipulated heartbeat unconsciously influenced the opinions and judgments—the emotional reactions—of the subjects.

Popular culture in the form of TV, movies, and books has glamorized the use of polygraphs in police dramas. The same media has also latched on to the study of facial expressions to detect lying and emotion-based cues in crime shows. Psychologist Paul Ekman (2003) has spent his career exploring how facial expressions correspond to emotions. Ekman showed how our basic emotional repertoire is innate and that facial expressions are universal. He tested remote tribespeople in New Guinea showing them pictures of faces expressing different emotions. They interpreted emotional meaning the same way as modern, technological people. Ekman tested other cultures and found people understood emotions in facial expressions similarly.

Ekman's work fleshed out Charles Darwin's ideas in *The Expression of the Emotions in Man and Animals* to which Ekman wrote an introduction in recent editions. Both men saw the connection between emotion and facial expressions as a continuum of the innate manifestation of evolutionary adaptation. Darwin noted that people blind since birth have the same facial expressions as sighted people. People have an exceptional ability to discern small differences in facial features and expressions. Among the thousands of people we interact with, we are invariably able to recognize each person individually and separately from every other acquaintance. As social beings, we make automatic, unconscious judgments of faces based on experience and heuristics. Given the importance of social interaction in human societies, the ability to detect not only individuals from each other, but also the smallest emotional indicators is crucial to managing cooperation and conflict.

Pinker (2009) corroborates the study of facial emotions as a key indicator of true inner states.

> Facial expressions are hard to fake. People don't really believe that the grinning flight attendant is happy to see them. That is because a social smile is formed with a different configuration of muscles from the genuine smile of pleasure. A social smile is executed by circuits

in the cerebral cortex that are under voluntary control; a smile of pleasure is executed by circuits in the limbic system and other brain systems and is involuntary. Anger, fear and sadness, too, recruit muscles that can't be controlled voluntarily, and the genuine expressions are hard to fake, though we can pantomime an approximation. (p. 415)

In our everyday lives we sense the world emotionally first and occasionally slap on conscious labels second, almost always to affirm the emotional judgment. Sometimes when we apply our attention to it, we can observe and detect our emotional state. When we attempt to alter our emotions, though, especially in times of extreme distress or upheaval, we find that it's extremely difficult, if not impossible, to do so. Our emotional complex has priority, and when we try to override it with consciousness, the best we do is suppress or redirect. The result is an array of consequences that, in the extreme, are internalized into physical or mental illness. Even minor repression of emotions can result in conflicted behaviors such as passive-aggressiveness, depression, neurosis, and stress reactions. Much of psychotherapy is the study of how people compensate when they are unable to express their emotions, and it is the emotions themselves that serve as the avenue to healing. In *The Healing Power of Emotion*, Colwyn Trevarthen (2009) describes their psychological importance.

> Emotions have healing power because they are active regulators of vitality in movement and the primary mediators of social life. From infancy, emotions protect and sustain the mobile embodied spirit and oppose stress. And they do so in relationships between persons who share purposes and interests intimately. By marking experiences with feelings, emotions allow us to retain a record of the benefits and risks of behaviors, and they give values to the intentions and goal objects of those behaviors. Most importantly, human emotions link persons in the life of family and community; they com-

> municate the well-being, cooperation, and conflicts of
> our engaged lives. (p. 55)

Human language and cognition are both qualitatively and quantitatively different from other animals, yet from the earlier examination of consciousness, we know they do not trump our innate dispositions. While the basis for studying humans is often what they report or what they claim they believe, cognitive scientists know that such reporting and belief is fraught with bias and misperception. The scientific observer cannot help but note what people think and say, but we learn that what people say and believe is not always, or even mostly, what is actually happening beneath the surface. Beliefs are emotion-based cognitions raised to the level of consciousness and have little to do with reason or rationality. Although we can learn a lot by asking human subjects to report their beliefs, we must keep in perspective the differences between what people state and their underlying disposition. Research into cognition and consciousness utilize many different techniques to evaluate and separate people's true intentions and subliminal feelings in order to evade belief traps. Many fascinating studies highlight the discrepancies and discontinuities between what people think they know and what they show they know.

In his book, *The Emotional Brain: The Mysterious Underpinnings of Emotional Life,* LeDoux (1996) calls emotions "neural systems that mediate behavioral interactions with the environment, particularly behaviors that take care of fundamental problems of survival." (p. 125) Ancient, adaptive emotions remain critical to Homo sapiens' evolutionary success. The fact that religious behaviors have emotional consequences means that those behaviors have value and importance. Otherwise humans would not have evolved religious behaviors that elicit emotional reactions in the first place. Emotions have the advantage that they can be observed and measured physiologically, which makes them amenable to scientific inquiry. The emotions generated by religion are available for measurement, unlike beliefs. Because emotions adaptively evolved, they provide a means to judge religion for evolutionary fitness and ultimately a theory for the origin of religion.

With that we next explore the biology of ritual. Several times to this point I have alluded to five ritual behaviors: music, dance, art, mythology, and prayer. The next chapter presages the last section of the book where five rituals types are examined in detail as representative of religious behavior.

# CHAPTER 7

## BIOLOGY AND RITUAL

In human culture is the preservation of wildness.
*Wendell Berry*

We turn to ritual, the actions that tie emotions to religious behaviors. For thousands of years and in all cultures, people engaged in music and art, danced in rhythmic movements, and told stories that today we call mythologies. Prayer, too, is a religious ritual and is functionally akin to these other rituals. These original ritual practices were mostly or even strictly for religious purposes, and not for mundane or secular reasons like they can be today. However, the functions of these ritual behaviors are not substantially different today than they were tens of thousands of years ago. Research shows that human rituals stimulate our emotional brain centers. That means these behaviors evolved. We are predisposed to do these behaviors, and we inherit the genes that motivate us to enact religious rituals. Getting pleasure from ritual behavior *didn't just happen or solely arise as a byproduct*. The trick is to deconstruct why and how rituals are adaptive. Leveraging ritual behaviors as the currency of religious practice is the key to revealing the link between emotions and religion, which is to quiet consciousness. But why do I emphasize these five particular rituals when there are many other types of rituals like rites of passage, sacrifice, festivals, and many others?

# Rites of Passage

Rites of passage are usually religion-driven ceremonies incurred at various life stages in tribal and modern cultures. According to Arnold Van Gennep's (1960) seminal book *Rites of Passage*, rituals, particularly rites of passage, move initiates through three stages: separation, transition, and incorporation or rebirth. (p. 11) The first stage, separation, may or may not be a physical separation from the society, but is always a metaphorical separation from the past. In the case of the adolescent rite of passage, the separation is from childhood. In marriage it is a removal from single status. This separation is like a loss or sacrifice, even a symbolic or metaphorical death. In the course of the ritual, the initiate prepares to leave her old mundane life and enter the sacred second stage, transition. The transition stage is typically when the initiate is emotionally stressed with the intent to break down psychic barriers and expose the emotional soul to the sacred where transformation can take place. Following the sometimes unsparing ordeals of transition, the initiate is incorporated or welcomed back into society in a new role.

Perhaps the most important rite of passage is the transition from child to adult. In traditional societies adolescents endure strict rites designed to convert them to adulthood in terms of recognition and responsibility. Even though these types of religious and secular rites still exist in modern society—bar mitzvahs, confirmations, graduations—their sacred aspect is much reduced. Some of these modern rites are performed within the religious sanctuary and framework, but they are watered-down versions of the often brutal, emotionally wrenching rites of passage in tribal cultures. In a tilt to the need to undergo and complete this most relevant rite, the modern teenager unconsciously gravitates towards cultural manifestations of revolt against the social order. This is not different from the past, but was manipulated through brutish initiation rites in traditional societies to leverage the adolescent's innate desire to acquire adulthood.

Today this rebellion is understood as a rejection of parents' and schools' authoritarianism, but this separation should be more properly seen as the first stage of ritual and the desire to descend into the transition phase where the adolescent meets the sacred. For many teens military basic training serves as the process that administers the physical and mental rigors that restructure the emotional psyche and converts children into adults. In the course of basic training, the drill sergeant exorcises the identities of the recruits, a symbolic death of the individual, a step in breaking them down in preparation for rebuilding them as soldiers. The armed services provide the third stage of ritual, which is incorporation, the return to mundane life, but now the teenager is an adult with adult expectations, tasks, and responsibilities.

Why are these rites of passage necessary? Why can't people move through these developmental phases without the help of ritual? For animals with little or no higher-order consciousness, genetically modulated instincts synthesize and generate behavior at every stage of development. Like other animals, the human transition from adolescent to adult involves various physiological changes, but cognitive ones as well, and these cognitive-specific changes are not divorced from their physiological foundations. The prefrontal cortex is one of the last brain areas to complete full maturation, which is achieved in early adulthood. Humans, however, have the capacity to hold contingent information. Whereas pre-human animals simply undergo the pubescent transformation under innate neural and hormonal controls, for humans, having been thrust out of metaphorical Eden, the adaptive instincts are no longer the sole source of instruction. With the added complexities of local and conditional culture, teens cannot simply make the ontogenic (developmental) transition without dealing with the overhead of nurture and society.

Achieving adulthood involves both innate physiological changes and the "tribal" knowledge necessary to perform culture-specific tasks and responsibilities. However, unmethodical consciousness, whose efficacy is a crapshoot in any given moment, is also undergoing rapid maturation. Consciousness is completely insufficient to counsel and guide the initiate during the turbulent transition into adulthood. Culturally acquired knowledge that serves temporally and locally doesn't promote the necessary biologically-based movement from one developmental stage to the next and is inadequate by itself to trigger and complete the move. Physical brain development requires biologically-informed assistance in the form of adaptive emotions. Restructuring the initiate at a deep emotional level integrates both the innate and conscious aspects, which is accomplished through rites of passage. These rites, richly tied to music, myth, and other rituals activate emotional processes to drive these maturational changes. Biology come first; consciousness runs a distant second. We'll look at some specific examples of rites and their effects on initiates in the chapters on dance and myth. The adolescent rite of passage parallels a developmental change that has important biological components: puberty in all its physiological and cognitive manifestations.

Rites of passage are important religious traditions, but the variety of practices makes it difficult to identify a commonality among them. They describe many different behaviors, but rather than trying to find unifying threads to pull together a specific meaning or definition, I summon the lowest common denominator of ritual behavior, the underlying actions that make up rites of passage as well as other rituals like sacrifices and ceremonies. I focus on music, dance, art, mythology, and prayer. These are the typical and frequent behaviors that comprise most rituals regardless of the rituals' purposes and methodologies. This level of observing ritual has the added advantage that we can study behaviors through an ethological lens, looking at ritual movements and actions, surveying rites from the point of view of animal behavior.

## The Ethological Lens

Because specific beliefs are not a fruitful avenue to understand the origins of religion, the quest to comprehend religion, and human nature in general, warrants additional, alternative approaches. Indeed, we don't ask other species what they're thinking or what they believe. Obviously, we are limited by the lack of interspecies language, but the ethologists, the scientists who study animal behavior, analyze animal moods and intentions based on their overt actions. Animals display various forms of communication including vocalizations and body language, which provides a rich dialect for scrutinizing meaning. Canine dispositions are easily assessed by body position such as a wagging or lowered tail, bared teeth, ears flattened or up, and other indicators. Can we apply the same approach to humans? Can we understand human behavior based on what people do rather than what they say or think? We've looked at a slew of studies that show people's actual intentions or feelings are often not their stated understanding. In fact, people are ignorant of the reasons for their inner states most of the time. When we assess people ethologically, we don't ask them overtly for intention. People have body language just like other animals as revealed, for example, by Paul Ekman's facial emotion studies.

When promulgating an ethological approach towards humanity, we are challenged to adhere to strict principles of animal behavior. Little about human behavior is simple and straightforward, so studying people through an ethological lens is not clean either. For those imbued in human exceptionalism—that humans are superior to other life forms—equating animal behavior with human behavior may be anathema. Nevertheless, human behavior is derived and driven by the same mechanisms as the rest of the animal kingdom. That isn't to say we can be glib about comparing human and animal bases for motivation. When I ask, "What do people do?" we are observing ourselves, which is problematic at many levels. In addition to the uncertainty and self-reflection bias we all bring to the table, we humans are indeed significantly different than the rest of the animal kingdom, and our ritual and religious behaviors reflect that in spades. When other animals display ritual behaviors, they are overtly physical movements, and, at the same time, we don't presume to completely understand animals' internal motivations. Human ritual can be both external and internal. Dancing and singing is external, but listening to music, meditation, reading, or watching a drama may involve little more than eye movement or even less. A whole lot is happening in the brain, yet it is opaque except on those extremely rare occasions when modern scientific instruments peer inside, or elaborate experiments are undertaken.

Ellen Dissanayake (2006) in the School of Music at the University of Washington researches and writes about the evolutionary origins of art. She recognizes the need to approach early human aesthetic expression like music and visual art from a behavioral biological perspective. In *Ritual and Ritualization: Musical Means of Conveying and Shaping Emotion in Humans and Other Animals,* she says, "This essay uses a new departure by taking an ethological approach to questions of musical experience—i.e., treating music as a behavior that evolved in ancestral humans because it contributed to their survival and reproductive success." She goes on to say, "In an ethological view, the biological purpose of emotions is to motivate behavior—to make us respond appropriately to the sorts of occurrences in the environment that could affect us, for good or ill. In this sense, then, musical experience was originally functional." (pp. 31-32)

Professor of Psychiatry Jay Feierman (2009), also promotes an ethological strategy to understanding religion. While he says most religious practice is culturally learned, he identifies one particular innate type of religious behavior.

> There is a Type I [biologically evolving] religious behavior that appears to be present in all the major religions of the world and at least some tribal religions...What can be seen is a local variation of make-oneself-lower-or-smaller-or-more-vulnerable behavior (LSV behavior)...LSV behavior is an ancient, coordinated motor pattern whose various forms can be traced back through the earliest vertebrates. (p. 77)

LSV behavior is seen in all the monotheistic religions as various forms of prostration, bowing, and kneeling. It typically represents a submissive posture in relationship to a dominant God. The dominance hierarchy is a common feature of interactions within human and animal societies and holds a special role in prayer rituals.

> Variations of the LSV behavior [are] associated with the nonvocal aspect of petitioning prayer in all major and at least some tribal religions of the world. Christians, Hindus, Buddhists, Muslims, and Jews all use different variations of the LSV theme. The eyes are often closed during prayer, making the praying individual

even more vulnerable. Christians bow their heads and put their hands together in front of their chests in the nonvocal aspect of petitioning prayer. Most Christians pray with their hands in front pressed together pointing upward. However, members of the Church of Jesus Christ of Latter-day Saints (Mormon) faith often pray by folding both arms across their chest. Some Christian denominations also kneel at times. Sometimes Pentecostal Christians pray by putting their empty (weaponless) hands over their heads similar to signs of surrender. Hindus can sit with their hands up. Buddhists exhibit various LSV behaviors when petitioning in front of statues of the Buddha for enlightenment. Muslims pray on their knees (smaller) and get even smaller, lower, and more vulnerable by putting their forehead on the ground with their eyes downward. Orthodox Jews as well as Muslims bow back and forth, which lowers them when they read sacred texts in prayer. (p. 77)

LSV behavior is just one example of ritual behavior that has the scientific advantage of being observeable and measureable in religious contexts. That said, I won't spend time analyzing the fine motor movements of ritual activities. While there may be cases where it's unclear if actions constitute ritual behavior, in general, we recognize when people engage in music, dance, making or viewing art, or reading, watching, or listening to mythology (books, movies, TV, plays, poetry in contemporary culture). These observable human actions provide a starting point for our ethological approach. And this is why I don't include other types of ritual such as sacrifice or rites of passage in this analysis. They are obviously religious rituals, but they aren't as amenable to ethological study. Sacrifice and rites of passage can mean very different things in different cultures and cannot be specifically identified behaviorally compared to music and dance, which can be delineated by a fairly limited set of behaviors. And in most cases, rites of passage, festivals, and other rituals contain the five basic ritual behaviors. Music, dance, art, mythology, and prayer are the building blocks of more complex rituals.

Undoubtedly, though, there will be debate about ascribing ritual as the basis of all ethological religious experience especially as some rituals have changed dramatically in recent history. Many rituals have been coopted by big business in modern societies with music, books, and movies (visual myths) raking in billions of dollars a year. However, no human activity exists isolated from cultural modification. It's the lock and key once again. Regardless of the milieu, the ability to enjoy music, dance, art, and myth are the instinctual brain latches that require cultural keys to open. The innate urge to engage in ritual behaviors remains, but the context created by a particular society modifies and adjusts the ritual activities. We now have corporations that privatize and own ritual content. That doesn't mean that the original purpose and drive is different. We now have to purchase ritual satisfaction, whereas formerly, the historical cost of ritual used to be the participatory requirement. As child or adult, male or female, every person in the tribe had their role to fulfill in the ritual act. Perhaps you would have to pay the shaman in chickens or tobacco for services rendered, but the very fact that we're willing to spend (sometimes lots of) money to obtain ritual interaction adds credence to the psychic need it serves. In our secular society, the satisfaction of participating in music, dance, art, or mythology remains, whether as actor or observer. Though its importance and significance within the culture has changed, ritual behavior remains the currency of religion.

The fact that humans universally embrace ritual practices, and did so 50,000 to perhaps more than 100,000 years ago, indicates a critical launch point. When people dance, sing or play music, make visual art, or watch, narrate or act out fiction, they are practicing what were originally the sacred acts. Historical and contemporary pre-literate tribes told myths of their gods conspiring, warring, wooing, and copulating, exactly the same as their own tribal behaviors. Archeologists find various artifacts left behind by tribespeople, usually utilitarian items such as pottery, arrows, and or other tools, but they also find carvings, petroglyphs, and pictographs that had no apparent practical purpose. Tribespeople added non-utilitarian patterns and motifs to their pots, clothes, and other practical crafts that depicted people, animals, and sometimes just symbols and patterns inscrutable to modern interpretation, yet these ritual activities are understood as expressions of tribal religion and spirituality.

The religious context for believing in gods is gone for atheists and many agnostics, but all ritual behaviors continue to have emotional consequences even in secular societies. Since emotional responses evolved to solve the dilemmas of survival, it begs for us to analyze these originally religious behaviors within their evolutionary context. We look at these ostensibly impractical ritual activities to see how to comprehend them akin to how we understand dogs' wagging tails. The ethological investigation of behavior requires not only understanding the function of the behavior but its adaptiveness. How does ritual behavior benefit the human animal?

## The Ritual Swamp

Why have we humans acquired these ritual behaviors that stimulate emotions? In Boyer and Liénard's (2006) article *Why Ritualized Behavior?*, the authors identify the overt movements of ritual. They assert that rituals are "intuitively recognizable by their stereotypy, rigidity, repetition, and *apparent lack of rational motivation.*" (emphasis added) (p. 595) Of course, the interpretation of the reason for these actions is a bit more problematic. The paper scrutinizes ritual behavior by obsessive-compulsives, rituals associated with life-stage changes as well as cultural rituals associated with religion.

The article describes how young children go through a ritualization phase "starting at age 2 and peaking in middle childhood" (p. 596) in which repetitive actions allay such potential anxieties as fear of strangers, loss of special attachments, and cleanliness. Life-stage changes such as becoming a parent can lead to unacceptable thoughts about harm being done to the baby resulting in sustained ritualization. The authors make the case that pathological ritual behaviors such as OCD and "normal" cultural rituals span a spectrum of intensity but are not qualitatively different.

For Boyer and Liénard, ritual is a non-adaptive byproduct, (p. 609) although they note that the cognitive consequences of ritual cause "the 'swamping' of working memory which permits the temporary suppression of intrusive thoughts." (p. 605) Working memory describes a variety of cognitive functions that are part of higher-order consciousness and is sometimes called the central executive, the top decision-making apparatus in the brain. Working memory includes features such as attention, response preparation, goal-attainment, planning, sequential memory, temporal-order memory, and information integration. "Working memory not only serves to focus attention and make decisions but also serves as the chief liaison to long-term memory systems and to language comprehension and production." (Coolidge, 2005, p. 7) In other words, by swamping working memory ritual inhibits aspects of higher-order consciousness. Shades of The Split Hypothesis, but why should there be these unwelcome deliberations, these intrusive thoughts in the first place that ritual serves to swamp?

In all cases of ritual they describe, Boyer and Liénard accord some unwanted aspect of cognition—unacceptable or distressing ideas, images, or urges—invading the mind, and ritual is the defensive response. "Security-motivation systems are engaged. This may be because of potential danger cues in the environment, information imparted by other people, self-generated thoughts, or intrusions." (Boyer and Liénard, 2006, p. 601)

Boyer and Liénard call the tendency of intrusive thoughts to ensue from potential danger cues the Potential Hazard Repertoire (PHR). This has an uncanny similarity to the Hyperactive Agency Detection Device. To review, HADD theory states that humans are naturally prone to designate external meaning and causality to unknown, potentially dangerous environmental stimuli, even minor ones, ultimately leading to the invention of supernatural entities—the basis of gods. The security assessments of the PHR lead to extreme apprehension that overestimates risks and danger. People must respond to these perceived threats with action—action-sequences, action-flow, and action-parsing—each its own component in the ritual process to allay fear. As a result of ritual activity "the intrusive themes are temporarily pushed away from conscious access, resulting in a short-lived reduction in anxiety level." (p. 601)

The authors recognize similarities between the pathological rituals of OCD and the "normal" culturally sanctioned rituals that constitute religious behaviors. Both "showed that the same themes recur over and over again in both domains." (p. 608) Ultimately, Boyer and Liénard conclude, "It is a cognitive and evolutionary puzzle that humans perform rituals, given the waste of time and resources involved...Ritualization may be seen as an occasional by-product of specific precaution systems and action-parsing capacities in humans." (p. 612)

Both HADD and PHR consider people's risky state of existence, which is reasonable since life can be fraught with peril, but why is this different from other animals? All have nervous systems designed to alert them to danger and provide fight or flight responses as necessary. To their credit, Boyer and Liénard explore possible reasons for the evolution of ritual behavior, but they presuppose the question in terms of hazard detection. They can't get past the belief that hazard detection is the normative response to the distressing ideas and thoughts people have. They limit their options prematurely.

HADD and PHR neglect to explain why people have an extra layer of cautionary cognitive response. To the best of our knowledge, no other animals have these hyper-stimulating cognitions. No one claims non-human animals utilize ritual for thought suppression. Animals' survival depends on detecting actual threats and acting appropriately, not dealing with intrusive thoughts and anxieties of possible or imagined threats. In the moment of actual danger, repetitive ritual behaviors are usually not the optimal response. While animals do exhibit ritual behaviors, they do so for specific communication purposes that are understood to be adaptive. Religious rituals, however, are practiced universally, so the challenge is to explain why ritual swamps working memory in all people, and why ritual activity would persist and be desirable.

Many rituals result in radical alterations of consciousness. As we will see in succeeding chapters about the specific ritual forms — music, dance, art, prayer — altered states of consciousness such as trance or quiescent meditative states are frequent outcomes of ritual behavior. It's extremely difficult to reconcile such extreme behavioral changes as being the result of agency detection or hazard repertoire. Meeting one's spirit guide after days or weeks of a brutal rite of passage is hardly the means to ameliorate the fear of unknown hazards. In fact, such rites create uncertainty, terror, stress, and misery leading to the purposive breakdown of regular consciousness. Harsh rites of passage in traditional societies intentionally instigate the collapse of normal sensibilities resulting in altered states. These merciless rites of passage are dramatic examples of The Split Hypothesis in which religious ritual swamps or suppresses extended human cognitive capacities such as working memory and the central executive, likely the source of anxiety-generating intrusive thoughts. Dissanayake (2008b) borrows from Cosmides and Tooby.

> During human evolution, hominid brain organization eventually enabled what evolutionary psychologists have called "decoupling" and "metarepresentation." Instead of reacting to events as they occurred or following the promptings of instinct, ancestral humans at some point could remember past events that were desirable or undesirable and then try to control—recreate or avoid—them in the future. (p. 179)

The reduced role of instinct was accompanied by the elaboration of cognitive functions such as working memory in higher-order consciousness, but not all aspects of embellished consciousness were favorable or advantageous. Early Homo's neural advancements, like all evolutionary changes incurred negative consequences as well as positive ones. The great knowledge humans acquired included the perception of open-ended possibilities for choice and action for which the conscious individual often could not determine an absolutely correct result or even a modest preference. The awareness of this irresolvable situation was a constant source of internal tension and discord. Ritual and religion evolved to counteract this problem and temporarily relieve this conflict.

*Intrusive thoughts* are the detritus of our internal conversation, a characteristic of higher-order consciousness. As much as any other aspect of consciousness, the constant background noise of our private discussion represents the disadvantage of consciousness. It generates its clamor due to its functional nature. Our conscious discourse throws out possibilities and suggestions, but they are usually rationalizations and projections of emotionally-based heuristics based on sensory input. Sometimes the notions are cautionary warning of possible problems, but they can also be innocuous such as daydreams that run a pleasant storyline. Our inner thoughts go off leash and run wild, and we often enjoy it. At the same time, it is the nature of consciousness to tout its own importance, to whisper that it is in control, watching, observing, and concocting the next plan of action. For the most part, however, humans do not act based on this conscious dialog but rather from emotionally-generated directives.

Why does consciousness perform this way? Why do we have this nutty function that causes us to believe in its sway when it's mostly toothless? Despite what Einstein thought about randomness and probability in quantum theory (God doesn't play dice), evolution proceeds based on random mutations, and rarely some mutations result in advantages. Consciousness is an accumulation of mutations that gave early humans an edge up through the ability to hold more than one or two concepts at once for parallel comparison and evaluation, but the mechanism to accomplish this does so with significant downsides, an overflow of extra neural effort that distracts and disrupts. The Split Hypothesis proposes that religion and its associated ritual behaviors function to inhibit the distortions of consciousness. Religious rituals are formal procedures to fulfill the need people have to quiet the noise of their incessant consciousness. There is no need to invoke hazard detection and precaution systems.

By the way, the Boyer and Liénard *Why Ritualized Behavior?* article is an excellent example of unintended consequences. Early in this book, I said that experiments have not been designed to specifically test The Split Hypothesis, which is necessary to validate it. However, I claim that many studies already exist to support The Split Hypothesis. This paper stating that ritual is a response to anxiety-producing intrusive thoughts is an academic work that unwittingly addresses The Split Hypothesis fairly directly.

In commentary following Boyer and Liénard's article, Alcorta and Sosis contend human ritual behavior is an evolved mechanism for facilitating social interaction. This is the group cohesion explanation for ritual and religion, but sociality is a secondary aspect of ritual. We observe that religious ritual takes place primarily in groups, but it doesn't have to. People invoke rituals such as prayer for very personal reasons in solitary circumstances. Today music, dance, prayer, art, and mythology are enjoined both individually and communally and probably were in ancient times as well. By first principles, the level at which we evaluate the cause and effect of ritual is the individual. Behaviors like religion and ritual begin with discrete brain activation.

More importantly, Alcorta and Sosis discuss neural activity during ritual, an important link between overt, observed behavior and its underlying purpose. Ritual, they say, promotes associational learning and enhances long-term memory. They note that brain neuroimaging reveals that the sustained attention or vigilance during ritual activity increases activation of right hemisphere prefrontal and superior parietal cortices. This promotes social-emotional information processing, forefronts negative appraisal systems, and elicits holistic, gestalt thinking. The right hemisphere's posterior association cortex, they state, is important for processing new information, anticipating consequences, and determining emergency reactions. (Boyer and Liénard, 2006, p. 613) Ritual behavior redirects brain resources to holistic, right brain functions and emotional centers. Emotional modification is the essential mechanism through which ritual effects the human actor, but these other ramifications raise fascinating implications suggesting additional future refinements of The Split Hypothesis and ways of interpreting ritual's effect on consciousness and the brain.

The psychic benefits of ritual have interesting parallels to recent trends in psychotherapy. Where once therapy was cognitive—the "talking cure" in which realization of repressed experiences and feelings led to psychological healing—a newer modified goal of psychotherapy is to help challenge the borders of people's affective tolerance. People who have dysfunctional emotional responses because of life trauma or other psychic insults are encouraged to test their emotions in the safety of a supportive therapeutic environment. The therapists role is to help guide the client to experience emotions that previously had been toxic without letting them wallow in dysfunctional habits or evade threatening emotions altogether. There are strong analogies between religious ritual and psychotherapy through their conscious and unconscious manipulation of emotions. Some, including several from the Jungian camp, suggest that modern psychotherapy is a substitute for the traditional role of religious ritual now missing in our modern societies. All told, this strongly suggests that intrinsic, unconscious knowledge systems are the beneficiaries of ritual vis-à-vis distracting conscious thought. Ritual encourages and supports important cognitive functionality in humans.

Early humans didn't *just happen* to engage in ritual because a human *decided* to have an enjoyable emotional reaction to activities such as music or dancing nor did they automatically embrace ritual as an accidental byproduct of other cognitions. Byproduct explanations are simply palliatives for being unable to build a cogent case for the origins of religious ritual. Rituals exist because there is affirming emotional feedback for practicing them. Ritual behaviors are engaged in and enjoyed universally and account for an extremely high resource commitment in all cultures. The fact that a wide variety of ritual behaviors exist, and humans universally seek them out, indicates inborn predispositions for ritual that directly integrate with emotional centers in the brain. There is evolutionary cause or purpose to ritual phenomena, which is to suppress or inhibit the din of intrusive higher-order consciousness. Hundreds of millions of years of trial and error have honed how our emotions effect and control us, not just the past few million years of hominid evolution. This fine-tuning has resulted in the hugely successful animal, Homo sapiens. Emotions provide the means for the human organism to survive by automatically and unconsciously guiding it to develop and thrive. Consciousness has its role contributing to human success, but it is far less significant than most people believe and has glaring drawbacks as well.

The next five chapters evaluate the major ritual types and explore how these activities improve evolutionary success. I draw comparisons between ritual and emotional healing through therapy and also look at further evidence that these ritual behaviors have an hereditary basis in the brain. We look at rituals to see how they enact the functional role of religion, which is to inhibit consciousness, promote emotions, and bring us closer to our instinctual being.

# Chapter 8

## Music and Religion: It's About the Music, Man

> We need magic and bliss, and power and myth, and celebration and religion in our lives and music is a good way to encapsulate a lot of it.
> *Jerry Garcia*

> Music is the only true religion. It promises to make us happy, and it does.
> *Frank Zappa*

Finally, we begin to examine the religious rituals themselves. The Split Hypothesis asks the reader to accept proposes that cultural rituals involving music, dance, mythology, and art are manifestations of religious feeling and intent even in our modern, secular society. With that in mind, we ask why music is compelling? You'd be hard pressed to find anyone who doesn't like some form of music. People sense and feel that music stimulates emotions. In our modern consumer society, it's the unusual person who doesn't put a good deal of energy into collecting and listening to music. Why is this engagement with music so pervasive when many believe music has no practical benefit? Some claim music, like religion, has no innate cause and is a byproduct, even while it may serve to enhance social cohesiveness and increase cooperation. If we are innately wired for it, what is its genetic purpose or advantage? Why does music elicit emotions, the repertoire of behaviors that contribute to survival and evolutionary success? The Split Hypothesis accounts for our attraction to music based on the evidence for innate brain foundations for music and the emotional changes that occur under the influence of music. A different approach to the efficacy of music is its use in various therapies both psychological and physiological. We will look at evidence that music has behavioral and analgesic (pain-killing) effects, which are examples of actual adaptive benefits necessary to make the case that music increases evolutionary fitness.

Like religion, music is a universal experience. It's pervasive throughout all cultures, however, like religion, the purpose and origin of music continues to befuddle. The existing theories for the evolution of making and enjoying music, as with other human tendencies, vary indicating no particular common, fundamental understanding. Atran and Norenzayan (2004) write, "Much of the intimate connection between music and religion remains a puzzle." (p. 717) Music's ubiquity is a powerful *de facto* indication that it has a genetic basis, but there are several additional biological attributes that buttress the case for music's innateness. Music summons auditory, learning, language, and emotional systems. There are specific brain regions or functions dedicated to processing music. One way we know this is due to instances of brain damage that selectively impede musical savvy and enjoyment. We will look in more detail at these and other measures for how music impacts us.

The *coup d'grace* for an innate basis for music would be to find actual genes that impact music capacity. As we will see, some preliminary studies support this contention. The last piece of the music puzzle is to show that musical perceptions and integration are evolved adaptions. This would then support the claim that religion, of which music is a behavioral component, is similarly evolved and adaptive. Of course, the claim here is that the purpose of music is to allay consciousness in order to access adaptive emotions. While we saw in the previous chapter how rituals hinder intrusive thoughts, more research is needed specifically designed to address the inter-relationship between the inhibition of consciousness and emotions.

Despite convincing evidence for an innate propensity for music, the academic community is far from consensus. Steven Brown (2003), Director of the NeuroArts Lab at McMaster University, researches the neural correlates of the arts. In his short article, *Biomusicology and Three Biological Paradoxes About Music*, Brown lays out the main challenges confronting those who ask if and how music fits into the human evolutionary game plan. The first paradox lies with music's apparent lack of survival value. Darwin was among those to bemoan that music had no obvious purpose or contribution to human fitness and reproductive success. Not only is it difficult to align music with increased evolutionary fitness, but it actually seems to have a deleterious cost. If nothing else, music distracts from gathering food, building shelter, defending territory, or any other usual means to enhance survival. Darwin tries to circumvent this situation by invoking sexual selection. Music, he says, is used in courtship rituals and enhances mating behavior. This is certainly true in some specific instances but falls far short of accounting for all instances of music.

## The Cultural Paradox

Another way people try to fit music into evolutionary adaptation theory is through the social cohesion narrative. Brown says, "Music is the ideal synchronization device and is quite reasonable to assume that it evolved as a cooperative mechanism to coordinate action and promote cohesion at the group level." (p. 16) I've previously described that this is a secondary consequence of music and other ritual behaviors. While music is often viewed for its social context in pre-literate tribes, this may be due as much to the fact that tribal people were rarely alone in the first place. People are social animals, so rituals involving music developed within tribal settings where individual expression and participation in music outside of the tribe was rare. However, if the function of music was strictly for the purpose of strengthening communal interaction, then the desire to connect with others would be the primary result of musical motivation, and there wouldn't be a positive motive to experience music alone. People in contemporary cultures listen to music alone, whether in their cars, in their homes, and now everywhere on their personal music players.

The fact that modern people enjoy music outside the group context means there must first be a reason to appreciate music at the individual level. One historical example of a single person summoning music was when a tribesman was ambushed by the enemy tribe. Huron or Iroquois raiders who captured an enemy warrior inflicted many days of the most heinous torture on the prisoner before finally dispatching him. "They also made him sing his personal chant" throughout his ordeal. (Trigger, 1987, p. 72) Every Indian knew that if captured, he would have to sing his personal song as a means to allay unimaginable suffering and not show weakness before the enemy.

It's true that music enhances the social dynamic and draws people together, but a more rudimentary explanation is called for based on individual responsiveness to music. The result of experiencing music in a collective setting helps people identify with each other by leveraging empathetic affect, so it's not wrong to say that music contributes to group unity, but it is wrong to say music evolved exclusively or initially for this purpose. The cohesion brought about by music is an additional adaptive elaboration of individual emotional stimulation. The sympathetic emotions elicited by music are the base mechanisms for social cohesion and can be stimulated by other ritual means as well.

To understand the adaptive purpose of music I again ask, why do humans need the social connection function of music when even our closest relatives, the chimps and gorillas, have nothing like it and have intensely social organizations as do thousands of other species with elaborate eusocial mechanisms? The cognitive differences between the other apes and humans must be addressed first before vaulting to group cohesion stories. Emotions under control of the limbic system, but also modulated by other areas of the cortex, are the internal machinery that underlie the bonds between individuals and promote sociality. It is emotion, one organism at a time, enhanced by ritual activities, that is the means to facilitate the interaction between members of the tribe.

Brown identifies the cultural paradox—the second of his music paradoxes—as music's cross-pollination with other rituals. Music does not exist in isolation and is closely tied to dance and other forms of physical movement as well as literature and mythology. The lyrics of songs can be as much a story or poem as they are music. Traditional liturgical music includes rhythmic chanting or recitation of verse with or without melody and is as much prayer as music. This paradox is only a challenge if dance, myth (poetry and literature), and other ritual behaviors intertwined with music are not understood to serve the same purpose for people as music does. The role of music for humanity is the same as these other behaviors. Music, dance, art, myth and prayer put the individual in touch with adaptive emotions, which is advantageous and thereby increases evolutionary fitness. Music evolved as one of the ritual practices designed to obscure consciousness so the emotional system, which maintains homeostasis and therefore survival, can maintain its predominance. Dance and movement in particular are closely associated with music primarily through the common characteristic of rhythm, which we will look at in the next chapter.

In the previous chapter I briefly examined rites of passage, the ceremonial practices cultures use to transition initiates from one life stage to the next. Music often plays an important role in those rites, traditionally as well as currently. It's especially notable in modern adolescent development where it makes up for insufficient or nonexistent rites of passage. Listening to or playing music carries the once religious ritual function into the secular sphere. In *Traces of the Spirit: The Religious Dimensions of Popular Music,* Robin Sylvan (2002) argues that,

> Religion and God are not dead, but very much alive and well and dancing to the beat of popular music; the religious impulse has simply migrated to another sector of the culture, a sector in which religious sensibilities have flourished and made an enormous impact on a large portion of the population...Because conventional wisdom has taught us to regard popular music as trivial forms of secular entertainment, these religious

dimensions remain hidden from view, marginalized and misunderstood. (p. 3)

Music has been an avenue of teenage defiance at least since Elvis Presley swung his hips suggestively and perhaps even when bobby soxers swooned at Frank Sinatra's crooning. Historical lack of memory hides even earlier incarnations of musical rebellion, or perhaps the advent of mass media, beginning with records and radio, enabled such adulation. In any case, modern music creates the setting for the teenager's recalcitrance, and today we see in their behavior and embellishments further expression of their discontent—wearing black clothes, dyeing their hair, body tattoos, skin piercings, casual sex, and taking drugs for recreation rather than medicine. In previous generations the evidence of disobedience was long hair on males, tie-dye clothes, free love, and taking drugs for recreation rather than medicine.

The music concert is a secular ritual. Wearing the bands' t-shirts, dancing, and singing the lyrics intensify the internal emotions and resulting outward empathies that bond the participants and help them identify with the band and each other. These experiences are in no way restricted to adolescents. Many who love music enjoy the live performance, which enhances the emotional flavor of the music, partly because of the crowd but also the presence of the entertainer to whom some amount of transference takes place. The performer assumes a role of responsibility for the audience to both carry and deliver the projected feelings of the songs, unintentionally (or intentionally) acting as the shaman or spiritual leader. The musical stars, like movie stars, become the target of idolatry, heaped with a fame far beyond the actuality of their real-life incarnation.

The logos of rock bands that appeal to youth sometimes display skeletons or skulls or have lyrics that offer themes of destruction, sex, and drugs—every parent's nightmare. The emphasis on destructive iconography is classic symbolism for the most universal mythological themes: death and resurrection. It is not meant to be actual death, but rather the death of the child psychically in preparation for rebirth as the adult member of the tribe or society. The attempt at ritual that secular music provides doesn't typically move past the second stage—transition. Without complete ritual support for all phases of the rite of passage, the young men and women are stuck in transition and can't get out, what some call the Peter Pan syndrome or *puer aeternus* (eternal boy). We see the consequences in youth who can't find direction in their lives and meander aimlessly, unable to make personal and professional commitments.

When people aggregate at raves, concerts, county fair shows, or even make their own music in their living rooms, they are honoring and fulfilling their intrinsic desire for religious experience in the form of music. Obviously, people don't think about it that way, but that is, nevertheless, what is happening. Music achieves the same result in non-religious communities worldwide that it does for traditional religions; it elicits emotional feeling. This is why interpreting religion based on religious assemblies and doctrine is not as meaningful. Yes, the church, temple, and mosque embrace the collective of religious devotees, but the originating expression of religious fervor exists intrinsically in spite of or regardless of the institutional hierarchy.

Much popular music is about amorous expressions or frustration with one's object of desire. It is not ironic that music deals with proclamations of love or broken hearts. This is due to the nature of sexual attraction, this most instinctive of behaviors. It is exactly because love and sex are so biological and not rational that the emotional messages of music are the avenue for expressing this passion. Music and other arts are the language of love precisely because they are averse to and untapped by practical consciousness. This is akin to Darwin's sexual selection grounds for music, but while sexual selection doesn't account for all musical conduct, it closely ties music to our innate biology.

The seed of religion starts in the brain, in the individual first and foremost, and the religious function of music exists and is expressed in each person regardless of any existing institutionalized church framework or even if people self-identify as atheist or agnostic. Without the individual capacity to have religious or spiritual feelings, the churches and temples garner no traction. Still, more than any other of the religiously-originated ritual behaviors, music has moved from its religious context to the profane, but that transition only emphasizes its real purpose. Music does for people in the mundane, non-sacred space exactly what it does in the extrinsically religious, which is why religious behavior like music transcends the religious institution and is as popular as ever. All people have the potential to touch the divine, or, more materialistically, they have the inborn capacity to have religious feeling. Music is one ritual behavior that continues to put us in touch with our inner emotional spirit and has the parallel effect of suppressing consciousness.

## The Neural Paradox

The neural paradox is Brown's third problem concerning music. Not only does music not have obvious survival value according to conventional wisdom, but it doesn't have cognitive value. There's no reason to believe that a person deprived of music will suffer any consequences, so some suggest it is at best a byproduct of other cognitive functions. The biggest problem here, of course, is the lack of a coherent theory for music's adaptiveness and therefore benefit. The Split Hypothesis addresses this, but we need to work through the research that shows music leverages the same emotion brain regions as other adaptive behavioral responses.

Isabelle Peretz, Professor of Psychology at the University of Montreal, studies the neurocognition of music. In *Towards a Neurobiology of Musical Emotions*, a chapter in the book, *Music and Emotion: Theory and Research*, Peretz (2001) reviews which brain regions are activated by music, particularly emotional ones. While she acknowledges that, as always, much more research needs to be done, remarkable progress has been made over the past few years that begins to fill in the riddle of music and the brain. Peretz begins by citing studies demonstrating that people in diverse cultures identify the same emotional content and intention in music. Societies as diverse as Hindustani, Japanese, Chinese, and Western are able to recognize joy, anger, and sadness in each others' music.

These findings point to the existence of some invariance in expressing basic emotions across musical cultures. Although non-Western participants may have assimilated the rules of Western music through exposure, it is remarkable how quickly cues to musical emotions, such as mode, which appear to be so culture-specific, can be internalized by listeners of a different culture. This flexibility is suggestive of an underlying universal bias on which listeners build their own cultural variants and assimilate those of distant cultures. (p. 101)

Emotions are evolved adaptations, and this suggests at least some of the emotional responsiveness to music is predetermined. Peretz describes a study that shows that infants as young as six months have a preference for their own mother's singing even more than her speech. When six-month-old infants were exposed to videotaped performances of their own mothers,

The infants showed more sustained attention and engagement to mothers' singing episodes than to their speaking episodes. The observation that emotional communication through singing is powerful for infants, even for hearing newborns of deaf parents, is consistent with the proposal of biological preparedness for music. (p. 103)

Humans are predisposed to be receptive to music, and, as we grow, we learn to like the specific types of music we experience—the music our family, friends, and society expose us to. We acquire our specific preferences for music through cultural transmission just as our culture dictates which language we learn, but the capacity for both music and language is innate.

Studies show the brain has distinct physiological responses to music. Jaak Panksepp (1995) at Washington State University looked at several variables surrounding the phenomenon known as chills, an emotional reaction, also known as "shivers down the spine." Chills are easily detected and measured, unlike some of the other ways researchers judge people's response to music—subjects' verbal or written interpretations or even brain scans. Subjects chose music that reliably gave them chills and, in the course of listening to their preferred music during the experiment, experienced chills as well. (p. 171) In another study Anne Blood and Robert Zatorre (2001) at the Montreal Neuropsychiatric Institute of McGill University showed how music positively affects the brain reward system that causes the chills response. Besides the chills sensations, subjects had increased heart rate, electromyogram (skeletal muscle excitation), and respiration depth, indicating changes in autonomic (involuntary) activity connected to emotions. Increasing chills intensity correlated to increased blood flow to the brain structures associated with reward. "The pattern of activity observed here in correlation with music-induced chills is similar to that observed in other brain imaging studies of euphoria and/or pleasant emotion." (p. 11821)

The correlation between the brain, specific emotional moods, and styles of music is becoming well understood.

> Music is reliably described at the level of basic emotions. The sad excerpts had slow tempos, minor harmonies, and fairly constant ranges of pitch and dynamics. The fear excerpts had rapid tempos, dissonant harmonies, and large variations of dynamics and pitch. The happy excerpts had relatively rapid tempos, dancelike rhythms, major harmonies, and relatively constant ranges of pitch and dynamics. (Krumhansl, 2002, p. 46)

Besides seeing an overall physiological response to music, scientists who study how the brain integrates music have found that there are specific neural areas involved in perceiving, processing, and reporting music. Music in the brain is not random.

> Neurological studies have documented numerous interesting brain lesions that lead to specific losses of musical function while sparing other cognitive capacities, and conversely, brain lesions that destroy much cognitive functioning but that preserve music. (Brown, 2003, p. 16)

Peretz (2001) describes a woman who had bilateral brain damage to the auditory cortex. Her language abilities, memory, and intelligence were normal. She was able to differentiate the emotional content of music — which music was happy or sad. Where she failed was in her ability to recognize music. "When presented with the melody of *Happy Birthday* without its lyrics, [the patient] IR would say 'I don't know that tune but it sounds happy.' " (p. 105)

This has analogies to blindsight, the condition in which a person is ostensibly blind, but is able to point to a light despite claiming that she is guessing the direction of the light source. These different instances of brain lesions show remarkable similarities in that only certain components of perception and integration are compromised, which help identify the role of neural circuits. The patient, IR, could still detect the emotion in the music that she couldn't name.

> CN, another patient with bilateral lesions to the auditory cortex and severe recognition problems for melodies that were once highly familiar to her, made a similarly interesting comment. When listening to the famous Adagio of Albinoni taken from her own record collection, CN first said that she had never heard the piece before. Suddenly, she said: "It makes me feel sad...the feeling makes me think of Albinoni's Adagio." In short, both IR and CN were unable to recognize melodies that were highly familiar to them before the brain accident, yet they were able to do so via their emotional responses. (p. 105)

Different neural pathways are responsible for perception, recognition (memory), and emotional responses to music, Peretz says. "Severe deficits in perception and memorization of music can leave emotional judgments of music unimpaired. Such a spectacular isolation of emotional judgments of music suggests the presence of an emotional neural pathway for music." (p. 106) The development of these pathways are encoded in the human genome. Learning or conditioning can modify the strength of these pathways but not their origination, which form under genetic directives.

Researchers ask whether the emotions stimulated by music are qualitatively the same as emotions generated by other perceptions and behaviors. Music, it turns out, excites the very same emotional brain regions as other sources of emotion. Brain scans show emotional responses to music cause changes in limbic and paralimbic areas, both of which modulate emotions, as well as in the neocortex for both dissonance (music evoking negative feelings) and consonance (music evoking positive feelings). However, dissonance triggers somewhat different limbic areas compared to consonance. (Brown, 2003, p. 2033; Blood, et al., 1999, pp. 382-3) These activations occur whether the music is familiar or unfamiliar. From an emotional point of view, prior association of musical memory is not required to elicit an affective reaction for either positively or negatively perceived music. This helps explain why disparate cultures can recognize the mood in music despite not being familiar with it. Peretz says, "There is a distinct emotional pathway for music processing, and that this neural pathway may differ according to the emotion considered." (Peretz, 2001, p. 105)

The researchers also found that positive emotional response was buoyed by decreased activity in brain regions associated with negative emotions. The different emotions generated by different musical forms excite emotion-specific pathways. This indicates that there are separate pathways for music recognition versus emotional judging of the music and even the style of music—whether the music is sad, scary, or happy. This is confirmed by the tragic yet elucidating studies of brain-damaged individuals.

> There is clear evidence that specific emotions can be lost after brain damage. This is the case for the recognition of "scary", and to some extent, "sad", music after damage to the amygdala, and of the preference for consonance over dissonance after lesion to the parahippocampal gyrus. (p. 105)

# A Musical Ontogeny

How is it that early humans even had the tendency to have feelings for music in the first place? One possibility derives from ritual communication theory. Ritual communications in animals are vocalizations and display behaviors for purposes of courtship, dominance displays, mother-infant contact, and other forms of social interaction. Some propose proto-human music came from prosody, the rhythms and intonations of speech, and other vocalizations such as laughing, crying, and perhaps other physiological rhythmic patterns. Certainly both human and non-human infants are soothed when held against the parents' chest, which is likely due to the parents' rhythmic breathing and heartbeat. Panksepp and Trevarthen (2008) suggest the,

> Evolutionary roots of musicality must lie in the repetitive rhythms and emotions at the source of moving...Musical dynamics resemble the dynamic of emotive movements and feelings evident in the ritual behaviors of communicating animals...We believe that an innate rhythmic musicality provides the prosodic background for all of our lyrical urges to communicate affectively. (p. 108)

Ellen Dissanayake, who I mentioned in the previous chapter for endorsing an ethological approach to studying art and ritual, asserts that human musicality first developed from the cooing and babbling exchanges between infants and their mothers. Called *motherese,* this pseudo-language could have been the source of spoken language as much as for music. In fact Dissanayake makes this case for the arts in general in her paper *The Poetics of Babytalk* with collaborator David Miall. (Miall and Dissanayake, 2003)

> The preverbal competencies and sensitivities utilized in babytalk are in themselves the rudimentary affective and aesthetic elements that human individuals and societies ultimately build upon in an ordered and sophisticated manner when they engage in the arts. (p. 355)

The intimate rhythm and pitch of motherese, she suggests, may be the precursor to vocalized music and is part of an emotionally-based bonding behavior. The vocal interactions between mother and child is a type of ritual communication, which may have been generalized into more elaborate features and led to the development of language, music, or both. Infants' preference for their mothers' singing supports this claim. Whether from motherese or other type of ritual communication, there were any number of organic mechanisms that could have contributed to the evolution of music. Peretz (2001) says,

> Music is particularly suited (or designed) to invade or co-opt emotion circuits that have evolved for biologically important sounds...Musical emotions might invade these evolved circuits for vocal emotions and adjust them for its particularities, (p. 115)

although she acknowledges that the evidence for this is weak. (p. 117)

Motherese and other rhymthic ritual communication forms that may have been leveraged by an incipient musical capacity don't explain why music evolved to contribute to the capacity for and appreciation of music, only how it might have arisen. Why was music compelling and attractive and why did humans develop means to elaborate its expression? We still have the onus of determining what forces led to the selection for individuals who, by luck of their genetics, refashioned existing proto-musical biological phenomena into an appreciation of pitch and rhythm. Many who study the biology of music ponder the significance of music's evolutionary value.

> Music recruits neural systems of reward and emotion similar to those known to respond specifically to biologically relevant stimuli, such as food and sex...This is quite remarkable, because music is neither strictly necessary for biological survival or reproduction. (Blood and Zatorre, 2001, p. 11823)

This quote screams out that music is an evolved adaptation that undergirds evolutionary success. Music acts on the brain just like any other stimulus that arouses our adaptive emotions. Music may not be absolutely required for survival, but that doesn't mean it doesn't have adaptive value, and that's the question that needs addressing.

While it isn't a great leap from the natural rhythms of life to simple musical engagement by early Homo, the fantastic elaboration of music to the complex forms they now take didn't happen "just because they could." Early humans didn't suddenly "decide" to embrace music. The dung beetle eats dung because the insect accidentally evolved to thrive by eating it, not because it just happened to decide to want or like it. Similarly, why didn't ritual vocalizations and rhythms generate more elaborate musical forms in other animals. Some have suggested, more poetically than scientifically, that animal vocalizations and ritual behaviors are musical. The aesthetic pleasure people get from bird songs is anthropomorphic, a transference of human emotional meaning onto bird calls. Even if we cast a wide net to consider this, the "music" of other animals is still functional and adaptive for the particular species. Birds' songs are serious business whether for establishing territory, defense and warning, courtship, or calling their young. The important point is that music-like behaviors evolved to fulfill the functional requirements necessary for the animal's survival and reproduction, and it is no different for humans.

Again, the assumption is that, for the brain's emotional circuits to have evolved to respond to music, there had to be a selective advantage. Human music is not simply a byproduct or benign mistake. The evolved elaboration for musical feelings required that emotions elicited by music increased fitness or they wouldn't have been selected for. It had to fulfill an adaptive requirement that benefited its owners for the experience of music to infiltrate neural circuits, reinforce positive emotional feedback, and be ubiquitous throughout all cultures. Otherwise there would have been no reason for music to take hold and be the extensive affective force it is. To have insinuated itself at the micro level into so many separate neural pathways in the brain and at the macro level in every culture in the world, music simply could not have arisen solely as an accidental byproduct of other mechanisms.

In early stages of human evolution prior to the diasporas out of Africa, some individuals had mutations that predisposed them to experience emotions due to repetitive beats and tone, perhaps based on existing biological rhythms. In some (but not all) of those individuals, music-caused emotions had the unintended, accidental consequence of inhibiting the noise of consciousness by swamping working memory (in one example we looked at). This promoted evolutionary success in those humans who had this necessary combination of traits to offset the drawbacks of consciousness, which was rapidly (in evolutionary time) evolving in parallel with music and other ritual behaviors. The people with these traits reproduced preferentially because, without conscious intention or awareness, they balanced their tenuous consciousness with their emotional needs, selecting the benefits of consciousness but suppressing its noisy distractions, and the genes for music spread. These humans who emigrated from Africa carried the genetic traits for engaging in musical behaviors (and other rituals) throughout the earth.

In The Split Hypothesis of religion, music functions as a means to incite the emotions at the expense of consciousness. It's not enough to say that music provokes feelings, though it does. For the hypothesis to be substantiated, we need to show not only that consciousness is hindered, but that music provides something beneficial and adaptive, whether through limbic arousal or some other means. In the previous chapter, I cited the work of Boyer and Liénard who asserted that rituals swamp working memory, but they did so by comparing ritual behavior to OCD and other pathologies. In any case, the authors never claimed that swamping working memory was a solution to a problem such as consciousness that needed fixing. The research is lacking to show that music suppresses or inhibits consciousness per se. A consensus for the definition and mechanism of higher-order consciousness remains elusive, which makes understanding the interaction of music and consciousness more difficult. Also research has not been designed with this goal in mind because The Split Hypothesis has not been considered. Nevertheless, evidence exists that music is beneficial.

# Music as Therapy

Music evokes emotions and these music-elicited emotions utilize the same brain regions and pathways as other emotions, including the reward and motivation areas. This section shows that music specifically benefits people, which completes the picture that music is an evolved adaptation. If I claim that music stimulates adaptive emotions, then I need to show the physiological and psychological advantages music provides. Neuroscientists and psychologists are beginning to flesh out the interaction between music, emotions, and health, both mentally and physically. While we look at some examples of how people benefit from music, it is important to understand that adaptive emotions can act restoratively regardless of whether ritually induced or not. "Just as emotionally traumatic events can tear apart the fabric of individual psyches and families, emotions can also act as powerful catalysts for healing." (Trevarthen, 2009, p. viii)

Research affirms that music has therapeutic powers. This comes primarily from medical studies in hospital situations and psychological perspectives for people with mental challenges as well as a continuum of conditions in between. In addition, music is shown to assist with cognitive tasks in non-medical or non-therapeutic situations. Therapists use music to help people with attention deficit disorders, learning disabilities, and other issues. Studies indicate that music can be used to combat depression, alleviate symptoms of cerebral palsy, and enhance children's reading and writing skills. When music accompanies memorization tasks, the memorizers recall their lessons better than those who memorized without it. Music even boosts play behavior. "Joyous music (Irish jigs) can increase overall movements in young children in the midst of rough-and-tumble play." (Panksepp and Bernatzky, 2002, pp. 140-141)

Hospitals have experimented with music before and after surgery to try to improve patient outcomes. A review of studies that used music as a non-pharmacological adjunct with surgery found music decreased anxiety, heart rate, and blood pressure, reduced the amount of sedatives and analgesics required, and increased relaxation and improved mood. (Nilsson, 2004; Bradt and Dileo, 2009)

Similar positive effects of music were seen in persons with coronary heart disease and cancer. While researchers have been very conservative interpreting results, the use of music has shown a consistent pattern for aiding people in hospital settings.

Age-related dementia refers to a number of progressive diseases that cause psychological impairments, most notably memory loss. Although there's no claim that music can cure or reverse the deterioration of dementia, music therapies are shown to lessen their symptoms. According to Panksepp and Bernatzky (2002), music slows the disease progression because it "tends to promote certain brain neurochemicals, especially brain NE (norepinephrine) activities, and hence facilitate attentional processes." (p. 148)

In contemporary society, we think of psychotherapy as an effort to correct or heal mental scars acquired from abusive or traumatic personal histories, but the use of music as a therapeutic agent goes back to the earliest cultures.

> A therapeutic role for music in the treatment of physical and emotional disease is found in many if not all non-Western cultures. "Music healing" is an ancient art that is at the root of what, in the 20th century, acquired the name of "music therapy"...This is the case in many cultures where disease is attributed to the bad humor of spirits and demons rather than to physiological causes. In such situations, the healer's singing becomes a means of assuaging angry spirits rather than directly soothing or helping patients. This occurs in the many cultures where shaman function as the culture's music healers, and where music is used to induce a state of trance in the shaman as a means of facilitating healing in people. Receptive singing seems to represent the ancient roots of the therapeutic use of music. (Brown, 2001, p. 129)

This intersection between music as therapy and folk healer also crosses into the realm of religious experience. As Sylvan (2005) argues, many people who deeply experience music portray the effect as religious-like. Words used to describe the transcendent musical experience are often the same words that mystics and meditators use to describe spiritual feelings. Sylvan offers this description of a modern-day rave. "Because of the high amplification and pounding insistence of house music beats, which are felt in the body as much as heard by the ears, the groove is often compelling to the point of trance induction for the dancers, carrying them beyond their normal consciousness into a powerful ecstatic state." (p. 20) Most researchers who look at the evolutionary basis of music look at the direct manifestation of music on the brain, not the corollary aspects such as how music effects other, consciousness-related cognitions, for example. Anecdotal descriptions must suffice for now.

People's neural response to music through emotional circuits and the empirical benefits of music makes a strong case for its adaptiveness, and therefore begs for its evolutionary importance to be explained. In a myriad of ways—psychologically, medically, socially—music is embedded in and aids people. From infants to seniors, music engages and enthralls. A rich anthropological trove of research shows music has existed in every known culture and had important ritual roles in each. Yes, music contributes to sexual selection, group cohesion, mother-infant bonding, and many other suggested reasons, but no one of these accounts for why it evolved to fulfill its valuable role. The Split Hypothesis, however, speaks directly to its eliciting emotions and subsumes all the other explanations as secondary consequences. Still, more direct experimental work is called for to elucidate the relationship between music and various aspects of cognition and consciousness.

In addition, if people are innately predisposed for music, we want to substantiate music's biological basis and find genes that code for musical interest and ability. Research is just beginning to make such inroads. A group led by the Department of Medical Genetics at the University of Helsinki has published articles contending they have evidence of genetic predispositions for musical talent. By tracking several hundred people within several Finnish families, they found positive correlations between several gene polymorphisms (variations) and musical aptitude. They sought associations between gene occurrences and musical characteristics such as auditory structuring ability, tests for pitch and time, and creativity in music (composing, improvising and/or arranging music). One gene in particular, called

AVPR1a, has strong links to musical ability. This gene is believed to be associated with attachment behavior, in other words, sociality, and will be cited again in the next chapter as a possible contributor to creative dance performance. (Ukkola, 2009, p. 1; Pulli, 2008, p. 451) There are also genetic abnormalities that impact musical skills and appreciation. Williams Syndrome, for example, results from the accidental deletion of about 15 genes in chromosome 7. It causes severe mental retardation as well as aortic constriction and "elfin" facial features. Oddly, many with this syndrome show remarkable music interest and, in some cases, unusual adeptness.

> Anecdotal evidence implies that some Williams people possess extraordinary musical talent. Even though their attention span for most tasks is short, many will listen to music, sing and play instruments with astonishing persistence. Most cannot read musical notes, yet some have perfect or nearly perfect pitch and an uncanny sense of rhythm. One boy quickly learned to play an extremely complex drumbeat in 7/4 time with one hand while drumming in 4/4 time with the other hand. A number of individuals retain complex music for years, remembering melodies and verses of long ballads; one even sings songs in 25 languages. Experienced Williams musicians also sing harmonies, improvise and compose lyrics readily. (Lenhoff, 2006, p. 68)

Studies indicate that Williams children "discriminate melodies well; they also show significantly more interest in and emotional responsivity to music than do subjects from the general population." (p. 68) While the mechanism for this attraction to music is unknown, the genetic correlation is striking and compelling.

Music evolved as one of the ritual religious behaviors. Regardless of modern music's dissociation from extrinsic religion and transition into the non-religious sphere, its function remains the same—to fulfill the task of delivering people to *in illo tempore,* where unconscious emotions reign foremost and return us to homeostasis, the physiological schema that promotes our survival. Proto-humans didn't choose to want or like music. Humans who happened to evolve a positive response to music through their neural reward systems and to balance their consciousness with emotional intuition benefited from music and were evolutionarily more successful. We see the results of music's benefits today in therapeutic environments. Music-incited emotions underlie various forms of psychotherapy as well as buttress people's welfare. Interestingly, the other ritual forms that will be discussed—art and dance particularly—also have their own versions of therapy and perform like music, both medically and psychologically. We look at the beneficial functions of other rituals in succeeding chapters.

# Chapter 9

# Dance and Ritual Movement

Dancers are the messengers of the gods.
*Martha Graham*

To dance is to be out of yourself. Larger, more beautiful,
more powerful.
*Agnes De Mille*

Like music and the other ritual behaviors, dance is a universal cultural activity as are related physical movement forms such as sport. From a strictly utilitarian perspective, these ritual movements are a waste of time, yet we recognize their religious involvement and purpose in tribal societies: to celebrate festivals, to honor ancestors, to heal the sick, to express grief and other feelings, and of course, as prayer when beseeching the gods for favor. In this chapter, we look at some of the prevalent explanations for why humans dance, the emerging neurological research on dance, and then take a small diversion into sports and other movement forms. We finish with the known benefits of dance and revisit The Split Hypothesis as a means of understanding dance as religious ritual.

Dance and music are closely tied through the common characteristic of rhythm. People unconsciously move, even small amounts, in response to music, but at a gross level, dance is different from music exactly because of the broader involvement of physical movement.

Like music, mythology is also an important sibling of dance, and often dance tells a historical myth. Dancers identify with or assume the character of animals whose story they portray, not only by mimicking animal movements but by adorning themselves with skins, feathers, or paint. Similarly, dancers can impersonate or embody deities or ancestor's spirits. Masks are a favorite means to achieve this. The Balinese mask dance is a classic example of a ritual that combines music, dance, and mythology. Ritual behaviors can overlap in various cultural incarnations and are a strong indication of their functional relatedness.

Some other examples of the many traditional dance rituals are: The Tarahumaras of Mexico enact several fiestas to make sure the deceased reach heaven. These complex festivals include several different dances performed by different groups, which are necessary to make sure the deceased do not return as animals and haunt the people. (Breeden, 1973, p. 187) The Dogon of West Africa also hold a ceremony in which the men dance so the soul of a deceased village elder can join the ancestors. (p. 28) The Somba of the Sahara dance with hoes to ensure a successful harvest. (p. 113) In the South American rain forest when a visiting tribe of Yanomamo enter a neighboring village, they dance to show bravery to their hosts prior to a feast. (p. 159) The Ainu, the indigenous people of the Japanese island of Hokkaido, dance as part of their bear sacrifice ceremony when the real animal is dispatched in order for its immortal soul to enter the spirit world and protect the people. (Severin, 1973, p. 231)

The dances of traditional cultures reflect components of Van Gennep's rites of passage formula: separation, transition, and incorporation or rebirth. Eliade (1964) describes the series of rituals necessary to induct Carib boys of Dutch Guinea (Suriname) into becoming shaman. In order to achieve shaman status the initiate must see the spirits that will assist him on his ecstatic, celestial journey. A group of six boys undergo initiation together. They live together in a hut apart from the rest of their group, the first phase of the rite, separation. For 24 days of the transition or liminal phase, the initiates undergo a variety of abnegations and ordeals. They endure periods of fasting save for the copious quantities of tobacco juice they are required to drink. They also smoke cigarettes and chew tobacco leaves to prepare themselves for the visions where they will meet the spirits. At night the boys are taught about these animal spirits they will encounter, and they dance and sing. "The dances imitate the movements of the animals of which the master has spoken during the teaching." After fasting and exhaustive dancing the boys are ready to have their first vision. "The master stretches several ropes at different heights, the apprentices dance on them in turn or swing in the air, holding on with their hands." (p. 128)

The goal of these rituals is to break down everyday consciousness and quell it. In the case of these shamanic initiations, the novices are taught what spirits they will see and how to embark on their ecstatic flight. This is not exactly getting in touch with one's emotions in the classic sense, but it's not clear what the unconscious consequences of the ritual are, other than to enable the frame of mind necessary to acquire the shaman's skills. Without the kinds of studies that can be done in modern settings, we don't know what effect these rituals have.

In contrast, our modern culture often presents music and dance as a show in which a few perform and many observe. Regardless of the many modern styles of dance performance, the goal is to create an empathic link between the dancers and their audience, to elicit emotional response just as music performers do with their audience. Of course, not all dance is performance. Movement and dance is enjoyed for its own sake in folk dancing, rock and rave concerts, and couples dancing such as the two-step, foxtrot, tango, and waltz. The teen dance is devised as an event approved for breaking personal space barriers and engaging in extended, formal touching. Young couples are not only allowed but encouraged (up to a point) to embrace during "slow dances." This invokes the sexual selection purpose of dance just as it is invoked for music. Many of the same reasons used to explain the purpose for music are also cited for dance.

Neuroscientist Ivar Hagendoorn (2003) has focused on dance's predictive quality. Using the analogy of sports, he points out that baseballs and tennis balls often move far too fast for players given the lag times of vision and brain processing. Athletes learn to overcome these deficiencies by getting very good at anticipating where the ball will go. Both the players and we as observers receive pleasure when the player correctly predicts the ball's location and hits it. Hagendoorn sees dance similarly.

> If the movement trajectory predicted by the brain coincides with the actual movement, we are filled with pleasure, which we ascribe to the movement that gave rise to it by calling the movement beautiful or graceful. In summary, when our expectations are fulfilled, when the brain's simulations are correct, we delight in grace or elegance; when they are challenged, we are pleasantly alarmed. (p. 21)

The tribal dance rituals described earlier are a far cry from addressing why dance, an elaborate and complex behavioral display, would have evolved just to set up a situation that enables completion of movement resulting in emotional satisfaction. It's certainly difficult to imagine that hours of continuous ritual dancing could engender positive emotion because of the anticipation of movement completion.

Hagendoorn cites Blood and Zatorre's study of musical chills as similar evidence of fulfillment of expectations and found the brain "map of [chills] activation overlaps considerably with the one that...I myself have sketched for the perception of dance. This may also explain why music and dance mix so well." (p. 21) Regardless of cause, the pleasure he describes is an emotional outcome. Hagendoorn addresses the appreciation of dance performance, but he presupposes the emotional gratification without asking why there would be a positive valence for dance whether performed or observed. Emotional efficacy is assumed without asking why this thing called dance should excite emotions in the first place. Why should rhythmic, repetitive body movements incite any affective response at all?

Hagendoorn does emphasize that humans have innate expectations for the completion of a sequence of anticipated movements. That's a very narrow view of all the manifestations of dance. The formal demonstration of dance for an audience is a relatively modern invention. Dance performance may be several thousand years old and was assuredly an art form that co-developed with drama. However, there are tens of thousands of years prior to that when tribal peoples danced in participatory ceremonies for much more varied reasons and in which the dance techniques were predetermined and repetitive with a minimal and predictable number of movements. Some of those tribal dances can be considered performances in the sense that some of the tribe watched, but the perception of the event was more about the content of the dance, its mythological significance, rather than the expected movement trajectory. While his analysis of dance is limited in scope, Hagendoorn correctly identifies the emotional outcome of dance as the end in itself.

Professors of Neuroscience J. Alexander Dale (2007) and Jeff Hollerman collaborated with dance professor Janyce Hyatt to propose a framework for the neuroscience of dance that emphasizes the dancer rather the audience. They boil down the definition of dance to two statements. First, "dance is an emotionally expressive use of the body" and secondly, "dance involves conscious choices made by the dancer regarding what to do, or not do." (p. 90) Rather than seeing dance as anticipation of movement and completion like Hagendoorn, these authors propose that decisions made prior to moving are a critical aspect of dance.

The first definition regarding emotional expression reinforces one of the essential tenets of The Split Hypothesis—that emotions are the universal response to religious ritual behavior. The second reason for dance applies primarily to complex choreographed dance. In contrast, tribal dance is highly stylized and repetitive. Even folk dancing, which may have more varied steps, is synchronized and formulaic, so there is very little choice of moves. The only opportunity for individual expression in synchronized group dances is the extent of enthusiasm or emotion. The authors acknowledge that their focus is on dance as performing art, and that there are other forms and definitions of dance. I mention this study as another example of the compendium of reasons offered for the purpose or function of dance. Conscious choice as a component of dance is an additional submission thrown into the varied and overly broad mix. Music, art, and mythology suffer similarly from the same "see what sticks" scattershot approach. The only consistent and pervasive feature of dance, music, and the other ritual behaviors is eliciting or invoking emotions.

Steven Brown (2008), who wrote the three paradoxes of music article discussed in the previous chapter, has mapped the brain's activity from dance. Brown and his associate, Lawrence Parsons, did this by having people lie with their heads in a PET scanner and move their feet in a specific dance pattern such as the tango. Assuming that the brain regions modulating dance movements act the same lying down as standing up, these dance movements not surprisingly involved the brain's sensorimotor regions—the areas responsible for detecting and controlling where the body is in space and directing the body how to move. These modules are located in the parietal lobe on the top middle of the brain. The parietal region is fed by various senses—vision, balance, and proprioception (the detectors in muscles that tell you where the various parts of your body are). A wide range of other brain areas are involved including the right putamen located in the basal ganglia, poised between the emotional limbic system and the neocortex. The basal ganglia influences the initiation and control of movement, which fits nicely with the current thread. Whereas music utilizes preexisting auditory brain mechanisms, dance borrows preexisting sensorimotor brain regions. This is intuitive but good to confirm.

Brown, who claimed music evolved to support communal interaction, takes dance in a different direction, as mythology and storytelling saying, "dance has a strong capacity for representation and imitation, which suggests that dance may have further served as an early form of language." (p. 83) Brown posits that the inferior frontal gyrus, the right-hemisphere homologue or mirror of the left hemisphere's Broca's language area, is the likely brain region involved in this gestural language capacity for imitation and ordering sequences of movement. Thus, according to Brown, dance did not likely facilitate acquisition of verbal language but rather evolved in part as an elaboration of emotional gesture or body language, a type of nonverbal communication. Dance's function of presenting mythologies is mentioned at the beginning of this chapter as one of dance's several societal roles. Narrative as ritual is discussed in the next chapter about mythology.

In his analysis of brain activity during dance movements, Brown also observed that the medial geniculate nucleus (MGN) is activated during the subjects' unconscious foot tapping in response to musical rhythm. Propitiously, the MGN is known to be an interpretive way station for relaying sound information between the inferior colliculus, a brain area that receives early auditory input from the ear, and the auditory cortex. This is an example of below consciousness perception of input before signals reach the "higher" cortex and how separate pathways work so people can feel the rhythm without necessarily consciously hearing it. Called unconscious entrainment, this process reflects our innate predilection for rhythm.

## Embodied Cognition

Not that long ago, the mind was studied as an isolated system detached from and uninfluenced by the physical body. The belief in a non-physical soul as separate from the body originated in the earliest tribes who buried their dead in order for the deceased to persist into the life beyond. Rene Descartes formalized this in philosophy when he said, "I think therefore I am." Those asserting this Cartesian approach often claimed a non-material or spiritual aspect to mind and soul that did not conform to the laws of physics.

This deeply held conviction in the separateness of the mind-soul and the body perseveres today and remains common in various religious, secular, and psychological constructs where mind and cognition are considered to belong to an autonomous plane of existence. Also known as dualism, this separation of mind and body is ironically exemplified by John Eccles, who won the the 1963 Nobel Prize in Physiology or Medicine for his research in neurophysiology and specifically for discovering the synapse. Despite his scientific background, he said, "each soul is a Divine creation, which is 'attached' to the growing fetus at some time between conception and birth. It is the certainty of the inner core of unique individuality that necessitates the 'Divine creation.' We submit that no other explanation is tenable." (Eccles and Robinson, 1985, p. 43)

While most religions promote the idea of soul and afterlife, from a scientific perspective the mind and body are interwoven systems that cannot be considered separately. *Embodied cognition* denotes this intimate connection, that the physical body interacts with and determines the nature of our minds. It is not coincidental that the word *emotion* is from the Latin meaning *move out*. Mentality and emotions are an embedded part of our biology just as movement is, so it isn't a surprise that cognition, based on the interaction of neurons, glial cells, and blood flow, is affected by physical activity. Emotions are the result of interactions between limbic and cortical brain regions and the endocrine (hormonal) system that sends its chemical messengers through the bloodstream. The sensorimotor areas of the brain, which regulate perception and movement, are richly connected to both the prefrontal cortex and limbic system. The interactions of movement, cognition, and emotions are a multi-feedback loop in which motor actions reinforce feelings and the feelings influence movement. This is illustrated in the well-documented phenomenon in which smiling, even a smile forced by a device that pushes the edges of the mouth up, leads to increases in positive associations. Paul Ekman's studies of facial expression and emotion are additional examples of how unconscious systems interact with mood and muscle, but the same forces impact the rest of the body. Facial muscles control emotional expressions, but behind them are the complex neural interactions that drive them. Embodied cognition science is rife with similar studies showing the tight interrelationship between mind and body. We saw other examples earlier in this book, for instance, when subjects primed with old age-related words walked more slowly after the experimental task.

Dance as ritual movement is a bridge between our physical and mental processes, but that makes the incorrect assumption that the mental and physical are separate entities. Movement and the brain are intertwined and inseparable. The sensorimotor cortex astride the border between the frontal and parietal lobes is just as required as are the muscles and peripheral nerves throughout the body for an organism to function. Emotions, movement, and mental cognition are not discrete entities; they are part of a highly integrated system that includes all the functions that support us.

Dance wrests emotions from participants, but dance would only do that if it was adaptive. Emotional brain regions aren't stimulated by random sensory or physiological events, otherwise an organism wouldn't respond appropriately to its environment. Adaptive behaviors such as eating and sex involve movements that, in conjunction with various sensory inputs, stimulate the brain's pleasure centers. The times we see animals enacting rhythmic, repetitive motions are during courtship rituals or dominance displays, which have obvious evolutionary purpose. Animals do not normally display repetitive dance-like behaviors without evolutionary motive, so why would humans? As I've emphasized before, for the brain's reward centers to light up in response to dance or any other behavior, there has to be an adaptive reason. Movement for its own sake without an obvious tangible benefit would have had a neutral or even negative consequence in the overall evolutionary picture, and dancing would not have evolved to trigger an emotional response in the various sensory-motor and affective brain regions. If dancing was only a non-adaptive byproduct of other behaviors, it would have been a waste of resources and selected against. At the very least, we wouldn't expect to observe it in all societies throughout the world. That dance evinces positive response means it benefits people's evolutionary fitness.

Besides investigating how dance benefits people and increases their evolutionary fitness, we want to see if there are genetic markers indicating predilections for dance, which would indicate that dance has evolutionary advantages. One of few such studies compared genetic correlations between dancers and sports athletes and zeroed in on a gene called AVPR1a, which stands for arginine vasopressin receptor 1A. AVPR1a is one of three receptors for the hormone vasopressin, which is primarily known for regulating water retention. Vasopressin is also thought to have a role in social behavior and is believed to influence the effectiveness of serotonin. The study found "highly significant differences in AVPR1a haplotype frequencies...between dancers and athletes," suggesting that people who prefer dancing to sports are predisposed by an allelic gene difference. Another gene, SLC6A4, which codes for a serotonin transporter, a protein that passes the neurotransmitter serotonin across cell membranes, also correlated similarly with AVPR1a. "Significant differences were observed in allele frequencies for both genes when dancers were compared to athletes as well as to nondancers/nonathletes." (Bachner-Melman, 2005, p. 395) The researchers propose,

> Serotonergic neurotransmission in some human studies appears to mediate human religious and spiritual experiences. We therefore hypothesize that the association between AVPR1a and SLC6A4 reflects the social communication, courtship, and spiritual facets of the dancing phenotype rather than other aspects of this complex phenotype, such as sensorimotor integration. (p. 394)

These types of genetic correlation studies are very preliminary and require much more work to confirm any genetic associations with dance. Nevertheless, initial evidence suggests that, in an as yet unknown way, the neurotransmitter serotonin affects areas of the brain involved in spirituality, either by producing more of the neurotransmitter or priming the brain regions to be more sensitive to it. For this to happen there have to be existing "spirituality" neural groups sensitive to such stimulations. Humans would have to be hard-wired for dance and religion.

In the previous chapter on music, I cited the work of Robin Sylvan (2005) who wrote about modern day raves as reproductions of traditional dance forms in which much of a tribe participated in either the dance or the music-making. The purpose of the dance ritual required personal involvement and was not an observer-performer relationship. Sylvan also pointed out that, in some cases, the throbbing, pulsing music induced trance states, a form of spirit possession or altered states of consciousness, the result of extended and heightened periods of dancing found in cultures throughout the world. The dancers engrossed in spirit possession are sometimes described as being in catatonic seizure states, shaking and convulsing violently, emitting guttural vocalizations such as grunts and groans. (p. 23) I believe it is safe to say these anecdotal, anthropological reports of trance and possession, when people exert themselves for hours in ritual dance, strongly point to a major encumbrance on the normal state of consciousness. While this possession state can result from extremely rigorous or exhaustive dance, it is just one end of the spectrum of dance affect. More research is necessary to evaluate the interrelationship between dance, biomotor components, cognition, and consciousness. Physiological benchmarks from dance and emotion provide plentiful study opportunities.

For what possible evolutionary reason would such drastic behaviors as dance-induced altered states of consciousness (ASC) exist in societies in every part of the world? Not only do we ask why people dance, but we are challenged to explain trance and possession, this extra-bizarre form of movement (from our modern point of view). Ecstatic or possession states are not all that different from other forms of ASC such as deep meditation or intense mystical experience, for example. Shamanism, ecstatic states, and spirit possession are enormous topics in themselves, but here the focus is on the relationship between consciousness and religious emotional expression, the dichotomies of The Split Hypothesis. Within this scope, these altered states are traditionally associated with religious experiences and are behavioral expressions that seriously impede everyday consciousness. The researchers who found a genetic link to dance suggest "that the association we observe between [the gene] SLC6A4 and dance is perhaps related to the need for altered consciousness states that subjects participating in and performing this art form sometimes have." (Bachner-Melman, 2005, p. 399) Dance sometimes engenders altered states, but this also results in the inhibition of higher-order consciousness. Dance, like music, mythology, prayer, and visual art rituals, all act to intercede with the human conscious flow of perception and cognition. We will examine ASCs in more detail in the chapter on prayer. Before looking at the benefits of dance, we explore other forms of movement.

# Going with the Flow

Music and dancing are not the only means by which physical movement can alter one's mental field. Rigorous tasks such as athletics can lead to altered consciousness as can abnegation techniques such as fasting, sensory deprivation, and mortification. A phenomenon called *flow* serves as an illustration of the psychological consequences of some instances of physical movement. Flow refers to the sense that a person is on automatic pilot and performing a task unconsciously or without thinking. Mihaly Csikszentmihalyi (1975), a Professor of Behavioral Sciences at the University of Chicago, coined the term, which,

> Denotes the holistic sensation present when we act with total involvement...It is the state in which action follows upon action according to an internal logic which seems to need no conscious intervention on our part. We experience it as a unified flowing from one moment to the next, in which we feel in control of our actions, and in which there is little distinction between self and environment; between stimulus and response; or between past, present, and future. (p. 43)

In baseball, when a batter is on a hot streak, sees the ball well or "fat," and consistently makes solid contact, he's in the flow, also called *in the zone* or *peak performance*. Another idiom sports announcers occasionally use for a player who's in the flow is *unconscious*. Csikszentmihalyi quotes a rock climber who said he was,

> So involved he might lose the consciousness of his own identity and melt into the rock...it's like when I was talking about things becoming "automatic"...almost like an egoless thing in a way—somehow the right thing is done without...thinking about it or doing anything at all...it just happens...and yet you're more concentrated. (p. 50)

A composer said,

> You yourself are in an ecstatic state to such a point that
> you feel as though you almost don't exist. I've experi-
> enced this time and again. My hand seems devoid of my-
> self, and I have nothing to do with what is happening. I
> just sit there watching in a state of awe and wonderment.
> And it just flows out by itself. (p. 50)

The flow experience is characterized by the merging of awareness
and action—the conscious observer we have inside us retreats temporarily, and we become completely focused on the task at hand. No
outside thoughts or higher level abstractions intervene in the process
of the moment. As long as the conscious voice remains quiet, flow
continues. As soon as consciousness disrupts, awareness becomes
divided between the task and the external voice, and flow stops.
The internal voice, the internal narrator, which some perceive as the
parental voice or superego, causes a shift in focus, typically slowing
effectiveness. Unlike some meditators, people experiencing flow do
not lose the perception of their physical body, and in fact, can feel a
heightened sense of their movement or thought processes, but those
processes are not impinged by awareness consciousness.

Flow does require a certain familiarity or expertise with the task
to be performed, but that doesn't mean a neophyte can't get into
the flow. A novice experiencing flow just won't perform at the same
level as an expert in the flow. Csikszentmihalyi says flow most often
occurs "in activities which have clearly established rules for action,
such as rituals, games, or participatory art forms like the dance."
(p. 45) By established rules he means activities that have a limited
and repetitive range of operations. Proficient athletes and musicians often attribute their success to muscle memory, the idea that
consciousness is not necessary or even desired to aid performance,
and that letting the actions flow unassailed by the thinking mind results in a preferential outcome. Part of the mental game in sports is
to quiet the internal discussion and let the inner knowledge of the
body come through. Both professional musicians and athletes testify that if they have to think about what they're doing, they won't

perform at their best.  But even for those of us who aren't top performers in the field, the same processes occur.  Most of our actions
occur below consciousness, an observer after the fact.  In instances
in which the typical routines fail or needed practices fall outside the
standard operating procedures, consciousness is called to assist with
driving practice routines and weighing novel evidence or options.
That slows the resulting output, however.

It is not the case that the brain is hyperactive during flow.  Daniel
Goleman (1995) writes in *Emotional Intelligence,*

> Watching someone in flow gives the impression that the
> difficult is easy; peak performance appears natural and
> ordinary.  This impression parallels what is going on
> within the brain, where a similar paradox is repeated:
> the most challenging tasks are done with a minimum of
> expenditure of mental energy.  In flow the brain is in a
> "cool" state, its arousal and inhibition of neural circuitry
> attuned to the demand of the moment.  When people
> are engaged in activities that effortlessly capture and
> hold their attention, their brain "quiets down" in the
> sense that there is a lessening of cortical arousal.  That
> discovery is remarkable, given that flow allow people
> to tackle the most challenging tasks in a given domain,
> whether playing against a chess master or solving a
> complex mathematical problem. The expectation would
> be that such challenging tasks would require more cor-
> tical activity, not less.  But a key to flow is that it occurs
> only within reach of the summit of ability, where skills
> are well-rehearsed and neural circuits are most efficient.
> (p. 92)

The implication is that conscious awareness is a brain energy hog
compared to flow.  Consciousness levies a greater tax on physiological resources.

Ornstein (1992) quotes the flow experience described by Formula 1
racer Ayrton Senna about racing in the Monaco Grand Prix, which
he won six times, more than anyone else.

I realized at that moment, suddenly that I was well over something conscious. Monaco is small and narrow, and at that moment, I had the feeling that I was in a tunnel — the circuit was just a tunnel for me. It was going-going-going and within the physical limit of the circuit, it was like I was on rails. Of course, I wasn't on rails. Then, suddenly, I realized it was too much. I slowed down. I drove myself slowly back to the pits and said to myself I shouldn't go out any more that day. Because for the moment I was vulnerable for extending my own limits, and the car's limits: limits that I had never touched before. I was not aware, exactly, of what was going on — I was just going-going-going. An amazing experience. (p. 140)

Csikszentmihalyi recognizes religious ritual as among the behaviors subject to the flow experience, and that exclusive human activities like ritual, art, and games are specifically designed to promote and elicit flow. In a not so subtle way, Csikszentmihalyi's flow theory is very similar to The Split Hypothesis but comes to it from a different direction. Both describe the reduction of consciousness in favor of intrinsic or subaware cognition. Both share a range of behaviors that fall under their rubric. The glaring difference is that sports and games have not specifically been included within the company of religious behavior. While this focus of religious behavior has been on a group of ritual behaviors — music, dance, art, prayer, and myth — they are certainly not the only human ritual activities. In *Religion: An Anthropological View*, Anthony F. C. Wallace (1966) names thirteen types of rituals including physiological exercise, which he differentiates from ritual dance. (p. 52) In one sense, dance could be a subset of exercise, but, as always, there is overlap, and categories are somewhat arbitrary. While not specified as ritual by Wallace, games and sports have many ritual features. Besides the opportunity for consciousness-altering flow, they are often performed recurrently, have a code of rules or doctrine, and are practiced socially and cooperatively.

The title of Csikszentmihalyi's article that's cited above is *Play and Intrinsic Rewards*. The thread throughout his analysis is that play, including adult play, is enjoyable. Play has an emotional currency, which means it taps into the human reward system and has evolutionary adaptive value, just like religion. Physical exercise such as play increases endorphins, the brain chemicals that act as endogenous analgesics—natural pain killers. The effect of intense exercise can result in the runner's high, which some describe as the euphoria felt after a long workout. For many years the relationship between endorphins and exercise was widely believed but not proven. A team at the University of Bonn, led by Henning Boecker (2008), showed that long-distance running indeed resulted in an elevated mood. The "release of endogenous opioids occurs in frontolimbic brain regions after sustained physical exercise and...there is a close correlation to perceived euphoria of runners. This suggests a specific role of the opioid system in the generation of the runner's high sensations." (p. 2530)

Games and sports occur in all cultures including traditional, preliterate ones, and have probably been around longer than agriculture. Some forms of organized competition are likely evolved ritualizations of dominance hierarchy and mate selection conflicts and may be a substitute for warfare in some cases. Other animals living in hierarchical societies have submissive behaviors that defuse aggression, and it is likely that sports developed similarly in order to avoid (excessive) physical harm. Play and athletics are rituals not generally thought to be religious in nature, but they share many characteristics in common. As ritualized behaviors, sports and play bypass consciousness to a great degree, which suggests that not all built-in human behaviors that demote consciousness are religious. Aspects of physical movement have many parallels to dance and, in any case, sports and games are further examples of human activities that are performed for emotional reward and pleasure.

# Dance and Movement as Therapy

The American Dance Therapy Association asserts movement therapy benefits the "emotional, cognitive, physical, and social integration of individuals. Dance/Movement Therapy (DMT) is practiced in mental health, rehabilitation, medical, educational, and forensic settings, and in nursing homes, day care centers, disease prevention, and health promotion programs." (American Dance Therapy Association) A great deal of research on the health effects of dance has been done, but the study of the putative benefits of dance is a mess for several reasons, one of which is dance's similarity to exercise. A slew of studies shows physical exercise has a wide range of benefits. Because dance requires physical effort, it is often conflated with exercise, which is not necessarily wrong, but it makes sifting out the dance-specific contributions more difficult. The following study reviews and summarizes fourteen papers that examined the effects of physical exercise on mental health.

> Aerobic exercise performed at a moderate intensity produces significantly greater positive psychological outcomes than does either high intensity aerobic exercise or anaerobic exercise. Additionally, no specific differences were discovered between various methods of aerobic exercise as long as it is conducted for over 20 minutes continuously. Low impact aerobic exercise, such as yoga or meditation was also found to have positive effects on mental health. (Cohen and Shamus, 2009, p. 1)

Are the benefits of dance simply the result of exercise or is there something unique to dance that isn't due to exercise?

Another challenge in sorting out the benefits of dance is the target subjects. The review of exercise's benefits quoted above specifically looked at the result of exercise on healthy individuals, but exercise has also been shown to help people with disease conditions and slow the brain's aging process. Does dance have the same efficaciousness for normal individuals as well as the aged and infirm? We look at the benefits of dance from both the perspective of healthy people and those who are not to see if dance has specific advantages that exercise strictly does not. Even defining what constitutes dance can be difficult, so analyzing the therapeutic value of dance and its outcomes is difficult. Indeed, research into the benefits of dance and movement are inconsistent for this reason. Dance in one study shows benefit while in another study, it doesn't.

To review, the reason that dance therapy is invoked in this treatise on religion is that for a ritual behavior to be adaptive, it has to be selected for and improve evolutionarily fitness. The behavior has to be beneficial. Random movements, even if repetitious, would not be expected *prima facie* to be useful or advantageous and, in fact, would most likely be deleterious to survival. If dance proves to be therapeutic, it strongly suggests that it is adaptive and therefore evolved, which also means there are genes that contribute to the urge to dance. Also, we cannot overlook that positive emotion from dance is evidence of its evolved function. We look at some of the available evidence to see if dance, independent of other activities or goals, is of value.

Parkinson's disease patients suffer impaired movement and coordination. Research shows benefits for Parkinson's patients from tai chi, which has been shown to help on various movement scales. Reinforcement for the benefits of dance also comes from studies showing dance improves multiple sclerosis patients' balance and motor coordination as well as for people with neurological damage due to traumatic brain injury and stroke. (Berrol, 1997, p. 135) In the case of Parkinson's, the benefits of dance and other movements is not a similar mechanism to the benefits gained from exercise. Gammon Earhart (2009) at the Washington University School of Medicine shows that dancing is a better therapeutic palliative for Parkinson's disease than regular exercise. "Significant improvements" from dancing were made in the Parkinson's patients' balance and speed of reaction that were not achieved through exercise. The dance program, which in Earhart's study was the Argentine tango, also proved to be very popular. Almost half of the subjects chose to continue the dance program in contrast to none who wished to continue with the regular exercise control program. (p. 234)

Earhart proposes several theories for how dance moderates Parkinson's: it's a social activity, it has cardiovascular benefits, and the practice required to perform the dance trains the person's movements. But the best reason is that dance bypasses the basal ganglia, a brain region damaged by Parkinson's. This theme of alternate pathways has been discussed before in regards to conscious versus unconscious control. The basal ganglia is involved in intentional movement control, but dancing is a repetitive series of movements. Once the person is trained, consciousness and intention are less necessary for the activity to take place. Just as in flow, handing over management to more automatic systems counterintuitively results in more control for the Parkinson's sufferers. This points back to The Split Hypothesis, in which the purpose of religion's ritual behaviors is to inhibit higher-order consciousness. This is another instance in which unconscious performance is superior to self-aware consciousness. Dance evolved to piggy-back on unconscious movement as a means to elicit emotions and avoid conscious interference. Because dance activates nonconscious pathways, dancing Parkinson's patients access brain motor controls that aren't as compromised by the disease.

In a study led by Joe Verghese (2003), published in the *New England Journal of Medicine*, cognitive or mentally stimulating activities such as reading, playing board games, and playing musical instruments, "were associated with a lower risk of dementia. Dancing was the only physical activity associated with a lower risk of dementia." The researchers found that other physical activities such as swimming, bicycling, walking for exercise, or climbing more than two flights of stairs had no impact on dementia outcomes. (p. 2512)

Other studies show different combinations of the effectiveness of dance. A group at the University of Nevada, Las Vegas, found that jazz dance taught to older women bolstered balance but did not impact cognition or mood. (Alpert, 2009, p. 108) This could be due to the different type of dance studied or that the dance was being taught rather than dancers engaging in a familiar, practiced dance that didn't require cognitive focus and concentration. Another challenge is to agree on standardized outcomes and what constitutes positive results. A pilot study at the MidState Medical Center in Connecticut found "a dance movement program that addressed the physical and emotional needs of women following treatment for breast cancer substantially improved a breast cancer-specific quality-of-life measure." (Sandel, 2005, p. 301) The improvement was based on one standardized questionnaire that had been validated in multiple previous studies and was used to evaluate the physical, social, functional, and emotional status of the cancer patients. Other measures the researchers looked at, such as body image and shoulder movement (compromised by cancer surgery), improved somewhat but were not statistically significant.

The researchers asked frankly if the positive results occurred due to social interactions or expectations of improvement, a kind of placebo effect, rather than the dance itself. At this point in the study of dance and movement, there is a great deal of inconsistency in the experimental results despite some evidence that dance improves people's outlook and well-being. Nevertheless, even that bastion of progressive thinking, the United States military, supports yoga and other "alternative" movement treatments as palliatives for PTSD and other ailments. (Reeves, 2010)

The implications of these studies are compelling, but none of them suggest why rhythm is so important to people as expressed through dance, music, and prayer, as well. Newberg (2002) scanned the brains of praying nuns and meditating Buddhists. Among the various brain regions activated by intense prayer and meditation was the orientation association area on the border of the temporo-parietal region. Newberg says, "Rhythmic behaviors can lead to unitary states by causing the orientation area to be blocked from neural flow." (p. 115) This orientation area is involved in self-identity and, when it is inhibited, people may lose their sense of self and physical boundaries. It may be crucially involved in the perception of conscious awareness and phenomena such as flow.

Interestingly, an idea called the psychodynamic model has become popular in some therapy circles. The premise is that the therapeutic process mimics or replaces the traditional role of ritual in our secular society. David R. Johnson (1998) makes the case that the therapeutic process imitates Van Gennep's three-step ritual process.

The psychodynamic model suggests that psychotherapeutic change occurs, first, through projection or externalization of unwanted or unknown parts of the self onto
play objects and behaviors; second, through the client's
rearrangement or transformation of these parts during
the play within the imaginal space and in the presence
of the therapist; and finally, through an acceptance or re-
internalization of these parts back into the self. Implicit
in this model is a movement outward (externalization) of
the unknown (unconscious), followed by their transformation in the therapeutic playscape, and finally a movement inward (internalization) of the known (conscious).
(p. 86)

These steps mirror Van Gennep's separation, transition, and incorporation model of ritual stages. Johnson (1995) promotes this
when he says in *The Therapeutic Use of Ritual and Ceremony in the
Treatment of Post-Traumatic Stress Disorder*, "Ritual and ceremony are
highly efficient vehicles for accessing and containing intense emotions evoked by traumatic experience." (p. 283) Ritual obfuscates
consciousness at the same time it processes emotions.

Irma Dosamantes-Beaudry (1998), Director of the Graduate
Dance/Movement Therapy Program at UCLA, fosters the psychodynamic model asserting, "regression to an infantile or instinctual
state can lead to a forward leap towards a new and creative organi-
zation of a person's sense of self." (p. 79) She goes on to specifically
cite Van Gennep's three phases of ritual and give examples of contemporary rituals in terms of the psychodynamic sequence.

Dosamantes-Beaudry also draws a comparison between traditional cultures' *soul* and modern cultures' *self.* In some tribes when
people get sick, they think it is a loss of soul. In contemporary
psychological terms, a person in need of therapy is suffering from
a loss of self due to internal conflicts between the person's true nature and forces in opposition to that nature. In both instances, the
sufferer needs to be restored through ritual. The therapist guides
the troubled person into separation, which in the psychodynamic
model is called regression—the projection of the internal struggle

out on to something external, typically the therapist. The therapist, or shaman in past times, guides the initiate through the practices or ordeals of the transition phase where the conflict is resolved or disease cured. Finally the healer leads the person back to incorporation or reintegration, ideally with a new, healthy, and competent perspective.

Jung (1933) understood this overlap between religion and psychotherapy as well. "Patients force the psychotherapist into the role of the priest, and expect and demand of him that he shall free them from their distress...We psychotherapists must occupy ourselves with problems which, strictly speaking, belong to the theologian." (p. 278)

Studies of the benefits of dance show inconsistent results. Not only does there need to be better standards for measuring the affective and cognitive impact of dance, there need to be standards established to ascertain if different forms of dance have different physiological consequences. In addition, studies are necessary to determine how dance impacts higher-order consciousness such as working memory, self-awareness, and decision-making. In the meantime, despite the varying dance study outcomes on health and cognition, there is abundant evidence that dance is useful and rewarding. Further work is necessary to clarify these benefits.

In preliterate cultures dance and movement assist people embody their emotions and desires, and in our high-tech society, the dance remains the same. The modern cultural permutations of dance have changed, but the original needs and urges to engage in this ritual persist. Dance and other forms of movement stimulate brain reward centers, which means that such activities are adaptive and selected for. People desire to dance, not because they suddenly or even slowly decided to like it, but because they evolved to receive both neural reward and evolutionary advantage from dance. That advantage is because dance, like other rituals, impedes higher-order consciousness and arouses adaptive affective systems—emotions.

Dance and movement therapies are one of the present-day, areligious methods for assisting people to address and integrate their desires, goals, and feelings that had been the historical realm of religion. Therapies exist for most art forms and these therapies are modern transformations of tribal ritual. Modern psychotherapy assumes much of the role of traditional religion, particularly in regards to creating a setting for personal ritual and healing. In combination with music, rhythmic movement produces a potent jolt to the brain that results in a vigorous affective state change. The brain's reward and pleasure response to rhythmic movement in general and dance specifically indicates that dance makes people feel better, and in terms of The Split Hypothesis, is one of the evolved devices that turn on the emotional complex at the expense of consciousness.

# Chapter 10

## Mythology: The Archetypal Stories

> People love stories. The human brain comes hard-wired,
> not just for language, but for narrative....
> Our brains really latch on to narrative, to story.
> There's always people ready to hear stories.
> *Leslie Marmon Silko*

For as long as we can determine, human culture has been resplendent with mythologies. Stories of gods don't leave a record in pre-literate tribes, but it's likely that myths were told at least as long as cave paintings and other art have been around. Mythologies remained vibrant as humans became agricultural and then established city-states and written language. The stories became codified into texts, some of which became the basis for hierarchical religions. Today, the fictional narratives permeate our lives, but instead of the Gods fighting and philandering, it's now mortals who fulfill the plot lines. We take for granted the obvious empathies we get when we identify with and project our own emotions into a mythical tale. Yet that same old question arises as to why no other animal does this, only humans. The amount of effort given to transmitting mythologies is resources absconded from other, more important activities that presumably promote preferential survival and success. Why is it necessary to seek that emotional high from mythology and fiction? It seems to occur for no other reason than an ongoing desire to trigger emotion for its own sake, and that's true; yet there's more to the story.

Every traditional culture has its array of myths to describe its creation, its tales of the gods, and within these chronicles are morality parables instructing people how to live and behave or explanations for why the world exists as it does. For the vast majority of human existence, the fictional folklore of a culture was passed down through story-telling, and traditional myths were delivered by the elders sitting around the hearth, reciting the stories they learned from their forebears. Wallace (1966) says, "Cosmology and values are expressed in one or more myths. Myths are narratives telling of events in the careers of supernatural beings, among themselves and in company with humans." (p. 74) A cosmology is a culture's explanation for the creation of the universe and how it came to be populated with gods, creatures, and people.

Fiction, the modern incarnation of mythology, now entrances in plays, books, movies and television. Myth and fiction are siblings, except today the consumers of literature project their empathies onto mostly secular human fictional characters rather than a hallowed troop of gods, saints, spirits, and souls. Just as the ecology of music has changed over the centuries from primarily religious and ritual forms to the commercial, popular music of today, mythology has culturally evolved from a polytheistic pantheon of gods towards a monotheistic top god. More recently mythology has undergone a secular transformation into populist literature and fiction. The stories of gods' wars and triumphs, lust and illicit trysts—theatrics of the deities—are now portrayed in the same scenarios about humans, but in either case, they are creations of the human mind.

Establishing the similarities between mythology and fiction is important. Despite the inadequate knowledge of how mythology and literature work in the brain, I make the assumption that both utilize similar neural pathways and elicit similar emotional outcomes. Despite delineating religious mythologies as sacred while fiction is secular, the brain doesn't care when it comes to processing them. In terms of any evolutionary basis for mythology or literary fiction, I submit they arise from the same operators and therefore serve the same purpose. Not that everyone equates their own fiction and literature with mythology. For many, mythologies are other society's fabrications and fantasies, quaint stories to soothe the ignorant, whereas, in typical anthropocentric fashion, one's own stories and legends are manifestly factual and valid.

Unlike music and dance, the biological roots of mythology are currently farther removed from scientific inspection. The involvement of physical movement under the influence of rhythm has physiological consequences that can be measured, but storytelling does not necessarily require the physical commitment and engage the body to the degree that music and dance do—particularly for the audience. At its most basic level, the absorption of mythology requires virtually no movement, and even the narrator can divulge cultural lore only by talking. The emotional impact of myth is still quantifiable, however, but investigating the correlates of mythology on the brain is challenging. The scientific study of mythology remains primarily the purview of psychology, which is a more interpretive endeavor and less leveraged by the empirical method. What we do know is that, like music, people passionately engage in narrative; they seek out stories. Panksepp (2000) says, "What makes humans unique, perhaps more than anything else, is that we are a linguistically adept story-telling species. That is why so many different forms of mythology have captivated our cultural imaginations since the dawn of recorded history." (p. 126)

Also unlike music and dance, the religious connection to mythology is more obvious and accepted since the myth stories are often synonymous with religious teachings. Modern religions have sacred texts—the Bible, the Torah, the Quran (Koran), the Upanishads—that are the mythologies in written form. The crucifixion, regardless of the actual event, is a mythological story of sacrifice that every practicing Christian embraces. The resurrection is the redemption and rebirth of every person who takes Communion, this most essential ritual in the world's largest institutional religion, and is based on a mythic narrative in four roughly parallel parts or gospels plus some non-canonical gospels.

On the other hand, myth doesn't exist in a vacuum. In both traditional and modern cultures, myth overlaps and integrates with other ritual behaviors. In the previous chapter on dance, I pointed out that several cultures' dances were steeped in the fictive and unearthly peregrinations of deceased ancestors. Dance can also portray the spirits and gods creating or explaining the world, so at least one aspect of dance is the expression and embodiment of storytelling in which a story's emotional content is symbolized and concretized with movement. Popular songs frequently tell a brief tale: a love gone bad, a love desired, a life lost, a lesson learned. Operas and musical theater also combine narrative elements in a music and dance ritual synthesis. Despite mythology being somewhat dissimilar to music and dance in terms of immediate connections to religion or biology, their interplay through ritual establishes their functional relatedness; they are all ethological behaviors of religion.

## Pleasure, Fear, and the Theory of Mind

Fiction is fabricated and therefore "false." Fiction is an instance where humans decouple the merit or value from the entity being described. We can watch a TV crime drama without believing that the crime depicted actually happened or that the program is an endorsement of an illegal act. Tooby and Cosmides (2001) write,

> Fiction consists of representations in a special format, the narrative, that are attended to, valued, preserved, and transmitted because the mind detects that such bundles of representations have a powerfully organizing effect on our neurocognitive adaptations, even though the representations are not literally true. (p. 21)

Fiction allows the receiver of the narrative to mentally simulate possible encounters and tasks, knowing they aren't real and without having to have the actual experiences to comprehend their meaning and significance. This is the common explanation for why people voyeuristically observe fiction; it lets people participate and act in their own mental theater, cognitively rehearsing scenarios to weigh the likelihood of other's intentions or actions as well as their own. Humans can imagine and think about what others are thinking and feeling. The narrative episode inspires because of the magnificent human ability to visualize and experience what others experience. This is the theory of mind (ToM), which, as discussed in earlier chapters, works because people evolved to be keenly attuned to each other, to sense and judge each other's emotions and thoughts. ToM originated because of humanity's sophisticated sense of self versus non-self, this most essential dichotomy.

ToM is an impressive skill that, as far as we know, extends far beyond the abilities of other species and is an important reason why humans are capable of complex social relationships and culture. In the ever-demanding social dynamic of the tribe, dormitory, office, or neighborhood, rivals jockey for advantage and influence and for potential and actual resources whether food, money, or mates. Even beyond commerce and sexual negotiations, everybody has people they prefer more, and people they prefer less. People jostle for status and friendships that result in preferential associations. Social interaction requires a robust imagination and anticipation of the minds of co-conspirators and competitors.

People enjoy narrative fiction and consume theater, movies, poetry, and literature as a continuous ToM exercise and indulgence, but does this fulfill a complete explanation? In *How the Mind Works*, Pinker (2009) says consuming fiction is desirable because it tickles the pleasure centers, but he also realizes that people enjoy narratives that induce fear or sadness as well. (p. 540) Hamlet and MacBeth aren't exactly pick-me-ups. Hannibal Lecter, the serial murderer in *Silence of the Lambs*, doesn't cajole a warm, fuzzy feeling from the audience.

Pinker throws out several possible reasons for the attraction to tragic or scary plots including the intellectual status associated with watching art films, the need to balance reality with the predictable Hollywood happy ending, or the vicarious pleasure of being a fly on the wall observing other people's hardships as any good busy-body would do. He also solicits Paul Rozin's theory of benign masochism for the suffering some stories cause—people seek discomfort as a way to practice real-world scenarios. For those who seek the emotional jolt from cinematic axe murderers and chain-saw wielders, are they imagining what the psychotic mind is thinking or that of the hapless victim? Depends on the viewer, I suppose. Another possibility Pinker raises is that fiction provides information, which has a similar effect as benign masochism; we can observe situations and imagine or practice our response as if we were in that position. This is another version of practicing real-world scenarios. He goes on to elaborate the complex interaction strategies all people exercise in their daily social intercourse and the benefit of ersatz practice. It feels like he's throwing everything against the wall and hoping something will stick. This groping for different possibilities is not unusual when lacking an actual answer although Pinker is transparent about the mystery of art and literature. "Tens of thousands of scholars and millions of pages of scholarship have shed almost no light on the question of why people pursue the arts at all. The function of the arts is almost defiantly obsure." (p. 521)

Imagining ghouls, ghosts, and other demons in the classic haunted house film is beyond a coarse approximation of real enemies. The scary stories of witches and giants in fairy tales or poltergeists and possession in horror movies are not actual possible foes, incarnating personages far beyond anything that could really happen. These demonic character types exist in practically every culture as does the concept of soul possession, when an external spirit takes control of a person. The fascination with demons' intrusions in our lives is much closer in context to the supernatural myths of gods, to peoples' relationships with gods, not with other people real or imagined. Benign masochism sounds plausible enough superficially, but it's descriptive rather than explanatory and falls short of a complete answer. Yes, some people are drawn towards myths that incite strong, even negative, emotions. Recursive role-playing—rehearsing real-world scenarios—is accepted as an adequate explanation, but it isn't. Benign masochism fits our interpretation of the behavior but tells us nothing about why people seek such emotional stimulation. Similarly, the notion that fiction provides a mental rehearsal space has a smidgeon of truth to it, but it falls short of the whole story.

Like benign masochism, the Hyperactive Agency Detection Device is a description, not an explanation. In chapter 4, I said that HADD theory proposes that people, when faced with unknown, potentially threatening events, want to identify and assign labels to them, which, HADD proponents claim, leads to the creation of gods and other supernatural entities. Invoking concepts like folkpsychology and habits of mind, HADD theorists work hard to link unpredictability and alarm to the formation of mental representations of nonexistent beings. What is certain is that the two tendencies exist: people are on the alert for agency or causation, and people create mythological entities such as gods. The Hyperactive Agency Detection Device draws a connection between these two, but this connection suffers from the Texas Sharpshooter Fallacy. This fallacy describes how a Texan shoots holes in the side of a barn and then draws a target around the holes. In other words, since people invent gods, and people work to assign cause to unknown, potentially dangerous events, it must be that we invoke hyperactive agency detection by drawing this target around imagined gods.

The most efficient behavior for dealing with unidentified potential threats from an evolutionary perspective is to actually identify mysterious perceptions as accurately as possible. Creating imaginary beings would be of dubious adaptive value in the face of possible real hazards. I subscribe to Daniel Wegner's proposal that the creation of external, supernatural gods is due to the human inability to accurately assign causation, which is only an issue because higher-order consciousness gives humans the false sense of having this ability. Because the human mind is mostly incapable of accurately fixing causality to phenomena, people compensate by fabricating gods that assume responsibility for earthly events, relieving us mortals of this irresolvable burden. In a way, HADD is not completely wrong, but it is only one of many situations in which causality is unknown and certainly not the primary basis for the creation of gods.

Even if it we accept HADD's premise, the range of imaginary creatures and the extent of the intricate mythologies constructed around them is enormous. If humans needed to generate other-worldly targets on which to offload their fears, it wouldn't take an entire pantheon of divinities to accommodate the requirement. Those mythic, mystical creations called gods are not haphazard. The gods and other spectral beings who populate myths are transferences of our archetypal, innate psychic architecture. The gods of mythology are mirror reflections of the yearnings and fears that all humanity shares—stories of heroism, angst, love, betrayal, and triumph. What would have been truly remarkable is if the gods looked and behaved in ways that were not representative of real human activities or not manifestations of nature like throwing thunderbolts of lightning. Even the gods who take animal forms behave more like people than the animals they resemble. Causal reattribution is the reason that humans invented gods compensating for the shortcomings of higher-order consciousness, but it was the archetypes—psychological motifs or mental constructions—that gave them substance.

In a parallel universe the ability to have a theory of mind, to contemplate what others feel and think, could exist without the obsession with myth and literature. I can think about my boss's intentions without creating or imagining a story about how nonexistent people similarly interact. Just because people can sense what others are experiencing, doesn't explain why people create an additional degree of abstraction called fiction. Strictly speaking, the ability to perceive what others feel and think doesn't necessitate engaging in fictions. Mythology is an elaboration, an added layer of ToM as if people need additional, imagined ToM stimulation. This suggests that actual social ToM interactions are somehow inadequate and require additional exploration of fantasy realms. In the theory of mind, the most effective strategy would be to compare the target person's predicted belief and the person's resulting behavior. The vicarious entertainment garnered from a poem about wilderness or a slasher movie seems unlikely to specifically benefit one's sociability or defensive behavior whether in a metropolis or in a tribe.

The primary effect of narrative is the emotional impact of the ersatz experience rather than any calculated examination. As mentioned in the chapters on consciousness, the greater the emotion, the greater the likelihood the story will be retained in memory. For literary critics who intellectually analyze fiction, judgment of the quality of literature is the emotional truth conveyed despite the ostensibly rational approach. A story lacking feeling and passion is generally panned and disparaged. The practice or rehearsal that results from fiction is primarily emotional rather than consciously considered. The importance of emotion to the mythological experience has significance on two levels.

First, despite mythology's purported social purposes via ToM, the search for meaning in mythology first happens within each person. The individual experiences emotions when observing and practicing mythologies. As Joseph Carroll (2008) says in *An Evolutionary Paradigm for Literary Study*,

> Motivations, actions, and interpretive responses all originate in the neurological events in individual brains. Thoughts, feelings, and memories are lodged in individual brains, and individual persons form the central organizing units in narrative depictions. Authors and readers are individual persons, and characters in fiction are fictive individual persons. Because experience is individual, the analysis of fictional narrative is always, necessarily, psychological analysis. (p. 118)

Social relationships are based on emotional interplay between individuals. Whether socializing, scheming, or cooperating happens in tribal settings or the modern housewives of Dubuque, social guile and posturing manifests through emotionally-driven ploys. Cognitive calculations are more or less incidental.

Secondly, since the effects of mythology and literature takes place on an affective plane, I ask why emotions—adaptive, evolved behaviors—are stimulated by fiction. We accept that actual community interactions would generate significant emotional effects, but the question remains, from an evolutionary point of view, why should non-real re-creations do the same?

Out of the many theories of literature and mythology, I indulge in the psychological interpretations by Carl Jung and Joseph Campbell, who, as part of their theories, advocate a biological basis for mythology. Nevertheless, they are interpreting cultural stories and personal dreams, which is a psychological level of scrutiny, not so much biological. Even Jung's concept of a collective unconscious that girds his view of mythology, while based on his supposition that instincts drive mythic content, remains beyond the strict scope of the empirical method. Jung influenced Campbell, and both espoused that mythologies were not only a collection of stories and themes but were also consistently inhabited by psychological pro-jections, manifested characters who reappear widely in various cul-tures' myths. Just as ritual behaviors populate rites of passage, sac-rifice, and ceremonies, the recurring characters are psychological building blocks of mythologies. Just as language has innate com-ponents and is molded by culture, so too the mythic actors have many names and faces but ultimately represent a few prototypical personalities that humans project over and over again. With that caveat, we explore some theories of mythology that are consistent with The Split Hypothesis of religion while we anticipate the time when methods exist to formally test the biology of mythology.

## Joseph Campbell's Mythology

For 50 years Joseph Campbell taught, studied, and wrote about mythology as a professor at Sarah Lawrence College. For Campbell (1973), mythology was an innate expression of the mind and a col-lection of metaphors symbolizing the human condition. As he said in *Hero with a Thousand Faces*, "The symbols of mythology are not manufactured; they cannot be ordered, invented, or permanently suppressed. They are spontaneous productions of the psyche, and each bears within it, undamaged, the germ power of its source." (p. 4) Myth isn't random and both expresses and engages the fun-damental mind, but it isn't only learned and passed on. Myths are endemic within our brains.

Campbell (1990) specifies four functions of mythology. Two of them are reiterations of secondary consequences of religion that we've previously addressed: to explain the cosmic order of the uni-verse (answer the existential questions) and to preserve and support the group mind (group coherence). Campbell offers a third perspec-tive for mythology. Teamed with rites of passage, myths convey people through individual stages of development. Myths inform the universal rebirth that ritual repeatedly performs. "Rites, then," Campbell says, "together with the mythologies that support them, constitute the second womb, the matrix of the postnatal gestation of the placental Homo sapiens." (p. 55) In his typically enigmatic prose, Campbell posits that symbolic and metaphorical rebirth is a purpose of ritual, and mythologies help give meaning and context to the ritual process. Some of the earliest evidence of human ritual burial found tools, plants, and food in the graves, suggesting the survivors believed the deceased would be reborn to a new existence. In some burials, the corpses were fetally positioned indicating a womb-like potential for being born again. Campbell points out mythological symbols include other themes besides rebirth, and these themes are pervasive throughout all cultures.

> In primitive mythologies and rites, we find the image of the sun-door, the clashing rocks, death and resurrection, the Incarnation, the sacred marriage and father atonement, employed not haphazardly but in the same relationships as in the myths of the higher cultures. (p. 58)

Campbell's (2001) fourth and most important purpose of myth "is that of *reconciling consciousness* [emphasis added] to the preconditions of its own existence — that is, of aligning waking consciousness to the *mysterium tremendum* of the universe, as it is." (p. 2) The *mysterium tremendum*, literally "great mystery," is Rudolf Otto's term for the personal perception or sense of the transcendent, the spiritual, the awesomely powerful God. Campbell proposes that human consciousness must accommodate the fearsome, loving, and formidably overwhelming experience of the holy that is beyond any ability to fully comprehend. Touching the numinous or the divine is the highest expression of universal religious devotion, but consciousness cannot fathom this. By its very nature religion is irrational, at least from rational consciousness's point of view. The two concepts — the divine and consciousness — are foreign to each other and are incompatible modes of being. Campbell credits mythology as moderating or allying the two forces of consciousness and religion.

This last of Campbell's purposes of mythology is dangerously close to The Split Hypothesis in which religious behaviors are compensating mechanisms for higher-order consciousness. It takes only a slight reinterpretation to understand that the great mysteries refer to the unconscious frog-mind. People have no conscious insight into the inner workings of the mind, which, during the evolutionary period that consciousness and religion were developing, was a source of inner turmoil. The processes primarily responsible for an organism's well-being were inaccessible to incipient consciousness. Consciousness was beginning to play a role, and the bright light it shone gave humans self-reflection while the historically dark, unconscious cognitive processes sometimes became symbolized or concretized in consciousness through ritual as religious spirituality.

Another approach Campbell (1973) takes for the purpose of myth that borrows heavily from Jung and Freud is psychotherapeutic. The unconscious is awash with hidden, repressed forces, some of which try to thrust their way to the conscious surface. The pressure of the unconscious disfigures and distends and may burst out as unwanted feelings or may remain bottled up causing internal conflicts that might be redirected uncontrollably or impulsively and labeled as neurosis or worse. They are the "inconvenient or resisted psychological powers that we have not thought or dared to integrate into our lives." (p. 8) This twist reframes the discussion into the psychological rather than the religious, but the essence of The Split remains. Religion's toolbox, myth and ritual, preside over the tug-of-war between the historical antagonists: the conscious and unconscious. Myth and ritual are methods to overcome overactive and irresolute consciousness and return to emotion's unconscious biological heritage. Today the psychoanalyst performs the role once exclusively belonging to the clergy class.

## Jung and the Collective Unconscious

Carl Jung explored folkloric realms and sought to understand myth's inherent importance as he delved into the human psyche. Campbell (2001) credits Jung as an important influence that led him to understand the nature of mythology.

> While times and conditions change drastically, the subject of historical conditioning throughout the centuries, that is the complex psychological unity we call the human person, remains a constant. What Adolph Bastian described as "elementary ideas," and Jung referred to as

"archetypes of the collective unconscious" are the biologically rooted motivating powers and connoted references for the mythologies that, cast in the metaphors of changing historical and cultural periods, remain themselves constant. (p. 6)

The myths that arise from the collective unconscious are populated by the archetypes, the prototypical characters that are held in our inherited memories. Examples are mother, father, male (animus), and female (anima), trickster, and shadow. Every person has inherited drives within them both anticipating and expressing these archetypes given the appropriate environmental cues—the lock and key. Jung (1990) elaborates the connection between myth and archetypes.

From the unconscious there emanate determining influences which, independently of tradition, guarantee in every single individual a similarity and even a sameness of experience, and also of the way it is represented imaginatively. One of the main proofs of this is the almost universal parallelism between mythological motifs, which, on account of their quality as primordial images I have called archetypes. (p. 58)

Although labeled, for example, as mother, father, anima, and animus, the archetypes are not external entities. They do not refer to one's actual mother and father. They are evolved predispositions each person carries psychically. Jung said the animus, the male principle, and anima, the female principle, are not primarily about representing one's own genetic gender; rather the animus is the woman's projection of her male archetype, and the anima is the man's projection of his female archetype. Jung said all people carry the full archetypal complement. Of course, these inherited archetypal principles are heavily influenced by life experiences—learning and conditioning. The mother archetype is the baby's internal, nonconscious expectation to bond with a nurturer who will not only feed, but love and minister to it during those first crucial years of development. Anything that impedes the baby receiving the care it needs frustrates the archetypal intent and can cause compensating mechanisms in the infant, always less than ideal.

Archetypes inhabit myths throughout all traditions. Campbell (2001) says, "Practically every mythology in the world has used this 'elementary' or co-natural idea of a virgin birth to refer to a spiritual rather than historical reality." (p. 7) The Aztec legend of the birth of Quetzalcoatl suggests he lived as both man and god. He was born of the virgin goddess Coatlicue or Chimalman and his father resided only in heaven. The Babylonian/Sumerian god Tammuz was born on December 25 to the Virgin Myrrha—also the mother of Adonis in Greek myth. Mary is thought to be derived from Myrrha. As Campbell says, the list of cultures containing this mythic form is long, but regardless of the specific storyline and culture, the stories have the same psychic meaning for all people. The virgin birth is not the historical event, but rather the metaphorical divine awakening or birth of the holy in each person symbolized by the god-child.

Mythologies are metaphors that represent innate, psychobiological drives and predispositions. I began this book with the Garden of Eden myth, a metaphor which represents the acquisition of consciousness leading to the quagmire of the human condition. Religion co-evolved with consciousness to accommodate and ameliorate the downsides of consciousness. Humans throughout time and geography share similar mythical themes and stories. These scenarios are not only common to all peoples but exist in and derive from the inherited memories of the species, hence Jung's provenance for the collective unconscious. Tooby and Cosmides call them innate concepts. These biologically-based mental entities exist in the unconscious in the sense that we are unaware of their source, but that is only a perspective relative to consciousness. It is consciousness which allows us to see and explore the archetypes through mythology, but that's like saying our breathing and heartbeat are in our unconscious. We've learned their purpose and functional mechanism, but it isn't our consciousness that gives breath, heartbeat, or mythology their genesis; rather they preexist, and we understand them after the fact. The collective unconscious is an endowment of our species regardless of our awareness and engagement in it.

To some the archetypes and collective unconscious sound like fantastical, new-age claptrap. For the rigorously scientific, the link between Jung's archetypes and the world of biology is legitimately unsatisfactory. Missing from the psychologists' discussion of the collective unconscious is the explicit genetic evidence for the inheritance of mental representations or archetypes. For the collective unconscious to be a valid theory, we ideally want to identify the inborn components that contribute to the archetypes; at a minimum to show that some mental functions have a genetic aspect; that some mental tendencies are transmitted through the DNA. In Jung's time there was no way to show this beyond observing inheritance patterns, and even that was dicey as behaviorism, the prevailing psychological model of the early twentieth century, dictated that children observed and acquired their behaviors from their parents and society, which masked any innate contribution.

Some people continue to argue that learning and conditioning decides a child's personality relative to genetics, which has limited or no impact. An obstinate prejudice persists against hints of genetic determinism, particularly when it implies limits to human potential. Some people discount genetic contributions to behavior because of their sociopolitical agenda, but it's also easy to disregard inherited behavior if only because it's hidden and not easily observed.

Scholars are frustrated by their inability to evaluate the collective unconscious with empirical precision. I raised this caveat earlier in this chapter, but little behavior is understood at the genetic level. Cosmides and Tooby (1997) point out the difficulty of identifying genetically based behavior, which they call instinct blindness.

> Our natural competences—our abilities to see, to speak, to find someone beautiful, to reciprocate a favor, to fear disease, to fall in love, to initiate an attack, to experience moral outrage, to navigate a landscape, and myriad others—are possible only because there is a vast and heterogeneous array of complex computational machinery supporting and regulating these activities. This machinery works so well that we don't even realize that it exists. We all suffer from instinct blindness. (para. 8)

Stating that homologous mythical themes are prevalent around the world is not evidence by itself that myths are psychologically innate ideas. The alternative to myths being innate concepts is that myths randomly developed early in human evolution and were conveyed as the first humans traveled out of Africa. Either that or after the African diaspora, the stories were transmitted like bartered goods from group to group. Because people perceive myths as traditionally inculcated, as culturally bequeathed by the elders, many believe that myths are arbitrary stories that blindly continue to get passed on.

There are two problems with this interpretation. Since no one alive is a witness to the beginning of myth-telling, we suffer the Richard Dawkins' paradox of who designed the designer? In *God Delusion* Dawkins deftly uses this argument to disparage so-called proofs of God's existence, but it also poses the issue of how the first mythologies arose. Of course mythologies are passed down, but that doesn't mean they are only cultural and don't have evolved origins.

How did the first mythologies arise? Were they simply made up because someone had a hankering for telling a good yarn and suddenly had a receptive audience? It's a popular idea but completely without merit. If myths were transferred from generation to generation without any underlying systematic psychic requirement, we would expect that the desire for fiction and narrative wouldn't exist in many cultures. Some societies wouldn't have any mythologies. Where they did exist, the content of the myths would diverge widely. Like an epochal game of telephone, the stories would deviate over time. They would meander into very different tales, but that hasn't happened. The mythical narratives retain their historical similarities and remain pervasive throughout all cultures.

Mythologies may be perceived as acquired beliefs, but, like language, have a genetic basis. The basics of language—grammar and syntax—are universal or deep structures as Noam Chomsky called them. "In Chomsky's view, every child comes into the world fully equipped with the capacity for speech." (Stevens, 1982, p. 43) Though the words change from language to language, the underlying forms are the same. Like language, it is only the superficial permutations of myth that differ. The names of the mythical characters change, some of the story details are altered to match the culture, but the essence beneath the stories doesn't change. The desire and propensity for myth is inherited. "Mythology," Campbell (1990) says, "fosters a balanced intuitive and instinctive, as well as rational, ontogenesis, and throughout the domain of the species the morphology of this peculiar spiritual organ of Homo sapiens is no less constant than that of the well-known, readily recognizable human physique itself." (p. 59) Just like religion, both language and mythology have their roots in the DNA instructions that create the human brain. Whether from a psychological or biological perspective, mythology quietly contributes to religion by negotiating the inward, unconscious forces under the nose of consciousness's watchman.

## Biology and Archetypes

Associating genetic details with mental constructions such as archetypes remains an enormous challenge, but that doesn't mean there isn't any progress. A great deal of evidence for the innateness of behavior patterns exists and suggests links between the archetypes and biology. Research over the last fifty years shows that many aspects of behavior and personality, as well as of mental illnesses, have a genetic basis. Many gene variants cause mental disabilities, including diseases such as Alzheimer's, Huntington's Chorea, and the various trisomies in which a third chromosome is replicated rather than the normal two, the most common being Down Syndrome. Williams Syndrome is a genetic anomaly already mentioned in the chapter on music. Many mental illnesses such as schizophrenia, bipolar disorder, and depression have an inherited component. Schizophrenia in particular can be the result of allelic (gene) variations on as many as seven different chromosomes. (McGuffin, 2001)

Today the behaviorist model has been relegated to at least share a role with genetic predispositions for all aspects of behavior. A slew of research shows ever-increasingly that archetypes, innate concepts, or elementary ideas derive from genetic, inherited predispositions. We accept that mammal newborns have an instinct to suckle, but they also have innate drives to seek affection and comfort. Harry Harlow showed that rhesus macaque infants, when given a choice between a wire cage dummy mother with a bottle of milk tied to it or a dummy mother covered in cloth without a bottle attached, spend most of their time clinging to the cloth mother, going to the wire mother only long enough to feed. We presume the monkey's desire for physical closeness is instinctual, but we take for granted how it happens. It just does; it's in the genes, but there are complex neuroendocrine mechanisms driving it, and humans retain the same apparatuses. In the psychological realm, this relationship is called the mother-infant bond but manifests mythologically as the maternal archetype. We see human expression of the mythology in art in the many Mary and infant Jesus paintings and sculptures, for example, but many, if not most, cultures represent this archetype in art and legend as well.

In his book, *Archetypes: A Natural History of the Self*, Anthony Stevens (1982) makes the case for such a relationship between archetypes and heredity in humans. Archetypes "have a natural history: they are subject to the laws of evolution. In other words, *archetypes evolved through natural selection.*" [emphasis in original] (p. 17) Stevens described his own work and the work of John Bowlby, both of whom studied how young children formed attachments to parents or other caregivers. They investigated the behaviorist prediction that infants would become bonded to whomever fed them. Known as the Cupboard Love theory, the premise was that the child-caregiver attachment formed through food reward conditioning. Stevens and Bowlby each showed that children established attachments to caregivers based on other emotional interactions and preferences rather than who simply fed them. In the orphanage where Stevens did his observations, "the crucial factors leading up to the pairing off of a particular nurse with a particular child were not so much linked with routine feeding as with play, physical contact and social interaction." (p. 5) The babies had an inborn desire to be nurtured that was not satisfied simply by food rewards as behaviorists suggested. "Mothers and their infants had no need to learn to love one another: they were innately programmed to do so from birth. The formation of mother-infant attachment bonds is a direct expression of the genetic heritage of our species." (p. 3) Children innately require nurturing for both physical and emotional development, which is programmed and anticipated in the developing brain and is an expression of the maternal archetype.

Missing are the genetic details linking archetypes and the collective unconscious to behavior just as such direct links are missing for most other aspects of human behavior. Finding actual genes that affect mothers' and children's interactions would be compelling evidence of the innate aspect of the mother archetype. Some fruitful results come, for example, from the study of protein hormones that stimulate maternal behavior such as prolactin, oxytocin, and the related neuroendocrine complex of pituitary-hypothalamic releasing hormones that control them. The oxytocin gene (OXT) codes for the oxytocin hormone, and the oxytocin receptor gene (OXTR) codes for the receptor which binds to oxytocin. Oxytocin causes uterine contractions during childbirth, but is also shown to influence the mother's bonding behavior to her child. That, however, does not explain if oxytocin in infants effects their behavior. Does this natural hormone change the infant's interactions with its parents, an expression of the maternal archetype? A study that looked at oxytocin in infants was done by Ruth Feldman's lab in Israel. Instead of studying mothers, they looked at the relationship between fathers and their five-month-old infants. The fathers were given oxytocin while the researchers observed the father-infant interactions. Both the fathers' and children's oxytocin levels were measured despite no oxytocin given to the babies.

> OT [oxytocin] administration to [the] parent can have parallel effects on the child without direct hormonal manipulation to the infant...Oxytocin administration markedly increased the fathers' salivary OT, autonomic response during free play, and parenting behavior, particularly touch and social reciprocity. In parallel, the infants' peripheral OT increased, infant RSA [respiratory sinus arrhythmia; associated with infant responsiveness] was higher during social play, and infants

> displayed more social gaze and exploratory behavior, indicating greater social engagement when fathers inhaled OT. (Weisman, 2012, p. 986)

Babies respond to the fathers' increased social communication with both higher natural oxytocin levels and social interaction. This is all predicated on genetic instructions for these systems to work. The physiology does the heavy lifting and the human brain (sometimes) translates these biological forces into conscious feelings. People have a tendency to believe that their conscious brains put processes in motion, but the evidence is just the opposite; the internal operations have their own motivation and chronology; consciousness sometimes reflects that internal agency. All explanatory approaches for mythology, ritual, and religion in general must address this essential bottom-up reality and avoid a top-down strategy, or at least make it secondary.

The so-called nature-nurture debate is anachronistic and no longer an either-or issue. In reality it's a matter of degree. Nurture is certainly a major contributor to personality and development, but without the inborn propensity to demand maternal bonding, why should mom's ministrations matter to the infant one way or another? The neonate, if born as a blank slate, will learn to become socially adept when Mom is cuddly and gregarious or will be asocial when Mom is aloof or even hostile. That should be the end of it, but, in reality, children who lack fulfillment of their maternal archetype or suffer separation from their primary caregiver endure more consequences than would be predicted from a solely social-asocial scale. Children raised under difficult circumstances may struggle academically as well as socially. Frustrating the maternal archetype potentially causes a spectrum of problems including both mental and physical disease states: neurosis, depression, or worse. The observed consequences are far beyond the specific social dynamic predicted by a learning-only influence on development.

Women are biologically bound for child-bearing and nursing, and that includes the associated behavioral predispositions necessary to foster children's development. The resource commitment to chaperone children to adulthood is enormous for the woman compared to the father even when he diligently commits to help raise them. This state of affairs derives from hundreds of millions of years of evolution, and human gender roles were not freed from such obligations. Today, women in many societies can choose not to have children, but it's an inescapable fact that the women of the future will come mostly from women who valued being mothers, selecting against whatever non-maternal genetic dispositions may exist.

A pair of archetypes that also lend themselves to biological investigation are the anima—the female principle—and the animus—the male principle. While a great deal is already known about the X and Y chromosomes and their impact on primary and secondary sexual characteristics as well as sex-linked diseases, claiming genes account for variations in gender behavior is very controversial. Despite the obvious fact that, on average, the XY genotype (male) results in significantly larger stature and greater muscle mass than the XX genotype (female), there's resistance to assertions that these genotypes also result in differential behavioral dispositions. In many Western cultures, there's a hypersensitivity to attributing too much behavioral determinism to genetic causes, and not without good reason. In most, if not all, societies, women suffer from discrimination, not the least of which is unequal compensation in the workplace. At the same time, it is absolutely clear that men are overwhelmingly perpetrators of violence, including sexual violence and pedophilia. Those who yearn for the perfectabilty of humanity will side with nurture, blaming paternalistic social mores for male aggression, but that's far too simple an excuse. In societies that provide the latitude, some people grow up to reject their given and conditioned sexual identity and opt to live as their apparent non-genetic gender or even undergo surgery to change gender. On top of that, those who would deny genetic gender-based behavioral differences also reliably state, appropriately, that homosexuality is not a lifestyle choice or a result of nurture. Homosexuals were born that way. I wish the mood swings of pre-menstrual syndrome were conditioned so they could be unconditioned, but I doubt the idea of PMS reeducation camps would have effectiveness any more than so-called reparative therapy could cure homosexuality.

While a great deal of evidence exists for behavioral as well as physiological sexual dimorphism, such assertions challenge the efforts of those working to balance the cultural gender equation. Even if there are gender behavioral differences, that is no justification for stereotyped discrimination, which continues to be rampant. At the same time, there is no benefit in denying an honest appraisal of the scientific evidence that, on average, men and women are born with different behavioral predispositions. The science of sex differences is plentiful. In just two of thousands of gender studies, a group at the City University of New York found sensory gender-based visiospatial and color vision differences. "There are marked sex differences in vision...We find that males have significantly greater sensitivity for fine detail and for rapidly moving stimuli." (Abramov, 2012a, p. 1) "There are significant differences between males and females in the appearance of monochromatic lights...Across most of the visible spectrum males require a slightly longer wavelength than do females in order to experience the same hue." (Abramov, et al., 2012b, p. 11)

Gene-environment interactions are extremely complex. It's awkward enough separating out the social and political biases let alone the actual relative contributions of inheritance and socialization. Nevertheless, the study of the anima, animus, and archetypes in general are relevant particularly because they transcend genotypic heritage (XX, XY, or other) and provide a means to understand the breadth of the gender behavioral phenotype. A relatively new discovery, epigenetics, has gained traction in the last few decades. Epigenetics studies the factors that make genes active or inactive and find that, in some cases, a gene's activation state is passed to offspring. This means inheritance is not solely due to the DNA sequence. People can inherit the same gene but its on/off status results in differential gene expression. Evidence suggests that in some cases gender identification may be influenced by epigenetic changes, which may account for some gender dysphorias (gender identity conditions). Regardless of one's sex at birth or position along the male-female identity axis, the archetypal masculine and feminine can be explored without regard for gender preconceptions. Because both men and women each contain both the male and female archetypal principles, there is no intimation that one is superior to the other. They are complementary, interdependent, and each has both positive and negative aspects.

The anima and animus are archetypes that are expressed mythologically. In practice dreams and symbolic metaphor give substance and embodiment to these innate, archetypal tendencies. The yin-yang symbol of Taoist religious philosophy represents in graphic form the male-female duality, but represents other dualities as well.

> The yang principle is characterized as energetic, dynamic and assertive; its attributes are heat and light (symbolized by the sun and its rays); its realms are heaven and the spirit; in its phallic, penetrating aspect it arouses, fructifies and creates; in its aggressive form it combats and destroys; its orientation is essentially centrifugal, outgoing, extraverted; it is positive and impulsive, but also disciplined and ascetic.

> Whereas yang is assertive and initiating, the yin principle is passive and containing (symbolized by the moon and the cave); its realms are earth, nature and the womb, for it is essentially concerned with gestation, giving form to the energy of yang and bringing life out of darkness; its movement is centripetal, in-turning and introverted. (Stevens, 1982, p. 176)

The relationship between the X and Y chromosomes and the outward gender phenotype, both physical and behavioral, is complicated, but without a doubt, genetics plays an important role.

Jung and Campbell's interpretations of mythology stray from a rigorous empirical analysis of ritual behavior, and while remaining far from scientific revelation, they beg for physiological and genetic investigation. I happen to be fond of Jung's archetypes and collective unconscious, but how would scientists even approach the biology of the trickster or the shadow archetypes? While there's a long way to go to link psychological archetypes to biological processes, the archetypes provide a framework to understand how mythologies are populated. In the meantime I take on faith that, despite the relative paucity of empirical evidence for the biology of archetypes and the collective unconscious, there is, nevertheless, enough to maintain them for ongoing scientific appraisal. We wait to see how science confirms or refutes an inherited basis for religious ritual and mythology. However they are called and interpreted, innate drives give rise to archetypal, mythological characters in consciousness, which live as tales retold throughout world cultures. They have their basis in the biological brain and are the mental projections and psychological predispositions that consciousness perceives and hardly understands.

This book begins with the myth of creation for Judeo-Islam-Christian religions, Adam and Eve's expulsion from the Garden of Eden, but creation myths exist in many variations in virtually all other faiths and cultures. The Eden story is a metaphor for the actual cognitive evolution of the human mind, which is retained as an indistinct embodied genetic memory in the brain and is expressed and relived through mythic narratives. The fall from grace represents the evolutionary elevation of human cognition that results in the capacity for consciousness and metarepresentations, the ability to decouple information from the truth value of that information. This is the advent of dichotomous thinking in which entities no longer possess an absolute essence or meaning. Humans can fantasize and reason, which includes formulating possibilities that are counterfactual, but the great challenge for the evolving human, as for every organism, is how to live an adaptive life.

Since people acquired higher-order consciousness, they have incorrectly assumed that everything that consciousness provides is beneficial, but that is demonstrably wrong. Humans have the burden of trying to keep in check feverish higher-order consciousness that is noisy and sees too many choices. Like other ritual behaviors, the purpose of mythology is to ameliorate The Split, to accommodate the important but limited capability of higher-order consciousness by bringing humanity back in touch with its older, adaptive, emotional drives. Mythology generates emotions that arise from a deep ancestral well. It incarnates instincts in consciousness and activates adaptive behaviors to offset the vagaries that arise from consciousness. Mythology and other religious rituals help humans limit options and abide instinctual dictates that, over millions of years, have ensured survival and reproductive success. The mythology of the ejection from Eden symbolizes the human condition—The Split of mental processes into higher-order consciousness and religious belief and feeling—and it does this as an unconscious, unbidden innate proclivity. Mythology is a chronicle of humanity's evolutionary travail in response to the slapdash, confusing signals arising from consciousness.

Archetypes are often represented using symbols, which often take the form of people, but can depict many non-human forms as well. Animals are frequent symbols of the unconscious such as the coyote and raven, which symbolize the trickster in many cultures. Symbols such as the mandala don't have to be based on any real-life entity at all. The yin-yang symbol is a simple mandala, which represents the dichotomies of existence like animus-anima, conscious-unconscious—any human duality.

Symbolism informs literature, plays, and movies, but is also the fundamental substance of visual artwork: sculpture, paintings, and designs worked into cultural artifacts. Making art—symbolic representations—is another human activity that doesn't seem to serve an obvious adaptive purpose, yet within the context of The Split Hypothesis of religion, art is a ritual religious behavior. I explore the evolutionary function and purpose of art in the next chapter.

# CHAPTER 11

## ART: THE ARCHETYPAL IMAGES

Art is a lie which makes us see the truth
*Pablo Picasso*

Visual art is the earliest ritual activity known because it leaves a record. Cave paintings and the plump Venus statuettes that likely portrayed sexual desire and fertility are some of the discovered artifacts that predate agriculture and written language. Cave paintings and petroglyphs depict animals and humans, often as part of hunting scenes. Some rock artworks depict unidentifiable patterns that remain indecipherable to anthropologists. Art is integral to preliterate, tribal religious practice, and art certainly remains important to modern religions.

Christian churches always have a statue of Jesus on the cross along with Mary and child images. Elaborate stained glass windows suffuse the nave with light creating a sense of awe and sanctity. Yet art, like music and dance, has transcended into the mundane sphere and lost its sense of sacredness. Like the other ritual behaviors, its purpose and function continue to mystify. I examine some theories of neuroesthetics, which attempt to build a biological case for art appreciation. Then I look at existing evolutionary theories for art before showing how art as ritual behavior elicits emotion, which underlies every aspect of aesthetics regardless of theory.

Like ritual and religious behaviors in general, the function and purpose of the human predilection for art remains mysterious and controversial. The nature of artistic representations differs widely as do the explanations for why it engages people in all cultures. The exploration of art's meaning calls on psychology and evolutionary biology in addition, of course, to cognitive-level analyses by art critics. In this chapter I cherry-pick a few of the many proposed justifications for artistic participation to indicate their shortcomings while pointing out that they all acknowledge an emotional aspect. Given the intimate connection of art and emotion, I again draw on The Split Hypothesis to account for why humans are the only animal in which art exists and for whom it generates any response at all.

The oldest known cave drawings are estimated to be around 40,000 years old, which means this form of art existed at least eight times longer than any city-state (civilized) art forms. Archeological finds of powdered ocher, thought to be used as pigment for body ornamentation, date to 100,000 years ago, suggesting that humans may have performed aesthetic rituals far longer. Could a case be made that ritual burial was the first performance art? Not only were the dead buried, but they were often buried in east-west orientation and various artifacts were entombed with the deceased. A cave at Shanidar in Northern Iraq contained Neanderthal burial sites and has evidence of habitation dating back 100,000 years. Ralph Solecki and his team from Columbia University excavated the site and, at the 60,000 year level, found a grave containing several adults and an infant. Based on pollen samples from the excavation Solecki proposed that a body was laid on evergreen boughs and at least eight flower species were placed with it. In addition, some anthropologists think the flower types were not random but had medicinal properties or were colorful.

Burial is not normally thought of as art, but funeral rites and provisioning the dead show the people at that time had an aesthetic sensibility, which informs artistry. This is hugely significant as the first ritual burial constitutes a paramount cognitive delineation in human evolution. In order to bury their dead with flowers and other tributes, the Neanderthals or other early genus Homo had to have the self-awareness to recognize death as separate from life. The realization of a soul that continued to exist after death meant the body needed to be buried with accessories for the next life.

Higher-order consciousness retains the knowledge and awareness of the self and simultaneously others as separate from the self. The soul lives on because the memory of the person lives on. At the same time, mitigation for the angst of these realizations was forthcoming as religious ritual. Yes, the fear of death is a portion of the religious experience, but it's not the sole reason for religion any more than the urge to paint game animals on cave walls is. As Jungian psychologist Aniela Jaffé says,

> Man, with his symbol-making propensity, unconsciously transforms objects or forms into symbols (thereby endowing them with great psychological importance) and expresses them in both his religion and his visual art. The intertwined history of religion and art, reaching back to prehistoric times, is the record that our ancestors have left of the symbols that were meaningful and moving to them. Even today, as modern painting and sculpture show, the interplay of religion and art is still alive. (Jung, 1964, p. 232)

As humans approached the transition from hunter-gatherer to agriculturalist about 10,000 years ago, the amount and variety of art increased, or at least more was discovered due to its proximity in time. Not only were there more art forms, but aesthetics were worked into practical items. Pots and baskets had distinct patterns integrated into them. Bone awls had feather markings. Spears had animal head carvings. Adornments were not just practical for warmth and modesty—clothes also had modifications that distinguished one tribe from another, increasing in-group association. This aspect of traditional art, which persists in all aspects of modern society as well, is the motif, the patterned decorations applied to crafts and other human-manufactured creations. People in all cultures create abstract art that may or may not represent actual items but represent ideograms—symbols of an idea or thing.

The mandala and the Celtic knot are examples of designs that have their own significance apart from any tool or craft. The swastika was a popular design motif worked into artifacts throughout the world long before the Nazis appropriated it. Religious symbols like the cross and Star of David are simple line designs that have acquired immense significance in religious contexts. People learn to identify with their specific culture's motifs, but every person is predisposed to want to recognize and embrace those motifs, those artistic expressions used for communal accord. That requires a triggered emotional reaction based on familiarity and affiliation. There's nothing inherently appealing about motifs until metarepresentational meaning and emotional significance are applied to them. Motifs often garner association with gods or objects in the natural world, such as the sun or animals. Their real importance is the stimulation of feelings of amity and kinship within the tribe or identification with archetypal meaning such as being a brave, bear-like family protector. People assign meanings to motifs relevant to their culture, but the motifs themselves are ultimately just lines and patterns of color.

In modern times the sophistication and expansion of art's thematic content has blossomed. Art is integral to every culture and has transformed into very different forms and styles of expression, much of it irreligious. Artistic movements have resulted in various interpretations and schools: Romanticism, Impressionism, Surrealism, Abstract, and many more. Art critics and historians spend their time analyzing these different movements and styles which each have their own perspectives and meaning. Some of the art movements, like Romanticism, attempt to represent ideals or truths. Others promote points of view—propaganda—or capture an image for the historical record, and of course honor religious feeling. These viewpoints are high-level summations of particular trends and styles and are less than helpful for understanding the primal purpose of art. The arts are the shared communal property of the tribe and are where our aesthetic nature evolved. Art movements arising in recent history are derived from cultural changes, not biologically adaptive ones. These cultural displays don't eclipse the biological, only modify or elaborate them. Regardless of art movement, school, or period, the goal here is to find a unifying theme or purpose behind the creation and appreciation of visual art. We explore why art evolved among early Homo, but unlike our ability to view historically preserved art, we can only measure the effect of art on contemporary people.

## Beauty and Pleasure: Half the Story

To account for the ubiquity of art behavior, scientists and philosophers gyrate through a mental minefield. Placing the arts, and religion as well, into the paradigm of evolutionary biology challenges the best minds because the arts, very much like other ritual behaviors, are not utilitarian. Steven Pinker (2009) says art is useless in terms of behaviors that benefit survival and fitness and is incomprehensible to evolutionary biology. Although he is concerned with explaining the biologically adaptive mind, when faced with the seemingly unanswerable problem of how art and religion are advantageous and increase evolutionary fitness, he says, "that does not mean that I believe that everything the mind does is biologically adaptive." (p. 524) Ultimately Pinker says, art is a biologically pointless byproduct of the mind that borrows from the human propensity to pursue activities that activate our reward systems. "The visual arts are a perfect example of a technology designed to defeat the locks that safeguard our pleasure buttons and to press the buttons in various combinations." (p. 526) For Pinker art is like a parasite that avoids the host's defense mechanisms and latches on. In this case art attaches to the brain's reward system.

Pinker suffers from the same shortsightedness that Dawkins and others face when they accept that evolution would tolerate (in a non-anthropomorphic way) an expensive behavior that is not biologically adaptive. Pinker assumes that it's reasonable for art to trigger our reward systems because art is inherently pleasurable, but art is no more inherently pleasurable than dung is to dung beetles. Stimulation of neural reward centers may begin accidentally or randomly, but only persist over evolutionary time because, in the case of dung beetles, the animals evolved to extract energy from the nutrients they contain. Tooby and Cosmides (2001) rectify the argument by pointing out that for humans there's no intrinsic reason that certain visual perceptions should result in internal rewards.

These rewarding states of mind seem so natural to us — so obviously the product of the works of art themselves — that their existence seems to require no other explanation. But these experiences would not be possible unless the mind contained elaborate reward systems that produced them in response to some stimuli and not others...Evolutionary researchers want to know why the mind is designed to find stories [and other art forms] interesting. (p. 8)

The goal is to explain why the mind finds art rewarding rather than accepting as given that art should be inherently pleasurable. No other animal creates or appreciates art. (I don't care that apes and other animals can paint. It's meaningless in the natural world.) Why do humans have this "pointless" behavior if it doesn't increase individual fitness? When added to the other seemingly non-adaptive behaviors of music, dance, and mythology, art as accidental mind virus or pointless byproduct becomes particularly suspect. All these resource-sucking behaviors would not persevere without providing benefit, at least if you happen to accept evolution, the miserly accountant.

Are rendering beauty and deriving pleasure the primary response to and purpose of art? Picasso's *Guernica* is a great work of art, but "pleasure" would not be an adjective to describe experiencing it. Disturbing is more appropriate, so what is art if beauty and pleasure are not the only criteria? Can *Guernica* be called beautiful? Yes, in the sense that it's an expression of artistic skill and a stylized representation of, in this case, a horrific event. But what is the ultimate take-away? Many of Salvador Dali's surrealist paintings are unsettling, particularly his work *Face of War*. While we can appreciate the artist's rendering expertise, the immediate emotional response can be discomfort, revulsion, even fear. In addition, in the world of modern art, there are differences of opinion about the quality of artwork, so that while some may find the works of an artist beautiful, others find the same art callow, unskilled, and mediocre. Emotion is the only commonality to art, not beauty and pleasure.

Pinker (2009) cites overly sweet and fattening food (cheesecake) as evidence for non-adaptive behaviors that stroke our pleasure centers. But earlier in *How the Mind Works* he says,

> Before there was a sugar bowl, salt shaker, and butter dish on every table, and when lean years were never far away, one could never get too much sweet, salty, and fatty food. People do not divine what is adaptive for them or their genes; their genes give them thoughts and feelings that were adaptive in the environment in which the genes were selected. (p. 208)

If only he'd carried this through to his chapter on arts and religion. He's confabulating what is non-adaptive for the past several decades in modern society with what was adaptive for millions of years in all primate societies. It's fair to point out that what is adaptive at one time can become non-adaptive as the environment changes; however, Pinker uses this argument to posit that arts and religion are non-adaptive. Fewer than 100 years of environmental changes that possibly alter the appropriateness of eating large quantities of sugar, salt, and fat is not equivalent to artistic and ritual behaviors that arose as long as 50,000 years ago or more. The context of art has changed in modern times, but there's no reason to believe that this change in the contextual environment has changed the function of art. Even if partly true, people continue to enjoy and appreciate art for the same reasons they always have—emotional stimulation. That requires an adaptive, evolutionary explanation.

Not long ago the rigorous study of emotion, religion, and even consciousness were off limits because they were "soft science," but the gloves have come off, and they are all now fair fodder for research. This includes the arts, leading to the new discipline of neuroesthetics, which asks what is the neural basis of art? Making beauty and pleasure the goal or purpose of art prematurely sets an agenda for neuroesthetics. It assumes that brain pleasure centers and the beauty of art are in a subversive tandem, which, as I described above, is not the case. Art is not solely about beauty. The focus of this chapter is visual art, but music and dance are also art forms, which display beauty as well as other passions. Pinker, himself, alludes to the range of emotions elicited by different types of music and mythology; some music and stories can induce melancholy, pain, or pathos as well as happiness and joy. Some people like the thrill of riding a roller coaster; they like to be scared. It is more appropriate for aesthetics to be understood as causing any affective or feeling response, but changing this definition will have significant consequences to those who rely on beauty and pleasure to frame neuroaesthetic principles. This also suggests that emotion for the sake of emotion is desirable even if the feelings are negative. I don't mean to imply that thrill seekers really want to confront a masked person with a chainsaw, although mountain climbing or kayaking through rapids markedly increases one's risk of injury and death. Some people testify that they get a rush from challenging and overcoming high-risk tasks. Cheating death makes them feel more alive. I believe this has to do with activities that suppress consciousness, but that is anecdotal.

The Institute of Neuroesthetics at University College, London, "seeks to establish the biological and neurobiological foundations of aesthetic experience." (neuroesthetics.org) Fortunately, the Institute bases its efforts on three suppositions that don't restrict aesthetic valuation to beauty and pleasure.

- All visual art must obey the laws of the visual brain, whether in conception or in execution or in appreciation;
- Visual art has an overall function, which is an extension of the function of the visual brain, to acquire knowledge;
- Artists are, in a sense, neurologists who study the capacities of the visual brain with techniques that are unique to them.

Unfortunately, the Institute makes the overeager judgment that the function of visual art is to acquire knowledge although they are in good company. Pinker believes narrative fiction and the arts perform the knowledge function as well. The evidence, however, points to emotions as the end game of arts and mythology.

Is the predilection to visual art under genetic control? Does art improve people's survival and reproductive success or, as Pinker and others claim, are arts accidental byproducts of other functions? Pinker offers that the pleasure of art rides piggyback on the actions of the visual system—how the eye and brain cooperate to manifest cogent images. In order to examine the relationships between art, the visual system, reward centers and the brain in general, we look at the neural connections between vision and art.

## The Psychobiological Basis of Art Appreciation

The bases of art's thrall are physiological and psychological, which are not exclusive of each other. Researchers look at many different features to explain the attraction to art such as symmetry, simplicity, proximity, variability, order, and predictability. For example, in his paper, *Emotional Responses to Art*, Paul Silvia (2005) at the University of North Carolina, takes the psychological view that the appraisal of art and the resulting emotions are the bases of art's efficacy. Silvia describes the cognitive steps involved in determining interest after art appraisal. In this paradigm, the questions he explores are if and how much art appreciation is dependent on factors such as complexity, novelty, uncertainty, and conflict. In order for a person to be able to arrive at such evaluations, the person first has to appraise the object or event. Silvia says of the appraisal process,

> The first is a novelty check...Appraising something as new, unfamiliar, uncertain, complex, inconsistent, inchoate, and mysterious typifies this first appraisal...The second appraisal is a coping-potential check, which refers to an appraised ability to understand the new, unfamiliar, complex thing identified by the first appraisal. (p. 349)

Silvia describes experiments examining the relationships between appraisal, preference (pleasingness), and interest, and, in one case how complexity affects people's perceptions. The more complex a poem or visual artwork is, the less interest people show, although those who are better able to understand the content or meaning of complex items show higher interest in those items. While Silvia is correct that appraisal—subjective evaluation—is a necessary step in judging art or anything else for that matter, he stops short of connecting such appraisals to the brain's pleasure and aversion systems. "Emotional responses to art are traced to the unfolding of a set of cognitive appraisals, not to the operation of psychobiological reward and punishment systems." (p. 348) He rejects that cognitive appraisals are themselves dependent on and informed by those emotion-generating brain processes.

Appraisal describes activities common to any sensate animal who analyzes its environment to ascertain significance of external entities. For any animal, the world is complex and uncertain, and the nervous system is designed to construct a cogent world view by winnowing and parsing vast amounts of sensory information. People evaluate art, which results in emotion-based value judgments, but using these psychological processes tells us little about how or why art would have merit in the first place. We'll return to the psychology of art when we take a more evolutionary tack.

Pinker and other theorists equate the positive feedback between visual perception processes and the emotion centers as the underlying mechanism for the human apperception of pleasure or beauty. Ramachandran (1999) takes this approach to the significance of art by investigating the interaction of art and the visual system. In his article *The Science of Art*, with colleague William Hirstein, Ramachandran investigates eight visual laws or principles that influence our perception of art. Straddling the realms of neurophysiology and psychology, they investigate how sighted organisms select and refine visual information to quickly and accurately make sense of it and suggest that artists intentionally or unintentionally attempt to provoke specific visual responses using these principles.

The peak shift effect, for example, is the attraction to extreme or amplified characteristics. A baby seagull chick instinctively pecks at the red mark on its parent's bill, which incites the parent to regurgitate a meal for the chick. A long, thin brown stick with three red stripes is an example of the peak shift effect. It makes the chick peck at the marks more enthusiastically than one red mark even though the three-red-stripe stick doesn't look like an adult gull's head. Human examples of the peak shift effect are the Venus fig-

Figure 11.1: Woman of Willendorf, 28,000 – 25,000 B.C.E.

urines, carvings in which the oversized breasts and buttocks emphasize female secondary sexual characteristics. One of the most famous is the Woman of Willendorf estimated to have been made around 25,000 years ago. Ramachandran points to East Indian art from 800 AD that similarly depicts ample feminine curves as another instance of the artist using the female form to reveal the peak shift effect. What is it that makes the peak shift effect salient? The artist is exaggerating objects that already activate the limbic system, especially for males who are hard-wired to appreciate female secondary sex features. Like the three-red-stripe stick that excites the gull chick, the hyper-shapeliness of the Venus statuettes rouse the human male, and to some degree, the human female as well.

Visual detection and cognition are really a multitude of neural processes that contrive cogency from perceptions. Ramachandran points out that several of the artistic principles have the consequence of improving detection. Another visual principle, contrast extraction, is the propensity for certain visual receptive fields to attend to borders: highlight edges and reduce or suppress visual information that is homogeneous. The isolation principle uses contrast extraction and other mechanisms to highlight a single visual entity to amplify its signal and significance. This may partially account for the persistence of black and white photography as an art form. Both contrast extraction and isolation maximize efficiency and focus the viewer's attention. Organisms do this constantly as the world has far too much sensory stimulation to absorb. "This is why an outline drawing or sketch is more effective as 'art' than a full colour photograph," Ramachandran says. (p. 24) Without color information, the visual system has more resources to process edge detection and contrast. We integrate more content details in the image. Isolating visual information through contrast extraction and other visual processes helps the organism get to the essence of what's important about the sensory image.

Grouping, one of the eight visual principles, occurs when various objects in the perceived visual field combine to form an entity. When walking through the jungle, the visual field is awash with shades of green foliage, but the natives of the rainforest ecosystem are attuned to it and are able to detect objects of interest apart from the background visual noise. They are adept at visual grouping. Whenever an object coalesces in the visual field from among various visual points, the limbic system is excited. There's a reward, an *ah-ha* moment for identifying an object regardless of what's identified.

Binding, another of the visual principles, complements grouping. Once an image is extracted from the jumble of visual data, it is connected or bound to the entity it represents. This scenario posits two levels of visual perception and potential reward: the act of distinguishing imagery and then the analysis or identification of these objects. Each entails complex interactions between different brain modules and criteria that excite different aspects of the reward system. The grouping and binding abilities that detect a leopard visual object with its camouflage spots from amidst the foliage is a very important skill and assuredly increases fitness. The visual grouping of the object (SEPARATE FROM FOLIAGE) is a successful delineation that provides positive feedback in the milliseconds before binding occurs (LEOPARD!). They are separate processes that each provide a critical but different function, and each sends a different signal to reinforce the perception. Why should these visual properties of sighted animals have significance to art?

Ramachandran describes the relationship between these visual detection principles and the emotional centers as a two-way street, but in terms of art, his focus remains on the reward and pleasure centers. "There may be direct links in the brain between the [grouping and binding] processes that discover such correlations and the limbic areas which give rise to the pleasurable 'rewarding' sensations associated with 'feature binding.' " (p. 22) The act of perception and recognition provides neural reinforcement via the limbic system, which confirms the efficacy of the visual cognition. The organism perceives successful grouping because of positive, though not necessarily pleasurable, emotional response. The realization of an object in the visual cortex by itself has no feeling valence, which must be mediated further downstream by emotional brain regions. Assuredly the binding of the object to leopard sets off fear alarms, the amygdala being one of the neural response organs, but binding is a different pathway than grouping. Each process elicits different responses from the limbic and other emotional systems, which provide the affective sentiment that unconsciously informs and guides us.

Visual principles such as grouping and contrast extraction enable the detection of shapes and patterns. The peak shift effect draws on pre-existing dispositions to attract the viewer. So far the visual principles that Ramachandran lists are universal neural processes for all vision-enabled animals. There's nothing unique to suggest why human visual processes shared with other animals contribute to engagement in art. Pinker says images such as circles, squares, zigzags and other patterns trigger these perceptual analyzers, but again this is true for all sighted animals. Specific visual fields are designed to get excited by specific patterns. One receptive field fires in response to lines, while another fires for a line's specific angle or orientation, while yet another fires for the line's movement. Animals process images with analogous sets of receptive fields and neural mechanisms, yet they don't have any detectable response to anything humans would consider art. Ramachandran claims when the visual system identifies an object and the organism finds it interesting, "in some circumstances 'interesting' translates into 'pleasing,' " (p. 24) but animals can have similar positive emotional responses to "interesting" images. Processes shared with animals do nothing to help distinguish art and religion, which are uniquely human properties. The reward of detection, binding, or grouping is not the basis for why these patterns have artistic significance. The real question is, given the operational responses of the brain to visual cues, why do humans have any extraordinary reaction to inanimate, two-dimensional patterns of pigments or even three-dimensional stone sculptures?

A different aspect of the physiology of experiencing art is to measure the observer's galvanic skin conductance response (SCR), a measure of the autonomic nervous system's emotional response. SCR is one of the tests used in polygraphs, popularly known as lie detector tests. People have subtle but detectable changes that indicate an emotional reaction. Surprisingly, this has almost never been used to evaluate the effect of art. In one of the very few studies of the effect of art on SCR, a group at the National Aeronautics and Space Administration (NASA) showed subjects one of three artworks. One was a relatively realistic image of trees. The second was an impressionistic image of different trees, and the third was an abstract simple line drawing that looked somewhat like randomly placed stacks of pancakes. The control was a white panel. While exposed to an image, each participant performed a sequence of mental tasks that reliably induced stress (arithmetic, logical problem-solving, and creative thinking). While each mental task predictably raised the subject's stress level as measured by SCR, the amount of stress was mediated by the image. For the natural images — trees — the rise in SCR-measured stress was less than the control (white) image. The SCR was higher than the control for the abstract image, indicating the abstract image added stress. (Wise and Rosenberg, 1986) While this study doesn't tell us why people like art, it is apropos for determining which art moves people emotionally and, therefore, how art might impact the viewer.

# Evolutionary Theories of Art

In chapter 6 I submitted that anything that stimulates the pleasure centers is intrinsically adaptive by definition, but that includes the aversion and pain centers as well. The reward and aversion systems aren't just nice-to-haves. They are part of the essential adaptive and evolved behavioral complexes that ensure our continued survival. What happens if a non-adaptive behavior stimulates the pleasure centers? An extreme, contemporary example is drug addiction. Humans have figured out how to artificially excite the brain's reward regions; however chemical dependency results in higher mortality and lower reproductive success. As Richard Dawkins says, evolution punishes the smallest extravagance, and behaviors that don't contribute to fitness and reproductive success are winnowed away. Being vulnerable to pleasure center lock-picking is, in fact, detrimental. Stimuli that mimic reward systems without specific benefit are quite risky and lower fitness. Fooling the organism into performing non-adaptive behaviors by spoofing the pleasure centers will not be tolerated by merciless selection.

Pinker and others can't conceive how art is an evolved adaptation. Because he acknowledges that art sparks emotion, Pinker contrives a rationale for it. Lock-picking our reward centers is as creative an explanation as any other non-adaptive argument. Alternatively, some observers of the psychology of art attempt to show art *is* evolutionarily adaptive. Ellen Dissanayake (2011), whose ideas about ritual as ethology and the evolution of music were mentioned in previous chapters, has written several books and articles proposing that art improves evolutionary success. She hypothesizes two ways in which art benefits humans and is adaptive, both of which are also common explanations for how religion benefits people: reducing existential uncertainty and promoting the collective psyche of the tribe. Both are valid but fall short of an encompassing explanation for the adaptiveness of art. Why don't other animals require or utilize artistic behaviors? Or to turn the question around, why do humans need this adjunct to cooperation when thousands of animal species already have elaborate social interaction mechanisms? Why don't animals need to address their existential uncertainty?

Dissanayake proposes a common denominator to art: *making special*, which is defined in opposition to and relative to what is ordinary. Dance and poetry are art because movement or speech is exaggerated, embellished, and has a repetitive rhythm compared to "normal" behavior. Music similarly has, besides rhythmicity, variation in pitch which is far more varied than the speaking voice. *Making special* behaviors employ techniques like the peak shift effect, which use exaggeration to emphasize salient characteristics. *Making special* also avoids the problem of art as a means to promote beauty or pleasure. Some cultures encourage the application of body paint to skin, lips or fingernails, for example, or scarifying the skin with tribally-relevant patterns. These are forms of *making special* and attach meaning that is perceived emotionally. By distancing itself from normality, the effect of *making special* elevates art and design to have emotional valence or power. Dissanayake (2008a) gets it right because she acknowledges this essential role of emotions and offers that rituals are compelling because of associated aesthetic elements.

> I view ceremonial arts as the behavioral counterpart of religious beliefs. In this I also follow Radcliffe-Brown, who proposed that religion in small-scale societies was less a matter of beliefs than of rites, indeed that belief was an effect of rites...Beliefs and doctrines are like black and white outline drawings that require the color of emotion to become psychologically incorporated as a living, forceful presence. The arts in "rites" engage and shape emotion. (pp. 254-255)

This deemphasis of beliefs is in line with advocating for religious behavior from an ethological point of view. As discussed in the chapter on emotion and ritual, it's the actions of ritual that are not only measured and studied, but are informed by emotions, an important rationale in the understanding of consciousness and religion.

A criticism of Dissanayake's *making special* proposition is that it is vague and overly general, and she is keenly aware of this. In a response to critics, Dissanayake (2003) says,

> I don't define art as "making special," but in the sim-
> plest sense, I do think making special characterizes what
> artists of all kinds do. Even more, it describes a common
> trait that, in a Darwinian sense, is a noteworthy feature of
> human nature. My concern is to emphasize a simple ob-
> servation that evolutionary biologists tend to overlook:
> that humans sometimes are not content to leave ordinary
> reality alone. (p. 10)

At the beginning of this chapter I said that Neanderthal funerary
rituals may have been the first performance art. Burying the dead
in certain orientations with flowers and ornaments is clearly a case
of *making special,* which contributes to the emotional gravity for the
tribe performing the ritual. Dissanayake (1982) says,

> I do not then claim that one can *define* art as "making
> special," recognizing or conferring specialness. But this
> ability or propensity must be taken into account in any
> behavioral definition. I *will* claim that it is the root pro-
> clivity from which everything that we call art has come,
> and it seems to have appeared early in hominid evolu-
> tion. [Emphasis in original] (p. 148)

The sacred in Mircea Eliade's sacred and profane dichotomy is
eerily similar to *making special.* In Eliade's view there are special
times and circumstances that make places and events sacred, which
are different from regular or profane situations. Both concepts, *making special* and the sacred, tend to be defined in opposition to what is
not special and what is profane (not sacred), which devolves into a
circular definition. One only exists in terms of the other, but neither
is defined in its own right. I suggest the way to delineate them is
to describe sacred and *making special* behaviors as not directly contributing to survival in the classic sense. As I've said before, music,
art, dance, and mythology don't directly and obviously contribute
to the essential tasks of staying alive such as gathering food, building and maintaining shelter, defending the tribe, and, despite sexual selection arguments to the contrary, courting and mating. Yet
making sacred and *making special* are emotionally salient behaviors

not observed in other animals. Among the defining characteristics of the sacred and *making special* are that they are purportedly non-utilitarian yet adaptive human behaviors that elicit emotions.

*Making special* is a feature or motivational characteristic of art, but it still doesn't tell us why humans are attracted to art. The painting of a countryside is an optical illusion. It's a flat, two-dimensional plane with patterns of colored pigments applied to it. Yet when we look at a lush landscape illustration depicting soaring mountains, arching trees, and flowing rivers, we enjoy it because we can correlate the patterns to actual terrain and transfer that image content to the experience we have had of actually being in the midst of wild nature. We are binding images as metaphors to memories or feelings, which is the cognitive analysis that occurs after detection. But why should we have these pleasurable memories and feelings at all? Did we learn to like images of mountains, trees, and rivers? In his book, *The Art Instinct*, Denis Dutton (2009) makes a case why art is an evolutionary adaptation. He describes the attraction people have to landscapes that depict water, trees, animals, and people, which makes intuitive sense since these environments provide plentiful resources for a tribe to thrive. The allure of savanna and woodland, Dutton says, is not learned but is hard-wired having been acquired in evolutionary time. Dutton understands that humans evolved to be motivated by verdant habitats because tribes in those environments flourished, and we retain those desires as evidenced by recreational hiking and camping.

> The emotions felt by our distant ancestors toward advantageous landscapes are of little use today, since we are no longer nomadic hunters who survive off the land. Nevertheless, since we still have the souls of those ancient nomads, these emotions can flood into modern minds with surprising and unexpected intensity. (p. 27)

People like to go on hikes to look at expansive sweeps of mountain and valley as well as look at painted or photographed images of such landscapes, but we don't learn to like these scenes. Like a reflex, pleasure swells from adaptive emotional centers when we perceive forests and water. The ocean, too, is an abundant source of food and another vista of great enjoyment.

Pinker (2009) says, "the geometry of beauty is the visible signal of adaptively valuable objects: safe, food-rich, explorable, learnable habitats, and fertile, healthy dates, mates, and babies." (p. 526) However, neither Pinker nor Dutton address how reaping reward from observing rich flora is qualitatively different from what other animals experience. All animals desire and seek food-rich habitats and are programmed to recognize environmental cues that indicate favorable resources. All visual animals have neural processes that provide feedback to and from the limbic system when such pattern recognition takes place. Limbic activation gives meaning to perception and provides organisms with emotional direction at a nonconscious level. The positive feedback that animals experience from their preferred habitat is no different than what humans feel, but human feeling can rise to the level of conscious awareness. However, there's no basis to explain the human sensitivity to art by summoning pattern recognition, bilateral symmetry, novelty, variety and other visual neural mechanisms. Animals have the same visual neurophysiological mechanisms, but why did humans take aesthetics—emotional judgment—to a another plane? Beauty is a higher-order human interpretation based on a form of affective pleasure, but our animal relatives are concerned with beauty only insofar as it is a nonconscious, non-verbal emotional reaction, not a metaphorical abstraction. (Animals are selective about mates based on indications of reproductive potential, which in humans can incarnate as beauty.) It behooves us to distinguish between the primarily hard-wired perceptual apparatus and the elevation of aesthetics to art; why *making special?* Explaining art requires going beyond issues of perceptual processing.

# The Purpose of Art

The allure of resource-rich environments is an evolved predisposition, but that doesn't collate with any of the previous reasons given for why art is advantageous. Enjoying a landscape painting doesn't help explain or salve existential uncertainty nor does it help socially bind tribal citizens to each other. Landscape art is relished for its own sake based on emotional feedback and is one of the reasons art is compelling. And that annoying question remains: why did humans take the extra step of representing these images in the form of art and have emotionally salient responses? We can show two-dimensional pictures or paintings of ideal rodent landscapes to rodents, and they won't indicate any recognition or preference for them.

Dissanayake (2008a) points out that the human mind is qualitatively different from other animals in terms of learning, memory, foresight, imagination, and awareness while being less restricted by instincts. This leads to awareness of possibilities, inevitable unpredictability, and anxiety. She raises the appropriate concern that issues of human cognition must be incorporated into addressing art, ritual, and religion. "Uncertainty — leading to emotional investment or 'caring about' — was the original motivating impetus for the human invention of religion and its behavioral expression." (p. 19) She goes the extra step by calling out the emotional aspect. She realizes that art and religion have emotional provenance. The arts through ceremonial and ritual practices engage and shape emotion, which satisfies physical and psychological needs. "All these effects contribute to psychobiological homeostasis and thus to individuals' survival and reproductive success — i.e., fitness." (p. 22) Emotions are the actors in our play, and art serves to motivate them.

Like Dissanayake, Dutton (2009) recognized the human cognitive conundrum. Reiterating Cosmides and Tooby, he said, "The fact that human beings in the Pleistocene outgrew automatic animal instincts created problems of its own: confusion and uncertainty in choices available for action." (p. 120) He also understood the integral association of emotion and art. "This ready acceptance of emotion as coextensive with art, intrinsic to it, appears to be a bedrock fact of human nature and the nature of art; it could in principle have been otherwise, but it is not." (p. 122) Dutton cited the Harvard biologist E. O. Wilson (1998), who, in his book *Consilience: The Unity of Knowledge,* reasoned that human high intelligence,

> Gave early Homo sapiens a decisive edge over all competing animal species, but they also exacted a price we continue to pay, composed of the shocking recognition of the self, of the finiteness of personal existence, and of the chaos of the environment.
>
> These revelations, not disobedience to the gods, are what drove humankind from paradise. Homo sapiens is the only species to suffer psychological exile. All animals, while capable of some degree of specialized learning, are instinct driven.
>
> The dominating influence that spawned the arts was the need to impose order on the confusion caused by intelligence...When Homo-level intelligence was attained, it widened [the evolutionary] advantage by processing information well beyond the releaser cues. It permitted flexibility of response and the creation of mental scenarios that reached to distant places and far into the future. The evolving brain, nevertheless, could not convert to general intelligence alone; it could not turn into an all purpose computer. So in the course of evolution the animal instincts of survival and reproduction were transformed into the epigenetic algorithms of human nature. It was necessary to keep in place these inborn programs for the rapid acquisition of language, sexual conduct, and other processes of mental development. Had the algorithms been erased, the species would have faced extinction. (pp. 223-224)

Wilson's term *epigenetic algorithms* refers to the emotion-guided, combined influence of genetics and cultural learning on human development. Social behavior is an example of such development that draws on perception, memory, and emotional coloring, which biases the choices people make. Certain outcomes are more likely than others. It isn't a level playing field in the land of inheritance and conditioning.

Wilson, Dutton, and Dissanayake all comprehend the paramount human condition, that higher-order consciousness, or high intelligence as Wilson calls it, brought risk and drawbacks as well as advantage. The final step in this logical sequence is how religion and ritual, including art, solved this fundamental problem.

> There was not enough time for human heredity to cope with the vastness of the new contingent possibilities revealed by high intelligence...The arts filled the gap. Early humans invented them in an attempt to express and control through magic the abundance of the environment, the power of solidarity, and other forces in their lives that mattered most to survival and reproduction. The arts were the means by which these forces could be ritualized and expressed in a new, simulated reality. They drew consistency from their faithfulness to human nature, to the emotion-guided epigenetic rules...The arts still perform this primal function, and in much the same ancient way. Their quality is measured by their humanness, by the precision of the adherence to human nature. To an overwhelming degree that is what we mean when we speak of the true and beautiful in the arts. (p. 224)

Wilson alludes to early people's attempt to control their environment through magic. He cites cave paintings in which the animals are depicted as having arrows or spears through them and suggests the cave art projects and symbolizes people's goals and desires. Magic is a means people use to try to control outcomes, and hunters are trying to control the success of their hunt and to gain confidence. That may be true, but early tribal art exists in many more forms than cave paintings. Are tribal-specific patterns on pottery and baskets done to use magic to fill them with food? Are blankets similarly patterned to protect their wearers? Maybe, but even in tribal societies, there are too many ways art is used to claim it is just for magic.

Besides, magic is not a exactly a biological entity. The reason for art has to start with the emotional response, not the interpretation of meaning such as magic, which is a higher-order rationalization.

Another problem is that Wilson says humans invented art as if it was a choice. This is the dung beetle dilemma again because it assumes that by creating art, people will naturally have an emotional response. There is no inherent reason why art should suddenly elicit emotions in early tribal people just because someone *decided* to create art such as cave paintings. Wilson addresses this problem saying the choice to create art ties into the emotion-based epigenetic rules, especially the innate aspect "of adherence to human nature." Somehow early humans engaged in art that happened to align with adaptive emotions. He's nibbling around the important issues of emotion and adaptation, but he doesn't need to cite "control through magic" as a means to improve people's status. Wilson correctly identifies the need to retain fealty to emotion-guided human nature. It's simply that rituals such as art incur adaptive, innate emotional response and quiet consciousness.

Wilson, Dutton, and Dissanayake each lay out the same basic explanation for the development of art and ritual religion: these behaviors are the result or consequence of the downsides of newly evolved human cognition. All three recognize that emotions are embedded aspects of ritual and religion. They all implicitly suggest that ritual art had the consequence of coping with higher-order consciousness. Humans developed art and religion as a means to manage the vexations raised by contingent high intelligence, but it wasn't a choice; it was an evolved adaptation.

The mechanism that gives motifs and art meaning is that these images can be symbolic or representative of entities other than the image itself. This association of images and ideas beyond the actuality of the image itself is metaphor, which is one of Ramachandran's eight visual principles, and the only one that isn't a function shared with other animals (except the great apes perhaps). Art as metaphor is a feature that, though dependent on the mechanistic neural processes common to all visual animals, is powerfully important in humans. Metaphor is possible in humans because they developed cognitive powers to perceive the self in opposition to non-self, the first essential dichotomy, so they can then symbolize other things they observe as separate from the things themselves. They can create representations of their mentality, their archetypal impulses. Wilson identifies archetypal projections, a type of metaphor, as a vital result of human brain evolution.

> Certain thoughts and behavior are more effective than others in the emotional responses they cause and the frequency with which they intrude on reverie and creative thought. They bias cultural evolution toward the invention of archetypes, the widely recurring abstractions and core narratives that are dominant themes in the arts. Examples of archetypes...are Oedipean tragedy...and the serpent images of myth and religion. (pp. 217-218)

Artistic images evoke feelings that arise from our ancient, inherited mythic well and mix with experience. A landscape is just one of many images residing in the collective unconscious, just as sexually provocative images of the preferred gender cause arousal. For art that represents realistic objects—nudes, melting clocks, paintings or sculptures of infant Jesus and mother Mary—the emotional impact results from the affective meaning of the objects to the viewer, the personal associations and experiences overlaid on innate predispositions—Wilson's epigenetic rules. The artist's stylistic presentation greatly influences the manner in which art is interpreted and felt. Clocks, while real, don't normally melt. Salvador Dali triggers analogies (metaphors) with his painting *The Persistence of Memory* by playing with the melting clock images. When people create and view art, the symbolic representations stir up a combination of archetypal forces and learned connections, and it is the human ability to create metaphor that makes this possible.

Patterns that represent real things easily invoke affective associations, which is why many people find modern art that veers from realistic depictions challenging. Piet Mondrian and Jackson Pollock are the epitome of artists whose abstract paintings are the antithesis of realism. The art critics describe Mondrian's rectangular patterns that only use black, white, and the three primary colors as

Figure 11.2: Mandala pattern

breaking down the visible world into its most fundamental, minimalist structure—horizontal and vertical elements that represent the paradigm of opposites. The simplicity of the straight edges removes distractions from the viewer, some claim, and reveals objects' essences. Pollock became famous for throwing or splattering paint onto canvas. Critics are divided as to the quality and historical value of his paintings although his works have sold for millions of dollars.

Any art, but particularly abstract art whose content evades conscious recognition through binding—the images can't be given obvious labels identifying what they are—can be like gazing into a fire and getting lost in it, spacing out. The seemingly arbitrary patterns in folk and tribal art can often lead to mild dissociation, the feeling of disconnection or detachment. It's the opposite of binding, of making a connection to a known thing. What abstract art does, as do motifs in general, is what all ritual does: besides inducing emotions it interferes with higher cognition such as working memory. Viewing art, whether realistic or abstract, can impede the flow of consciousness much as music and dance does. Artistic enhancements sometimes have repetitive patterns of blocks and lines, which intrigue and appeal to us but without any clear association. They are found in furniture, fabrics, baskets, and pottery; whatever humans make is usually adorned with aesthetic flair. Abstract art evinces connections personal to the viewer, and people draw their own meaning and interpretation similarly to how a Rorschach test is used or how someone might relate a cloud's shape to a face, animal, or other object. Artwork stirs emotions and intrudes on awareness consciousness, which has the corollary consequence of limiting the purposive internal dialog. This dissociation integrated with the suppression of higher-order consciousness is characteristic of all ritual. We'll discuss dissociation further in the next chapter on prayer. I make this claim about art based on the skimpiest of evidence, but The Split Hypothesis is proposed first in order for experiments to be designed to test it.

The action of creating metaphor is part of what establishes something as sacred or making special. The sacred act or object assumes a significance beyond its mundane existence. Dutton (2009) explains how the most ordinary things can assume importance. "Rocks are passive recipients of action, not initiators of it. Stories are essentially about agency and emotion, which generally rules out a central place for rocks as main characters, unless they can be converted metaphorically or symbolically into humanlike entities." (p. 117) The human ability to create metaphor is an enormous topic unto itself. It is at once a consequence and cause of human higher-order consciousness. It begs us to ask how metaphor fits into the evolutionary story of humanity. It may be that metaphor is a more essential and defining characteristic of Homo sapiens than even religion, but that is a discussion for a different day. (See Lakoff and Johnson, 1999, for an in-depth discussion of metaphor.) For now, metaphor is the mechanism that makes art vital. Metaphor is the cognitive tool that attaches emotions to art by transforming the commonplace with affective spirit. Art as a consequence of metaphor brings out the emotional content of visual imagery. Based on the premise that tens of thousands of years of emotional responsiveness to art can't be a fluke, mistake, or accidental lock-picking, we would still like empirical confirmation that art and other rituals improve human evolutionary fitness. To test this we would ideally like to observe that people who indulge in art in various forms compared to those who don't are more evolutionary successful. That is a high bar, but as in other ritual forms, we can observe that art improves people's lives in tangible ways.

## Art Therapy

The proposals for the evolution of art are disparate and far-flung showing nothing close to any kind of consensus. I, of course, propose that art evolved as a means to elicit emotions and overcome the distraction of consciousness, but much like mythology, art behaviors do not lend themselves easily to biological analysis. Indeed, art is a half-step beyond even mythology in our ability to link it to biology, and very little effort has been made to study the biology of art behavior. If it evolved, we need to show it is beneficial and improves fitness. The efficacy of art therapy is a first step towards establishing the facilitative role of art.

The American Art Therapy Association (AATA) advocates the creative process of art-making to enhance physical, mental, and emotional well-being. It is based on the proposition that artistic self-expression helps people to resolve conflicts and problems, develop interpersonal skills, manage behavior, reduce stress, and increase self-esteem. To support its efforts, the AATA publishes an *Art Therapy Outcome and Single Subject Studies* summary of art therapy research. It lists abstracts of studies that show improvements from art therapy for a wide variety of ailments and conditions including abuse, chemical dependency, traumatic brain injury, and developmental disabilities. The favorable outcomes due to art therapy are described in terms of positive behaviors such as increased attention, coordination, and self-esteem with less depression, anxiety, and impulsive behavior. In the study *Relieving Symptoms in Cancer: Innovative Use of Art Therapy*, (Nainis, 2006) researchers found art therapy alleviated eight out of nine psychological distress symptoms. There is no claim that art therapy helps cure cancer, but it significantly reduced pain, tiredness, and anxiety while improving appetite and well-being, suggesting art therapy is a valuable psychological tool.

Also appealing is the cancer and art therapy paper's rationale for how art therapy works.

> The objectives of art therapy are to use the creative process to allow awareness and expression of an individual's deepest emotions...The meaning and the power of these emotions often are not easily articulated using verbal communication. It is the art itself that provides a vehicle for expression. (p. 163)

It always comes back to emotions, the systemic behaviors that ensure evolutionary success. Art therapy creates conditions that enable patients to integrate their emotions in ways that aren't easily available to them as they mull their situation. What is it about human nature that necessitates additional mechanisms to elicit emotions? Are these benefits convenient coincidental consequences of lock-picking the pleasure centers, or is there a selective advantage to those who evolved to leverage ritual to overcome the shambles of consciousness? As of yet, there's little evidence that art acts to suppress consciousness.

Another attraction of The Split Hypothesis for those who abide by science is that it keeps universal human behaviors such as art, mythology, music, and dance within the sphere of evolutionary theory rather than making them exceptions. Fitting religion and ritual into a Darwinian framework avoids the myriad, ill-advised machinations scholars go through to account for them. Still, we need to have more measurable physiological indicators for art and other ritual behaviors so research can determine more precisely how they impact working memory, thinking, and other aspects of consciousness. To promote The Split Hypothesis to the rank of theory, research must show not only that ritual and religion elicit emotions, but which emotions happen, under which circumstances, and how these emotions promote fitness.

In the next chapter we arrive at the last ritual form to be discussed, prayer, a behavior that, like mythology, is virtually synonymous with religion. Unlike mythology, though, which in modern times has non-religious aspects, prayer is effectively always associated with religion.

# Chapter 12

## Prayer: Self-help for the Original Sin

The function of prayer is not to influence God,
but rather to change the nature of the one who prays.
*Soren Kierkegaard*

The last ritual I discuss is prayer, a decidedly religious behavior that requires faith and belief. Because prayer and religion are so closely intertwined, I interchange them liberally in this analysis. Despite this, everyone, even the non-religious, find themselves beseeching external entities for favor at one time or another. We look at the effects of prayer, which show that religious practice, on average, results in being healthier and happier. Also importantly, we look at the functions and purposes of prayer, one of which is that prayer is a self-administered placebo. We review the biology of placebo and religion's ability to not just provide psychological confidence and optimism, but to induce actual physiological enhancements. Then we examine some other behaviors that I somewhat arbitrarily lump into prayer—meditation, trance, and other activities identified as altered states of consciousness. All these aspects of ritual behavior do the same thing: reduce or dissociate consciousness from standard cognition.

The most common ritual activity associated with religion is prayer. In most every religion, people recite verses, both alone and in a congregation, as a quiet, inward activity, or with movements like singing, dancing, bowing, or kneeling. Petitionary prayer is the act of propitiating the gods and beseeching external forces for benefit, whether solace, comfort, or specific entreaties for aid: cure me of this disease, help me win the affections of my desire, help me score a goal so I can get a better contract next year. But for those who ask for favor, prayer is usually a two-way street. The supplicant knows she must offer God a bribe to be blessed by the big guy. "If you do this for me, I'll [quit smoking, lose weight, go to church, stop parking in handicapped spaces.]"

Not all prayer explicitly seeks aid. Many forms are simply expressions of adoration and dedication to a higher power. Praise prayer can simply be a remembrance that "I believe in you, and I subject myself to do your will." Many adjuncts accompany prayer. In Catholicism alone there are rosary beads, candles, incense, and, of course, images of Jesus, the cross, the Virgin Mary, and a plethora of saints.

Like other rituals, prayer follows Van Gennep's pattern of separation, transition, and incorporation. Going to church, temple, or mosque is to enter a holy place, which separates the individual from the mundane world. Once in the sacred sphere, the rituals, including prayer, begin. In this transition or liminal phase, congregants communicate with God or other numinous spirits. Communion is received, the prayers are recited, and the service completes. Leaving the church is the incorporation phase and the return to the secular world. Of course people don't need to go to church to pray, but the ritual pattern still holds. When people pray at home, they close their eyes, bow their heads, and perhaps put their hands together. This movement establishes the separate, sacred space and makes the moment special. Muslims prostrate themselves in prayer, which alters the environment for communing with God. While it may not be controversial that prayer is a religious ritual, the function of prayer is a bit more esoteric. Does prayer have a real effect on the supplicant? If so, how does prayer work and why?

Note: Intercessory prayer, praying to higher powers on behalf of someone else, has generated a great deal of interest in some corners. In this book, praying to help another person is of absolutely no concern. Only the effects of praying on the person doing the praying are discussed here.

## Efficacy of Prayer

Despite the perception of appealing to an external agent, the praying person attempts to alter her psychological stance, to change her own feelings. This once again raises the role of emotions on health. Emotional health also has implications for physical health. What is anecdotally called the mind-body connection is a very intricate interaction between neural and hormonal systems. In the chapter on emotions we saw how emotional health has an important impact on behavior and even intelligence. A compendium of studies shows that stress and depression inhibit the body's immune system and ability to fight disease.

> People who experienced chronic anxiety, long periods of sadness and pessimism, unremitting tension or incessant hostility, relentless cynicism or suspiciousness, were found to have double the risk of disease — including asthma, arthritis, headaches, peptic ulcers, and heart disease. (Goleman, 1995, p. 169)

The chapters on mythology and art were low points when applying biological methods to analyze ritual actions, but prayer lends itself to psychophysiological study much like music and dance. An avid and active research community has produced a prodigious body of research that focuses mostly on the psychological benefits of prayer. The results of these studies, not surprisingly, vary as there are many modes of prayer and ways to evaluate it. Much of the research literature is driven by Christian ideology, and religious authors strive to make a case for the benefits of Christian prayer. Despite their biases, we shouldn't necessarily discount their work.

Harold G. Koenig, M.D. (2008), author of *The Healing Power of Faith*, testified to the U.S. Congressional Subcommittee on Research and Science Education about religion, spirituality, and public health. Koenig promoted the premise that religion is a coping mechanism for dealing with a variety of maladies or anxieties, and people turned to prayer for dealing with depression, stress, and other emotional disorders. Based on his review of thousands of studies, greater involvement in religious activities in general resulted in lower rates of alcohol and drug abuse, crime, delinquency, and cigarette use as well as more physical exercise and other positive health practices. Religious practice led to improved outcomes for medical conditions such as cardiovascular disease, cancer, immune and endocrine function, HIV/AIDS, and other infections. Religious people were slower to develop age-related cognitive impairments like Alzheimer's, recover from surgery quicker, and had longer lives. Koenig acknowledged that the studies were far from unanimous in showing health benefits, but anywhere from 60% to 90% of the study categories showed some efficacy.

To offset the fervor for religion and prayer as medical treatment, a group from Columbia University in New York criticized the methodology and conclusions of many of the studies. The authors pointed out esoteric but important procedural issues such as failure to "control for multiple comparisons" or "for confounding variables and other covariates." (Sloan, 1999, p. 665) In part this means using measures such as frequency of church attendance and prayer, religious denomination, or degree of religious orthodoxy as the basis for improved outcomes paints with a broad brush. There may have been other lifestyle or demographic influences that affected the subjects that weren't adequately considered. When the studies were adjusted to take these issues into account, the efficacy of religion and prayer wasn't as pronounced, although in many cases, some amount of benefit remained.

As significantly, the conclusions of many of these studies were correlational, not causal. Francis and Evans (1995) admit that "while such studies [of the subjective effects of prayer] may demonstrate the beneficial nature of prayer, they cannot demonstrate the causal efficacy of prayer." (p. 377) That same broad brush insinuates that religious faith may be only one reason for boosts to health and well-being. Psychological-based studies do not show that prayer or religious practice are the direct basis of improvements.

Nevertheless, there remains a broader pursuit in many universities to understand the psychology of religion. Academics evaluate issues such as measure of religiousness, attitude formation, the development of moral judgment, and a slew of other psychosocial perspectives. They describe the cognitive aspect of spirituality from an observational point of view without the benefit of much evidence. "There are few hard empirical data supporting such results, but a substantial body of testimony and considerable theological and psychological theorizing maintain them." (Meadow, 1984, p. 120)

Such is the nature of investigation into the religious psyche, which is why descending into the underlying biological causes is more fruitful. Studies avoiding vague psychological parameters and focusing instead on direct physiological measures carry empirical clout. In one such physiological example, European collaborators compared the effects of reciting the Ave Maria prayer in Latin or a yoga mantra on subjects' breathing, blood pressure, and cerebral circulation. The researchers began by stating how they came to design the experiment.

> We serendipitously discovered that reciting the Ave Maria prayer and yoga mantras enhances and synchronizes inherent cardiovascular rhythms because it slows respiration to almost exactly six respirations per minute, which is essentially the same timing as that of endogenous circulatory rhythms. (Bernardi, 2001, p. 1446)

Lowering the breathing rate has positive effects on a variety of cardiovascular and respiratory functions such as blood pressure, oxygenation of the blood, and exercise tolerance that indicate overall health. "Slow respiration may reduce the deleterious effects of myocardial ischaemia [precursor to heart attack], and, in addition, it increases calmness and wellbeing." (p. 1447) Both the Ave Maria prayer and the yoga mantra slowed respiration to around six breaths per minute, which happened to coincide with a natural circulatory rhythm called the Mayer wave associated with improved cardiac and circulatory outcomes. The authors conclude, "The rosary might be viewed as a health practice as well as a religious practice." (p. 1449) While this study shows one form of prayer has efficacy through changing breathing rhythms, there are many other methods of prayer so the results cannot be inferred to apply to all prayer. As always, much more research needs to be done, but enough evidence exists to validate continued research into the relationship between prayer, religion, and psychophysiological health.

A different aspect for the study of prayer centers on brain scans. Newberg (2002), scanned the brains of praying nuns and Buddhist meditators to see which regions were either activated or inhibited. Interestingly, some of the papers on the benefits of prayer and religion include meditation practices since many find that meditation and prayer have similar characteristics. In his study, Newberg found both differences and similarities in the brains of meditators and prayers. The differences, Newberg says, were because the nuns silently prayed with thoughts of words compared to the Buddhists who meditated to empty the mind. Newberg labels these variations as the passive and active techniques for communing with the sacred. In the passive approach, used typically in meditation, the goal is to rid the mind of all thoughts and ideas. This means ignoring any input whether external or internal and results in silencing of the conscious mind. This is exhibited in brain scans by the inhibition of the attention association area in the prefrontal cortex. In the active approach, instead of clearing out thoughts, the praying person concentrates on a mantra, a saint, a chant, the image of God.

> The process begins just as in the passive approach, with the attention association area translating, into neurological terms, the conscious intention to pray. But in this case, since the intention is to focus more intensely upon some specific object or thought, the attention area facilitates, rather than inhibits, neural flow. (p. 120)

Where the active prayer and passive meditation techniques are similar is in their inhibition of the orientation association area (OAA) of the posterior superior parietal lobe. The OAA is responsible for the perception of oneself in space in order to navigate through the environment. People with damage to the OAA have difficulty moving in relation to the objects around them. They bump into things and have trouble with the most elementary tasks like sitting in a chair. The OAA then is involved in the perception of physical self and non-self objects. The meditator suppresses or loses the perception of self in terms of her surroundings.

> We discovered that both the nuns and the Buddhists...were able to deliberately reduce activity in their parietal lobes while meditating. Thus, it should come as no surprise that these individuals describe themselves as entering a state of timelessness and spacelessness, states commonly associated with spiritual, mystical, and transcendent experiences. (Newberg, 2006, p. 151)

The degree of blockage in the OAA for different types of prayer covers the spectrum, so a full mystical experience is one end of the transcendent moment while unconscious entrainment—bowing up and down or other rhythmic movements during prayer—is another.

Brain scans during prayer are a valuable addition to understanding the biology of prayer as is prayer's connection to physiology, as we saw in the Ave Maria prayer and yoga mantra study. Prayer, meditation, and, undoubtedly, other introspective practices alter brain activity in predictable ways, but there remains a big gap between these relatively shallow insights into prayer and its observed augmentation of well-being. Synchronization of breathing is a mechanism to improve circulatory health, and though this one example provides a reasonable appreciation of how prayer modifies physiology, we still have no real explanations for the potency of the many other styles of prayer.

Many of those who are indoctrinated in their faith embrace the stories of people who've been healed through prayer and belief. Religious people believe higher powers watching over them intervene in their lives to aid them. Researchers who study people with more religious involvement find the devout, besides being healthier, friendlier, and more cooperative, have better marriages and higher life satisfaction. (Koenig, 2008) For people to say the reason that the religious profit from prayer and devotion is because faith in God strengthens them becomes a self-fulfilling prophecy. People ask God to help them do what they already wish to do. It reaffirms what they already know and desire. Sensing that God blesses them provides the motivation to achieve their goals. It is through belief that religion leverages its health benefits. Although we mostly don't know why or how praying to and believing in God(s) reaps mental and physical rewards, we need to look at faith and belief, themselves, as creating the modes for reaping psychic rewards.

In Chapter 4 about the problem with consciousness, I referenced Daniel Wegner's idea that the human inability to accurately determine causation for one's own actions led to the belief in supernatural powers. People created gods primarily for attributing actions to external entities. There appears to be an additional mechanism for allegiance to spectral forces, which may tell us something about how people gain from prayer and religious practice: that belief, itself, has material consequence by means of the placebo effect, which is another way to overcome the handicaps of consciousness.

## The Placebo Effect

The placebo effect is a person's belief or expectation that a medication or procedure will lead to improvement of medical symptoms despite the drug or treatment being inactive or nonfunctioning. Most people understand that a placebo is a fake or non-effective treatment that fools a person into believing she is getting real medicine. A placebo can be an inert compound masquerading as a drug, a sham procedure, or simply the word and confidence of a medical professional or authority figure claiming a favorable result. It is the placebo effect in the form of religious faith that causes people to have superior health relative to non-religious people. This is also true in tribal societies where shamans or the tribal version of a health practitioner treats patients with a combination of native herbs and ritual. The herbs or other nostrums may or may not have therapeutic impact from a western science perspective, but the faith in the treatment enhances the outcome.

The purpose of dissecting the placebo effect is to show how be-lief leads to physiological changes, which fleshes out how religious faith results in benefits. The consistency with which prayer affects the brain as revealed in scans is a big step in that direction, but brain changes by themselves aren't enough to demonstrate how prayer and other religious behaviors are advantageous. Showing a link between religion and the physiology of health demonstrates how prayer and religious belief are evolved adaptations. Establishing that religion makes people healthier and less vulnerable to disease is an evolutionary boon and clearly increases fitness. But do scien-tists know how the placebo effect works? Is the brain so powerful that it alters a person's physiology? Why can't people consciously will themselves to health? Why do they need prayer and faith that is ultimately based on emotional, irrational relationships with mytho-logical beings?

Those who investigate the placebo effect caution that there are some misunderstandings about it. For example, inert compounds and communication of confidence in a treatment do not cause the effect. Rather, it's the patient's belief or expectations in the curative power that results in the healing. At the same time we will see sci-entists who define a type of placebo effect that is the result of condi-tioning, a form of learning. In this case, expectation is not the driver of the medical outcome.

Teasing apart the placebo effect gets even thornier as there are other aspects to consider. The placebo effect is used as a control in drug studies. To test the effectiveness of a drug in clinical develop-ment, half the subjects might get the real drug and half the subjects might get a sugar pill or other inert substance, but in neither case do they know which one they received. If the subjects who didn't get the drug but believe they did show changes that the drug is intended to cause, there's a chance that they have a placebo response, meaning they get better without the real drug. But people in drug or therapy studies may also improve for reasons other than either placebo or the drug being tested, which have names such as regression to the mean, spontaneous recovery, or demand characteristics—the ten-dency to comply with experimenters' expectations. (Wager, 2005b, p. 175) How much effect was really due to the drug, how much was due to the subjects' belief they would get better, and how much for other reasons? In addition, there are the investigators who claim that some reported placebo effects are due to reporting biases and statistical artifacts, so, as is usual in any scientific endeavor, there are disagreements and controversies.

With these caveats out of the way, there seems to be consensus that legitimate placebo effects are observed for Parkinson's disease, depression, and in particular, for pain. According to University of Colorado psychology professor, Tor Wager, (2005a) many other conditions are likely susceptible to the placebo effect but research so far is less than conclusive. (p. 23) University of Turin neuroscientist Fabrizio Benedetti (2005) reviewed the evidence for placebo's impact on depression and found a significant effect although a real drug treatment, fluoxetine (prozac), performed better to relieve depression than the relief experienced in the placebo group. Also, the actual drug had a wider impact on various brain regions than the placebo-induced brain changes. Nevertheless, "brain changes with placebo response, in fact, most closely match the active drug-response pattern to which it was experimentally yoked (conditioned)." (p. 10398) In other words, the placebo effect closely mimics the physiological action of actual drug treatment.

The role of placebo on pain has been well studied, and in many cases placebos reduce not just the perception of pain but the actual pain itself. Benedetti showed that the placebo effect impacts the brain's endogenous opioid system, the natural built-in painkillers, by acting on the prefrontal cortex, nucleus accumbens, anterior cingulate cortex, and anterior insular cortex brain regions. Not surprisingly, these regions are also part of the brain's reward system. The placebo effect—when people expect they will receive pain relief—alters pain perception by stimulating the opioid brain regions just like the pain-killing drugs. However, in the placebo instance, it's utilizing the endogenous, internal neurochemicals to activate the pain relief rather than exogenous pharmaceuticals.

> Expectation of analgesia is an important factor in the engagement of objective, neurochemical antinociceptive [anti-pain] responses to a placebo and, furthermore, that

these processes appear to involve the expectations of the perceived analgesic efficacy of the placebo, an effect that is mediated by endogenous opioid neurotransmission. (p. 10394)

Placebo is a *natural* painkiller that leverages existing pain-suppression systems.

Wager (2007) performed neuroimaging studies and found placebo-induced increases in opioid activity in similar limbic and paralimbic areas as Benedetti. Placebo subjects reported less pain, which corresponded to larger observed brain activity. "Overall," Wager said, "placebo treatment had widespread effects on endogenous opioid activity in cortical and subcortical regions critical for the determination of affective value and context-based control of pain." (p. 11060) Placebo relief was effective for both the psychological expectation of pain and the actual physiological pain. The placebo effect impacted the emotional aspect of pain as well.

Parkinson's symptoms—tremor and rigidity—are caused by damage to dopamine neurons primarily in the basal ganglia. Dopamine is necessary to stimulate circuits from the basal ganglia to the motor cortex that results in movement. We saw in the chapter on dance and movement that dance can alleviate some Parkinson's symptoms. Placebo-induced expectations have also led to improvement in Parkinson's patients. Raúl de la Fuente-Fernández (2001) and his team at the University of British Columbia told patients they were receiving an anti-Parkinson drug that would improve their movement, but some received a placebo. Results showed "evidence for substantial release of endogenous dopamine in the striatum of [Parkinson's] patients in response to placebo. Our findings indicate that the placebo effect in [Parkinson's] is powerful and is mediated through activation of the damaged nigrostriatal dopamine system." (p. 1164) Placebo in Parkinson's, like other placebo effects, activates built-in brain chemistry similarly to the real drugs, in this case by boosting dopamine production or potency. The placebo effect alters actual neurotransmission and is more than just "wishful thinking." The striatum of the basal ganglia is also part of the brain's reward system. For this reason de la Fuente-Fernández proposed the placebo-reward hypothesis specifically linking the placebo effect to the reward system. "Converging evidence from animal models and human imaging studies [implicates] the ventral striatum and orbital frontal cortex in the expectation and delivery of reward during various conditioned learning paradigms." (Benedetti, 2005, p. 10398) Placebo piggybacks on some of the same reward pathways and mechanisms that are involved in emotion regulation.

A functional non-drug therapy for Parkinson's is deep-brain stimulation in which electrodes are implanted in specific areas of the basal ganglia. Applying current to the electrodes can reduce the symptoms of Parkinson's, but those electrodes can also be used to record neuronal activity. Benedetti found that patients who positively responded to placebo experienced beneficial changes in neural firing patterns compared to subjects who did not respond to the placebo. "There was a nice correlation between the subjective reports of the patients, the clinical assessment of the neurologist, and the electrical activity of single neurons" for the placebo responders and nonresponders. (p. 10392) In other words, when the placebo didn't help, the neural firing rate didn't change, and the patients showed no outward motion improvement, whereas those who reacted positively to the placebo—exhibited better mood and movement—had improved neural firing.

The opioid system that is often the target of placebo action influences a wide range of physiological functions such as "the regulation of central stress responses and pain, hypothalamic-pituitary regulation of reproductive and stress hormones (e.g., ACTH and the immunologically active cortisol), and the adaptation and response to novel and emotionally salient stimuli." (p. 10393) This suggests that placebo may have more far-reaching ramifications. An entirely new field has arisen at this intersection of disease, brain, and behavior called psychoneuroimmunology. Psychological well-being, physiological health, the immune system, and the brain form an intricate and complex network that scientists are just beginning to wrap their heads around. Where it was once thought that the immune system and the central nervous system (brain and spinal cord) had little interaction, it is now known that the immune system has complex bidirectional communication with the brain and the endocrine system as well. For example, in a study by Robert Ader (2003) at the University of Rochester, mice were given cyclosporin A, an immunosuppressant used to prevent rejection of organ transplants, and a flavored drink. After repeatedly pairing a conditioned stimulus—a flavored drink, and the cyclosporin A—the unconditioned stimulus, the flavored drink alone produced a suppression of immune function. The conditioned immunosuppression response is a type of placebo effect because the flavored drink by itself has no immunosuppression function yet it stimulated physiological changes that it would not normally do.

This conditioned placebo response in animals is a different type of placebo effect than what we've been discussing up to this point, which is based on expectations. The general consensus is that expectation placebos won't work in animals since animals aren't aware of and don't anticipate the effects of a placebo or even an actual treatment. Alternatively, is there evidence that humans are susceptible to conditioning placebos? Efforts to perform such studies on humans found that "conditioned enhancement in human subjects are more difficult to implement than studies in animals and have yielded inconsistent results." (p. S52) Despite this, conditioning placebo effects in humans have been observed for childhood asthma and nausea due to chemotherapy. (p. S54)

If the conditioning placebo effect works on humans, patients do not need to know what is happening to them or believe that they are receiving a treatment. Conditioned patients exhibit the placebo effect through unconscious training. "The placebo effect seems to be a phenomenon that can be learned either consciously or unconsciously, depending on the system that is involved." (Benedetti, 2005, p. 10391) The interaction of conditioning and expectation in the placebo effect is even more complex according to a review by Stewart-Williams and Podd (2004) at Massey University in New Zealand. In many cases the two types of placebo effect may complement each other, making it more difficult to discern the influence of each. It may even be that expectation, itself, is based on conditioning. Expectation may not be the basis of the placebo effect at all, although the authors decide that expectancy is its own medium. "Classical conditioning is sometimes mediated by the creation or adjustment of an explicit expectancy, whereas in other cases the [conditioned stimulus-conditioned response] link is not mediated by conscious cognition." (p. 333) Ultimately, Stewart-Williams and Podd find that expectation stands on its own. "In some instances, such as the enhanced placebo analgesia...it appears that this conditioned placebo effect is mediated entirely by consciously accessible expectancies." (p. 338) While the debate rages as to the significance and mechanism of the placebo effect, there is enough evidence that at least some placebo effect in humans works through unconscious conditioning in addition to conscious expectation.

I indulge in this examination of the placebo effect because it is the mechanism that abets the potency of prayer. In the first part of this chapter, I reviewed evidence for the enhancements in health and well-being from prayer and religious belief. Do the strong indications for actual physiological changes due to both the placebo effect and prayer establish a case that prayer is a form of placebo? If prayer is shown to have some health-improving consequences and the expectation placebo effect leads to benefits as well, is this an example of the transitive property of mathematics. If A=B and B=C then A=C? Perhaps I'm stretching the analogy a bit, but the essence holds. Both the placebo effect and prayer can directly influence the brain's reward system as well as induce other physiological changes.

The next step is to directly test if prayer causes placebo-like effects. Such studies are fraught with methodological challenges, although many could be mitigated by thorough controls, as is done with the more sophisticated placebo experiments. The greatest problem is how to establish consistent prayer behavior. While placebo researchers can deliver specific doses of drugs or inert compounds, it isn't as easy to measure an amount of prayer even in a lab setting. Do different people pray with the same fervor and intention? Does the same person pray with equal intensity at different times? Despite these problems, the question is well worth pursuing. With experience the variables can be better understood and controlled.

For the expectancy placebo effect to work, does a priest or evangelist have similar sway as an authority figure such as a doctor or researcher? Can a person change her own attitude and health simply by stating a goal to achieve? The praying person could do this saying, "This medicine will cure me," or "God, make the medicine work for me." People petition God for succor, and some likely gain traction from their entreaties, but not just because they ask.

We think our consciousness intercepts the primarily verbal cues from prayer or from medical professionals or researchers who "apply" the placebo, but it isn't that simple. The critical operations in the reward center, which can drive real bodily changes, take place beyond conscious knowledge. Whether expectation is generated internally or externally, we don't know how to communicate to our own physiology, how to direct our internal processes. We don't have conscious access to the strings that pull this function or that mechanism. People are not privy to the source of their intrinsic emotions and find it nearly impossible to instigate or direct affective, consciously intended feelings at will.

While I describe instances where the placebo effect works, many functions are not susceptible to the placebo effect and even when a placebo does work, it doesn't necessarily work for all people. Simply delivering the message doesn't make placebo effective. The placebo effect and prayer work beneath awareness and beyond the reach of intention. Consciousness, in its ability to enable sophisticated communication, makes it possible for the self-healing apparatus to hand off the message, but thinking, by itself, doesn't achieve the goal. The patient—the praying person—has to believe, which happens on a non-rational, feeling level and transcends consciousness. A person who is more likely to have a positive placebo response and medical outcome has a more emotional and less conscious interaction with placebo stimulus. When the doctor says the treatment will work, the patient must believe it emotionally, not intellectually. When we say a person is optimistic and confident, we're saying that person has emotions of optimism and confidence. People must exercise their emotional systems, which, in some cases, are employed through religious belief and ritual practice. Being assured of therapeutic potency conveys the placebo message through affective means, stimulating neural activation of limbic and frontal cortical areas. The reward system is part of the infrastructure that serves behavior including ritual and religion. Consciousness may be a way station that interprets the message after the fact, but that message is handed off in an unconscious way that is opaque to the patient or subject. The more consciousness speaks, the less force the placebo effect carries.

My heuristic, my rule of thumb, is to ask why the placebo effect based on expectancy and prayer has any effect at all? Belief, central to human behavior, religious and otherwise, is also germane to the placebo effect, but why should it be? It's remarkable that humans evolved belief and faith in such a way as to so manifestly effect the dopamine reward system through prayer and placebo. This rather oddly evolved psychophysiological susceptibility didn't have to happen. It would be easy to imagine living life without it, but since it is pervasive, we are confronted with explaining this relationship between the brain's reward modules and belief. Just as we saw that ritual behaviors like music and dance achieve prominence in the human repertoire through activation of the pleasure centers, so, too, do prayer and the placebo effect. Accessing the reward system resulting in improved health and well-being directly attests to evolutionary selective advantage in people who maintain faith and belief. Placebo exists and is conserved because it activates the brain's limbic and prefrontal emotional pathways just like ritual behaviors. When viewed in this way, we can only conclude that prayer and the placebo effect evolved to stimulate adaptive emotional systems. Nothing other than evolution by natural selection would have led to this intricate complex. Anything that stimulates the brain's reward system for thousands of generations is inherently advantageous and adaptive. Indeed, all other explanations falter. These adaptations were only necessary because of the pitfalls and distractions of higher-order consciousness.

## Altered States of Consciousness

Humans display a range of behaviors termed altered states of consciousness (ASC), that, from a purely rational point of view, seem pointless and even non-adaptive, much like some claim about religion. There are so many forms and names for this spectrum of behaviors, ranging from dream consciousness to meditation to sleep and sensory deprivation to mystical ecstasies and catalepsy. Sometimes people refer to ASCs as spiritual higher states of consciousness, which muddies the meaning of consciousness. Trance or possession states describe a wide variety of ASCs typically associated with shamanic healing practices or rites of passage in tribal societies. The possessed person, often a shaman or mystic, is overtaken by extreme emotional frenzy and thought to be under control of outside forces or to be on a spirit quest traveling beyond one's normal plane of existence. "The shaman specializes in a trance during which his soul is believed to leave his body and ascend to the sky or descend to the underworld." (Eliade, 1964, p. 5) Trance is often induced by intense dancing or other exhaustive physical exertion, although other stimuli can lead to trance as well, such as extreme pain, fasting, drugs, or other stressors. Some of these dissociative states cross over into psychosis in terms of modern psychological convention, but they all describe rather universal behaviors.

I group these practices into this chapter on prayer for several reasons: they are often a form of entreaty to an externally-perceived, unearthly power; some of them are behaviorally and ritually similar to prayer; and some have physiological effects similar to prayer. These behaviors are integral to religious ritual in traditional societies and are brute force methods for inhibiting or altering higher-order consciousness. Of course, the practitioners of ASCs themselves see the proximal reasons to attain such states of dissociation from consciousness as helping to interact with their deities.

> In traditional societies—and to a considerable extent in modern societies as well—the context in which such (ASC) patterned states are viewed most often by the people concerned is one that we may broadly call "religious." I mean here that altered states tend to be spoken of in connection with supernatural entities such as "spirits" or "souls." (Bourguignon, 1973, p. 3)

Not only do ASCs assist with contacting the divine, but they perform pragmatic matters as well. "Practices that induce altered states of consciousness are often considered spiritual healing practices, since they are based on spiritual and supernatural beliefs in tribal societies. However, they can also be seen as psychological healing practices, or even psychotherapies in some cases." (Thomason, 2010, p. 1) Regardless of type of ASC, they all change the normal sense of being and put a damper on higher-order consciousness. Newberg (2002) says of praying nuns and meditating Buddhists,

> The mystical experiences of our subjects—the altered states of mind they described as the absorption of the self into something larger—were not the result of emotional mistakes or simple wishful thinking, but were associated instead with a series of observable neurological events, which, while unusual, are not outside the range of normal brain function. In other words, mystical experience is biologically, observably, and scientifically real. (p. 7)

Transcendental meditation has therapeutic value. Hundreds of studies attest to the benefits of TM specifically for health and cognitive function, and there are other types of meditation such as some forms of yoga that lead to benefits as well. TM itself requires training in order to perform and maximize its effectiveness. TM teachers recommend practicing for 20 minutes twice a day by concentrating on a mantra. "Sit in a comfortable fashion. Let your body relax and be at rest. As best you can, let your mind be quiet, letting go of plans and preoccupations. Then begin to recite inwardly the...phrases directed to yourself." (Kornfield, 1993, p. 19) When people enter into transcendental meditation practice, they are usually aware of the stated benefits of TM, a placebo suggestion, but people are typically unable to immediately turn off their stream of consciousness discourse, which is why meditation takes practice. People can't consciously turn off the mind's chatter at will. Mastering meditation is somewhat paradoxical because most of us don't know how not to try to achieve a goal. (Let go the conscious mind, Luke.) The esteemed Zen philosopher D. T. Suzuki (1994) said about the meditator,

> Let him not be concerned with ideas good or bad. Let him concentrate himself on the koan [Zen riddle], which is to think the unthinkable by going beyond the realm of thought. When the exercise is kept up persistently for a

sufficient space of time, disturbing thoughts will naturally cease to assert themselves and there will prevail a
state of oneness, which is however not to be understood
conceptually. (p. 105)

How do you not think about the white bear? So many of these spiritual practices including an abundance of new-age, self-help healing
techniques advocate turning off the thinking mind and going to a
place of mental blankness, what I called the null frog mind back in
the introduction. This is not accidental. The conscious mind interferes more than it aids and precipitates real physiological vexations.
This meditative mode of dissociation specifically targets the stream
of white noise in our heads.

Rites of passage and healing rituals can induce various types of
ASCs. The Salish Indians of the Pacific Coast use a variety of techniques to fix what they call spirit illness, which Western culture would
label as depression. These techniques include,

Sensory deprivation, sleep deprivation, kinetic stimulation, sonic driving [intense, persistent drumming], emotional arousal, and fasting, resulting in hypoglycemia
and dehydration. The physical training process includes repetitive dancing, drumming, hyperventilation,
increased motor activity, and exposure to extreme tem-
peratures. (Thomason, 2010, p. 3)

This Salish ritual, like most all ritual, adheres to Van Gennep's
three-step process. The first step, separation, is intended to symbolically kill off one's old life. The initiates are taken to a special
"smokehouse tent" where the torment begins. For four days the initiates are blindfolded and,

Subjected to kinetic stimulation (lifted up and dropped,
carried around, and whirled about) and acoustic stimulation (loud rapid drumming, rattling, singing, and
howling). This process is repeated four times until the
initiate is weak, pale, rigid, and appears lifeless on the
ground. The initiates...must lie still, cannot talk or move,

and have to fast (although they are teased and tested by people holding tasty bits of salmon held close to their mouths). (p. 3)

The next phase is physical endurance in which the poor souls swim in icy waters, run long distances barefoot, sometimes in snow, and dance endlessly to the drum, which drives them into an altered state receptive to witnessing the appearance of a guardian spirit in a dream or vision. While the initiates are in this liminal, second stage, low point of the rite, they receive the tribal mythological doctrine. Reintegration occurs when the initiates receive new clothes signifying their new adult role in the tribe and the cure of their spirit illness.

These practices that border on torture are taken to even further extremes in mortification rituals that intentionally induce suffering or pain in order to change waking consciousness. Self-flagellation is practiced by some Christians to honor the scourging of Christ and to atone for their sins. An annual crucifixion reenactment is performed in the Philippines, in which nails are literally driven through hands on a wooden cross. The Native American Sundance was made famous in the movie, *A Man Called Horse,* and is based on a real ritual. The initiate is lifted off the ground by ropes attached to animal bone or wood inserted under the pectoral skin. Typically these painful rituals lead to alterations in consciousness, which is believed to bring the initiate closer to the Great Spirit. Many tribal cultures practice scarification rituals during rites of passage, circumcision being a common one. These mortifications are a type of personal sacrifice, which venerates the deities, and hence is a form of supplication or prayer.

Sacrifice, which functions to propitiate the gods, need not be brutal to induce an altered state of consciousness. Sacrificial practices often involve offerings of food or other gifts to deities. Jews fast on Yom Kippur as do Muslims during daylight in the month of Ramadan. Proffering something of value to the divinities is a kind of economic transaction. I give you food, drink, tobacco, or abstinence, and in return you bring the rain for robust crops, buffalo for hunting, healing for sickness, or strength and courage to gain advantage in war. Literally "to make sacred," sacrifice, like ritual in general, creates a sacred space within which the participants can transcend to a spiritual plane. Once removed from the profane world, the sacrificers are immanent (at one) with the holy. The sacrosanct forces are powerful and not to be trivialized. All prescriptions must be followed exactly so as not to upset the gods and to be able to attain the consecrated state. Even modest sacrifice changes consciousness if only slightly. This act of propitiation sets a different mentality where regular, mundane rules don't apply, and the sacred activities are mandated and strictly enforced. The act of sacrifice suppresses ego desires, the normal state of affairs in consciousness, in service of the holy. Turning outward or away from the self changes the sacrificer's viewpoint. In a mundane perspective removed from religious context, sacrifice refers to an altruistic or selfless act on behalf of others. When spiritual, the sacrificer feels removed or insignificant in relation to the awesomeness of the powerful spirits. When profane, sacrifice puts the needs of others before the self.

Daniel Wegner (2002), who proposed that the invention of gods is due to the human inability to accurately assign causation, dedicated a chapter in his book, *The Illusion of Conscious Will*, to the phenomenon of hypnosis. According to Wegner, hypnosis works because of the human propensity to be swayed by others. "The induction of hypnosis is no different, in principle, from any attempt at direct social influence." (p. 273) The characteristics of inducing hypnosis in many ways resemble preparing for meditation. Being open to hypnosis requires relaxation and focused attention, but "hypnosis may be another version of the placebo effect," Wegner says, "a way in which people behave when they think something is going to have an influence on them." (p. 282) For example, skin warts have been shown to respond to both placebo and hypnosis treatments and maybe for the same reason. Pain, too, is modulated by both hypnosis and the placebo effect.

While hypnosis is not normally lumped into the same bucket as religion, a case could be made that forceful preachers and religious cult leaders exert the kind of influence that amounts to hypnosis. That kind of mental dominance is not a characteristic of intrinsic religion per se but is endemic to human nature in general and is commandeered by charismatic clergy and politicians. At least in some cases, though, hypnosis is used to help people deal with addiction, pain, and other issues susceptible to placebo or social influences. Wegner believes hypnosis derives in part from the loss of the sense of voluntariness, the perception that the cause of an action is not based on personal will. It is experimentally possible to make people believe they cause actions when they don't and don't cause actions when they do, and hypnosis leverages the latter. When a hypnotized person acts according to the hypnotizer's instructions, the act feels like it's motivated by an external force rather than by the hypnotized person, herself. "The presence of the hypnotist as a plausible cause of one's behavior reduces the degree to which one's own thoughts are interpreted as candidate causes and so reduces the sense of conscious will." (p. 308) This indicates a dissociation of ego consciousness and is another instance that describes how the conscious ego, where we think volition occurs, is rolled back in favor of unconscious processes. Our inherent suggestibility is an adaptive feature that may aid in social cohesion, but the mechanism by which this occurs happens in the unconscious and, under hypnosis, constitutes another example of an altered state of consciousness.

> The hypnotized person has the unique ability to achieve certain sorts of control over the mind and body that are not within the capability of the waking individual. It is as though in hypnosis a normal layer of conscious controlling apparatus is cleared away to yield a more subtle and efficacious set of techniques. A variety of self-control techniques that work without the exertion of conscious will—such as the response to placebos and expectations—may be models for the sorts of control that become available in hypnosis. (p. 311)

Altered states of consciousness feed directly into the maw of The Split Hypothesis that, on a regular basis, humans need to move out of their normal, conscious space and into a nonconscious place that happens to excite a panoply of emotions. Over and over again, whether through altered states, other religious rituals, or in other areas of life, the same theme arises: suppress, redirect, shut down, deviate from consciousness. Higher-order consciousness brings humans a wider range of cognitive options, but as much as it empowers people with a certain freedom from environmental constraints, it also raises difficult awareness of choices: fear, doubt, indecision. Religion co-evolved with consciousness and brought relief with belief unencumbered by conscious cognition. You didn't have to worry or think about the right thing to do, the correct action to take. Religious faith blotted out the negatives of dichotomous consciousness, brought ritual to the fore, and allowed innate resources to emanate. The actual behaviors that emerged from the development of religion rode shotgun on the brain's existing limbic and prefrontal pathways. Prayer and the placebo effect were adaptations that arose from this relationship between religion and the brain, between belief and reward. Humans evolved to engage in ritualized activity to leverage unconscious emotions, where most of the real business of living takes place.

# CHAPTER 13

## EPILOGUE—THE BEST BIOLOGY WE HAVE

Heaven and hell are within us...All the gods,
all the heavens, all the worlds, are within us.
*Joseph Campbell*

Those interested in the source of human religion and who don't depend on belief in supernatural entities ask, why did people acquire religion? To what ends or purpose did this seemingly irrational set of behaviors satisfy? Was is a glorious accident or did it have evolutionary intent? The existing theories for the derivation of religion each address a piece of the puzzle. For many, religion acts to bind groups of people socially. Others see religion as primarily acting to assuage the anxieties and concerns that arise from people asking existential questions. Why are we here? What is our purpose? In a similar vein, some believe religion acts to alleviate general fears from natural causes like impending death or other potential or actual disasters. Religion plays a part in all these aspects, but there is a more fundamental foundation that links them all together, which I have introduced as The Split Hypothesis—the adaptation in which intrinsic religion evolved as a compensating mechanism for consciousness, eliciting emotions, and suppressing the so-called rational, intelligent mind.

*it does do that, But adaptive? in the Darwinian sense?,*

255

## Standing on Shoulders

Despite the relatively new findings from biology and psychology on the role of the conscious and unconscious, one might have expected that there would have been a bit more foreshadowing of The Split Hypothesis of religion before now. The theory of the coevolution of consciousness and religion did have some predecessors, however. Carl Jung, Mircea Eliade, Joseph Campbell, and others understood the limited role of consciousness in human affairs and the instinctual nature of the human mind but lacked an evolutionary background and Darwinian perspective. Also predicting The Split Hypothesis was the book *The Dual Brain, Religion, and the Unconscious* by Professor of Psychiatry Sim Liddon (1989). Liddon drew upon William James' assertion that religion was an "invasion" from the unconscious. He adduced that strong emotions caused a shift from reason and conscious awareness to feelings that arose from the unconscious. This is reflected in the brain's two modes—the Gestalt, symbolic mode and the rational, thinking mode. Based on this dual brain model, Liddon realized that religion derived from emotions and was expressed by means of the non-linear holistic brain. Religion, he said,

> Is experienced primarily as feeling, rather than as an element in a rational structure. The image is felt as it reflects its connotative feelings, and expresses in symbolic form the feeling aspect of one's inner life. In such a case awareness lacks the assumptions of time, natural cause, and separateness of items in the world, which disrupts what we ordinarily experience as conscious awareness. As an "invasion" from the unconscious proceeds, the image within one's focal awareness becomes primarily a symbol of feelings, and the influence of structured understanding recedes into the background. (p. 166)

While he was on the right track, his approach was, like Jung, psychological, and it wasn't his purview to draw a broader stroke by addressing religion and the dual brain from a biological or evolutionary perspective. He also lacked all the research that had accumulated since his book's publication, although he did appreciate and include in his book the significance of Sperry and Gazzaniga's split-brain experiments, which helped establish much of his thesis.

The many scientists who have uncovered and described the intricacies of human brain function both before and after Liddon—Libet, LeDoux, Damasio, Ramachandran, Panksepp among them—realize that consciousness is not the controlling force in human life, and, in reality, is far less significant than most people assume. Timothy Wilson, John Bargh, and Daniel Wegner elaborate this theme of the automatic nature of human behavior and how our everyday existence is driven by the physiological mechanisms rendered through the spectrum of homeostatic emotions. These are some of the many scientists who indirectly contributed to The Split Hypothesis, but even without their work, the religious functions of Homo sapiens are evident intuitively. It is apparent through observation that religion suppresses higher-order consciousness and stimulates emotions, but to reach this realization requires breaking the ego lock of consciousness domination and deducing evolutionary justification. *what is it?*

This book couldn't have happened without those who managed to shed the shackles of the behaviorist dogma that dominated much of the twentieth century. I already alluded to the influence of Robert Ardrey and Desmond Morris, but a shout-out also goes to E. O. Wilson, who, in his landmark book *Sociobiology*, proposed that humans had instincts, that human behavior was not strictly enculturated. He received a great deal of criticism for this because it threatened people's sociopolitical beliefs, particularly the belief in the unlimited potential for human advancement. However, in the decades since Wilson first offered this, advances in genomic science amass and continue to confirm genetic contributions to behavior. *Darwin agreed*

Pinker and Dawkins, on the other hand, while great evolutionary biologists, are stuck without a good reason why religion is adaptive. Like the religious believers who leverage mythologies to acquire explanations for natural occurrences, they reasonably attempt to fill this cognitive deficit and engineer a story for the genesis of religion. Unfortunately, they contrive the non-adaptive byproduct solution of religion, which is peculiar and out of character for good scientists otherwise completely imbued in Darwinian evolution. The *Social glue. Yes* *non-adaptive?!*

non-adaptive byproduct—a questionable application of an idea with paltry scientific justification—leaves religion on the outside of evolution as a disowned bastard child. It's time to bring religion in from the cold and treat it with the same evolutionary gravity as any other set of animal behaviors. Or do these important scholars maintain the anthropocentric view that humans are substantially different than all other life forms so that exceptional new rules are needed? It's time to pull religion back into the evolutionary fold and hold fast for an adaptive story for the range of religious and ritual behaviors.

## Paradoxical Answers

Among those with the greatest vested interests in preserving the idea of the dominance of consciousness as a primary cognitive device are the academics and intellectuals, the philosopher-kings who (theoretically) use it the most and have the most to gain by maintaining its status. Scholars sustain the precedence of consciousness as the means to examine and analyze their disciplines of interest and perhaps even solve some of the big philosophical problems.

University professors are hardly alone in their prejudice that consciousness is a superior cognitive force. Most people, including myself, have the intuitive sense that their consciousness provides an interface to the environment where sensory input is mixed with historical memories, and the rational thinker calculates the next action. And on top of that, people are aware of and remember their actions and their intent. They sense their own control and volition in this process; they are aware that they are aware. People disbelieve that the most important aspects of their behavior are driven by unconscious processes. People just *know* that their consciousness is in charge. Consciousness tells them that this is so, except that consciousness is a deceiver. Consciousness takes credit for actions and obfuscates the truth. In a cruel irony, consciousness figuratively sits atop the brain and reports that it accomplishes actions and makes decisions, yet the scientific evidence tells us that it isn't so. This essential contradiction makes it difficult for people to accept that the monopoly claimed by higher-order consciousness is a

*finger bonding?!*

*yes*

problem and that religion acts to submerge it. While it's true that higher-order consciousness distinguishes humans from the rest of the animal kingdom, what's not true is that higher-order consciousness is solely beneficial and accurately informative.

Even Jung (1933) was conflicted about the role of consciousness. On the one hand he understood that the nature of consciousness was duality and awareness of life's struggles: to know pain and suffering, to be enlightened to the existence of problems. At the same time, he felt humans must engage their rational mind in order to overcome the challenge of duality. *Why a challenge?*

> The artful denial of the problem will not produce conviction; on the contrary, a wider and higher consciousness is called for to give us the certainty and clarity we need...When we must deal with problems, we instinctively refuse to try the way that leads through darkness and obscurity. We wish to hear only of unequivocal results, and completely forget that these results can only be brought about when we have ventured into and emerged again from the darkness. But to penetrate the darkness we must summon all the powers of enlightenment that consciousness can offer. (p. 111)

While Jung acknowledged that both a return to the darkness of the unconscious and its partnership with consciousness are necessary for people to cope with and integrate The Split, he intimates that the role of consciousness is at least as important as delving into the unconscious and perhaps even more necessary for healing.

In *How the Mind Works*, Pinker (2009) describes the shortcomings of human cognition and, in the process, he reveals the pitfalls of subsuming a theory of religion within rational consciousness: that a function of religion is to generate answers to life's quandaries. Pinker points out that, despite thousands of years of debate, "our minds lack the equipment to solve the major problems of philosophy." (pp. 562-3) He attributes this failure to resolve the metaphysical issues to a deficiency in human cognitive equipment. The human mind, Pinker says, is limited in its capability, which is clearly true, but he also makes the wholly unwarranted assumption that at

Yes

least one role of religion is to solve the same epistemological dilemmas that conscious human cognition is unable to do. "Beliefs about
a world of spirits...are hypotheses intended to explain certain data
that stymie our everyday theories," (p. 557) as if the purpose of religion is to replace rationality when its actual role is to suppress it.

different?

A different example Pinker cites as an instance of acquiring knowledge or garnering answers is fiction. The purpose of narrative stories, he says, is to role-play various possible scenarios in order to
anticipate community interactions in advance. Pinker suggests that
identifying with fictional characters prepares for strategic social intercourse and is not for decoding epistemological riddles, as he suggests consciousness and religion should. From Pinker's point of
view, religion and fiction are, for the most part, disconnected and
unrelated because the type of information sought is different.

NO

Pinker doesn't address if fiction's internal mental rehearsal works
more on a conscious awareness level or an unconscious emotional
level. Does the organism attempt to consciously acquire and process
knowledge about group interactions similarly to seeking answers
to the existential dilemmas or through intuitive, emotional operations? If the answer is that fiction elicits emotions through empathetic identification with characters in stories, then it would seem
that fiction and mythological ritual do not strive for factual or logical knowledge. If Pinker believes that fiction's (and therefore ritual
mythology's) role-playing function are incarnations of innate psychological tendencies augmented by theory of mind and sometimes
subsequently brought to conscious awareness, then perhaps he is
right; mythologies provide information to engender adaptive emotions and resolve the discordance of consciousness. What is

Born

it is
sold as
factual

this?

True

If religion functions to answer the existential mysteries in a logical or empirical way, it does a miserable job. It makes no sense that
religion and rituals like mythology and art should provide evidence-
based information as Pinker and others suggest. A thing called God
doesn't exist tangibly outside the human brain. A turtle does not
carry the world on its back, and Anansi the spider did not deliver
stories from gods to people. These myths are human fabrications.
Religion piles one set of fantasies on top of another by invoking all
kinds of imaginary beings and situations. If religion attempts to ex-

Bible

True

*TRUE*

plain the unknowable or the unknown, it does so with irrational and illogical answers, or, at best, metaphorical ones. Yet Pinker never-theless claims that our insufficient cognition shows religion's inad-equacy, so religion is not useful for rationally solving the big mys-*TRUE* teries. "[The human mind's inability to solve the epistemological dilemmas] does not justify religious or mystical beliefs but explains why they are futile." (p. 563) *Yes*

Well, that's exactly right, but the underlying supposition that re-ligion's function is to solve epistemological dilemmas with rational answers is wrong in the first place. Neither higher-order conscious-ness nor religion may be able to resolve epistemological dilemmas, but some philosophers and scientists say religion should be able to. Philosophers use cognitive tools within the rubric of higher-order consciousness and the central executive that provide logic and think-ing to attack the metaphysical quandaries. If the human rational mind is incapable of solving the big mysteries, certainly religion isn't going to either.

But within all this is this crazy paradox that asks, due to con-sciousness's insufficiencies, why should we expect consciousness to solve *either* the riddle of consciousness itself *or* the riddle of religion? And aren't I a pretender to this intellectual position by writing this book? Aren't I my own paradox? If consciousness is a weak and sub-servient tool of human cognition, how can I propose this hypothesis using my thinking and logical consciousness? How can any scien-tist make any progress if our consciousness is so impotent and fu-tile? But it's not. Despite its inadequacies, consciousness is still a powerful force, and no one is ready to or even capable of abandon-ing consciousness. Despite its deficiencies, consciousness is still an important device for thinking and rationality, in conjunction with our innate emotional intelligence. After all, we didn't achieve send-ing rockets into outer space, monkeying with genomic DNA, and splitting atoms without our consciousness. But it took a few million years growing our brain and developing this new cognitive niche to get to this point. Cultural change seems to be moving extremely rapidly right now, but for 99.9% of human existence, change was piecemeal. And it's far from clear if the upsides from these great accomplishments will be offset by the downsides.

This leaves us in the odd position of using the scientist's toolset that consciousness affords us to decipher the universe's puzzles, despite our misgivings about our limited cognitive abilities. It helps that we can now offload much intellectual inquiry to machines; let inanimate devices do the difficult detection and measurement work of scientific investigation, which obviates the normal prejudices and other shortcomings of the human mind. It's not perfect, but it's the right and necessary direction. The more we can remove human cognitive bias, the more we can be confident in empirical results.

Pinker (2009) extricates himself from this dilemma somewhat differently by stating that modern philosophers need to decipher the small, solvable issues until such time as the bigger issues become amenable. While acknowledging that our minds lack the ability to solve the big ticket questions, he, like many others, believes that consciousness can ultimately be an effective means to comprehension. The big philosophical problems "are perfectly tractable, and I see no reason that we should not have decades of progress and eventually a complete understanding" of them. (p. 563) That's undoubtedly true, but that isn't evidence for or against the relationship between higher-order consciousness and religion. It just means that science is a legitimate method to ask and answer the questions.

Many origin of religion writers recognize that religion elicits emotions, but invariably they assume that that is reasonable and doesn't require further explanation...except there is a very big reason, which is why should it? Emotional responses are evolutionarily adaptive behaviors and honed by natural selection. That begs for evolutionary appraisals of the selective value of religious emotions. Why isn't that line of thought more actively pursued? For those who don't believe religion evolved, it isn't a necessary pursuit in the first place. For some it isn't the intent to answer the role of emotions in religion but is a side note to other issues. Most of those who explicitly discuss the interactions between religion and emotion start with religion first and examine how emotion serves the religious function. They pose the question in reverse with religion as the target of inquiry and emotion as one of the supporting players. The proper question, at least evolutionarily, is why religious behavior impacts or affects emotions? But because the perspective is backwards, the necessary question can't be asked and answered, and a unifying theory of religion is unattainable.

The Split Hypothesis stages the argument that consciousness and religion co-evolved out of singular human cognition as separate but parallel entities, but that is a conceptual convenience, an artificial device to present it. Like all aspects of the brain and behavior, consciousness and religion are interdependent. That doesn't mean, however, that consciousness subsumes religion. Many people have the mistaken belief that the spiritual is inferior and ultimately owes allegiance to the conscious thinker. Because of the assumption that religion acts to answer the important philosophical questions, which it clearly doesn't do, rationalists try to make religion irrelevant by relegating it to the epistemological back of the bus. That misses the point of religion whose purpose is not to answer the metaphysical questions factually. Religion answers these questions metaphorically, embarking on a completely different arc than that dealt with by higher-order consciousness. Religion is its own cognitive complex which interacts with emotional systems and higher-order cognition to symbolize and manifest unconscious operations in consciousness. Religion and ritual permit people to release themselves from consciousness and offload the challenges of living from the thinking mind. To make religion subservient to consciousness sets the discussion on the wrong track before it gets started.

The unconscious is the label we put on all the processes and systems working away beneath our awareness that keep us alive and vital. However, in the minds of many the label *unconscious* connotes something lesser or inferior. Because of the blazing beam of consciousness, we think that accessing our unconscious through therapy, religion, or other techniques is a top-down movement from will and awareness to reveal the hidden unconscious below, yet the science says the unconscious is far more than 95% of what and who we are behaviorally. We only think we know what's happening when we register an event with consciousness. Without signing the consciousness log book, we are mostly unaware an event never took place. We are held hostage by the maniacal ego of consciousness, which like the naked monarch in the *Emperor's New Clothes*, tells us that it wears the royal ermine. We're told we must bow down, but in fact, it's all a ruse. In reality our lives are bottom-up. We are possessed by our biology for good or for ill. Humans have the same desires as other animals for food, safe environment, mates, and defense, but these desires are rendered through the filter of conscious biases and beliefs. Consciousness retains its illusion of power as a homunculus trying to manipulate the puppet strings, but in the last analysis is only marginally capable. Consciousness may help make incremental improvements that ease the problems of survival, but survival is primarily engineered by emotions and homeostasis. We animals, we human animals, live from our biology, which behaviorally dwells in our emotional unconscious.

Most people are immersed in an anthropocentric view of humanity as the conceptual and cosmological center of the universe. This is not a condemnation of humanity as all animals are encoded to act in their own self interest, which makes each organism the center of its own universe. But when conscious self-awareness is added to the mix, it becomes a relentless impulse. Our self-perception of free will leads to the leap of faith that our awesome cognition, the central executive, is in charge. It wants to be the center of attention, an unreserved and undeserved egomaniac. Just as people have beliefs about religion, they also have beliefs in the potency and viability of their own consciousness except they treat this as fact rather than belief. The influence of consciousness is assertive to the point that people believe in its (their) ability and want to protect it from derision and criticism. It defends itself against anything that attempts to undermine it. Consciousness is a devilish beast that tricks its animal owner into believing that consciousness itself is the master and directing the movie. It's hard to believe otherwise as our consciousness continually reaffirms this most basic assertion.

It's true we have advanced culture, and consciousness does impact our lives in important ways, but we nevertheless dupe ourselves into believing in our own enlightened prowess, that we retain authority over our lives and make rational choices. It isn't until the mid-20th century that the technology matures enough to uncouple our conscious thoughts from the actual underlying neurophysiological processes. When modern scientific techniques use disinterested machines to separate our conscious ability to think and analyze from our unconscious internal processes, it becomes apparent that consciousness is a belated and deficient player. A tide of research tells us that we aren't as in command as we think, and various unconscious physiological mechanisms have much more to do with who we are than we realize. It's time to call out the king of consciousness and put him in his place or at least acknowledge his rightful place beneath our inherent nature. It can be no other way, else we oppose ourselves and our lives become conflicted and impotent. The real *brains* of the operation are the emotions under the direction of the nervous and endocrine systems and produced by the genes. In this scenario our consciousness is more like the projectionist in a movie theater watching the movie go by, and occasionally we can stop the projector, edit in a snippet, and set it rolling again. The best we can do is insert a segment every now and then, but most of the time the movie is rushing on unbidden.

## Wanting Better Answers

It is common for someone to write a book bemoaning this or that aspect of the human condition, sometimes even a biological aspect. In the end, the author arrives at an optimistic solution for the welfare of the human species facilitated by our higher intelligence. In his book *On Aggression*, Konrad Lorenz (1967), one of the founders of ethology—the study of animal behavior—acknowledges several inborn reasons why humans fight and war with each other, yet he can't relinquish his hope that we have a way out of our self-destruction. "The need to control, by wise rational responsibility, all our emotional allegiances to cultural values is as great as, if not greater than, the necessity to keep in check our other instincts." (p. 265) His intent is noble, but I make no such apologies. This book about consciousness and religion changes nothing nor even suggests changes to humanity's tragic, exalted position. If this exposition reveals different or new perspectives, they are only explanatory and invoke no recommendations. I only try to accurately describe humanity's situation. Our inherent nature is the result of millions of years of evolution—the final arbiter of all life including humans.

The fact that our conscious, rational mind has limits doesn't nor shouldn't nor can't impede thinking. Whatever mental manipulations humans entertain, they will continue to entertain. Whether religious or not, people still feel the urge to engage the emotions that ensure well-being. The devout persist in celebrating spirituality, but now have a justification in the face of criticism for being intrinsically religious. For believers and non-believers alike, rightly condemn the political obstruction and hypocrisy of the religious institutions, but at least personal feelings of faith are inviolable. People continue to enjoy music, dance, and mythology as they always have. All this book does is deal with how and why, but completely abdicates on *should*. Religion has existed for tens of thousands of years, and despite the growth of agnosticism and atheism, the religious behaviors are universal and remain so. It can be no other way. People are essentially the same creatures that they were 10,000 years ago or two million years ago. People will always be both altruistic and selfish. We can neither override our innate aggression nor are we evolving into a new age of consciousness — at least nothing of significance in the near term. Genetic-based evolution takes thousands of generations to effect significant changes, and in any case, given the historical circumstances of constant, multifarious human warfare, there's no indication that natural selection is working against aggressive individuals or societies.

Evolution works its wonders (so far mostly) beyond human manipulations and regardless of mental intention — kind of like God. We are susceptible to Nature's whims, which can certainly be capricious, but it is beyond the pale of anything we know scientifically that we can change human nature, and I certainly don't advocate it. If unconscious homeostatic mechanisms are the primary drivers of survival and only marginally accessible to consciousness, the solutions to human predicaments will not be palpable. Externally attending to the unconscious — trying to modify the content residing below one's awareness — requires massive resources, if it can be done at all. It demands active practice and intervention to intentionally bring the unconscious and consciousness together and can't simply be turned on and off. The various psychological therapies, analytical being the first, along with music, art, dance, and others, are available to help integrate the conscious and unconscious. These therapies are the modern replacements in secular society of religious ritual. The styles have changed, but the function remains the same. Therapies rely on ritual behaviors that evolved explicitly for the purpose of subsuming higher-order consciousness.

For those who want a more definitive or hopeful scientific solution, the answer is evolution and natural selection will sort it out. Short of our complete annihilation from nuclear war and nuclear winter, we of the human race will endure the consequences of drastic climate change and race to overpopulation. This will mean a very long drawn out struggle for scarcer resources as regions of the world become uninhabitable due to rising oceans, expanding deserts, famine, and water shortages, to name a few obvious repercussions. These forces, along with the usual avarice of kings, dictators, and presidents (and now CEOs), will continue to result in regional and international conflicts as people fight to protect their wealth and territories just as they have done for millennia. These changes won't extinguish Homo sapiens in the short term. The bottom line is that death is the tool of natural selection, which doesn't care if men kill each other, or floods, famine, and disease do it. Religion and ritual will be there to help, console, encourage, and rationalize with or without consciousness.

There are those who say that humans are innately good and not evil, but these are arguments based on cultural and political beliefs. Belief is an endemic human characteristic and is based on emotions and cognitive biases, not logic or rationality. If you want to promulgate the worthy ideals of fraternity, equality, and liberty, you must address it with the understanding that you're swimming against forces that are easily manipulated. You can teach people to resist their inclinations, but realize that the least tug on the emotional triggers—hatred, terror, and mistrust—can send you back to square one in an instant. Playing on fear and demonizing the enemy rallies the masses every time regardless of education, technological achievements, or region. "My country is the best, and my culture's customs are superior." Beliefs, bound to xenophobia and patriotism, have deep biological, emotional roots. It will always be an uphill battle to overcome the instinctual predispositions.

## More Questions Raised Than Answered

For thousands of years philosophers pontificated on the human condition, and 150 years ago Darwin rewrote the paradigm by delineating evolution by natural selection. It's now time to plant a unifying garden to nurture an ecology for religion, ritual, and evolutionary biology. Until now there hasn't been an adequate biologically-based synthesis of religious behavior within the purview of evolution. The reason The Split Hypothesis of religion has traction is that it is primarily based on biological principles, along with a smattering of Jungian psychology. It addresses and marries the religious and ritual behaviors that have previously caused some authors to refer to them as enigmas or paradoxes within the evolutionary framework of natural selection, adaptation, and fitness. Because The Split Hypothesis of religion is new, no science has addressed it with direct research. The hypothesis is a proposition that is supported by a great deal of indirect evidence acquired from biology, psychology and anthropology for other purposes. When scientists take brain scans of praying nuns or meditators, they show that religious practices have measurable effects on the brain. Besides prayer, scientists are just beginning to measure brain changes during music and dance. These first baby steps raise more questions than they solve. Direct substantiation for The Split Hypothesis will be spotty until scientists design experiments that specifically ask the questions to confirm or reject. Questions to be pursued are:

- What are the effects of various religious behaviors on the emotions? Are there consistent correlations between religious behaviors and affective physiological processes? Do specific rituals elicit consistent and identifiable emotions or are the elicited emotions varied and inconsistent?
- Is the unconscious just a lofty appellation for the emotional homeostatic engine or does it exist as its own entity in some fashion? Does the unconscious closely interact with emotions or is it essentially the same entity and indistinguishable? From the brain's point of view what is the unconscious, really?

- Are there biological correlates of religion in the brain? Are innate archetypes the wellspring of mythological religion? How does religious belief affect internal physiology? How does religion alter the brain and psychological well-being?
- The recalcitrant problem of consciousness remains to be solved. I believe the function of consciousness will become clearer as its role in human affairs is deemphasized. What is the relationship between religion and consciousness? What does it mean to inhibit or suppress higher-order consciousness? In what ways do religious rituals impinge on or swamp higher-order consciousness? Does religious belief alter human cognitive capacity or capabilities? Does being a more rational, thinking person alter one's religious affinities and ritual behavior?
- How do the various ritual behaviors—minimally music, myth-telling, dance and other ritual movement, prayer, and art—integrate with and elaborate the religious experience? What are the physiological and psychological correlates to religion of listening to or playing music, dancing or watching dance, creating or viewing art? Does athletic activity produce the same effects on consciousness and physiology as some religious ritual activities?
- Evidence indicates that people who practice religion are psychologically better adjusted and are healthier than non-religious people. If so, why is that? Can non-religious people enjoy the benefits garnered by religious belief without having religious belief through secular ritual practice? Is the interaction between consciousness and belief or placebo involved in this difference? Can people survive and thrive without religion and ritual?

# Secular religion

Human religious behaviors have existed for at least fifty thousand years and resided in societies that breathed the sacred in every aspect. In the skeptical dance between human culture and biology, the last few hundred years have proven to be momentous. Today large segments of the population have abandoned their traditional religious heritage. In its place are a smattering of adjustments and compensations: science, excessive acquisition of wealth, secular rituals, neurosis, drug addiction, and depression. None of these are new, but it feels like they have become more prevalent in the new world order. In the chapter on music I discussed that adolescents frequently lack rites of passage to move them into the role of adulthood in modern society. The immense popularity of music provides a moderate but incomplete ceremonial experience, where youth gravitate towards the ritual stages of separation and transition. They embrace psychic symbols of transcendence and death, but lack effective and meaningful resurrection, ritual completion, and incorporation into society. The loss of spiritual meaning is not confined to teenagers. Jung (1933) called the dearth of ritual "the spiritual problem of modern man." (p. 226)

If anything illustrates the dangers of losing the divine, it is the psychological destruction of aboriginal societies when they come into contact with modern civilizations. Indigenous cultures suffer immense upheaval and collapse when their traditional way of life is taken from them. Native populations everywhere continue to cope with social malaises of violence, alcoholism, disruption of the family unit, suicide, and poverty, the rates of which are higher than the rest of the populations. Movements to preserve historical native cultures are on the rise, but they continue to struggle with the loss of cultural traditions as well as ongoing disenfranchisement and contradictory government policies. The loss of religious structure is not the only reason for their hardships, but it is certainly a critical part of it.

Beyond the special situation of indigenous peoples is evidence of a general cultural shift. In the United States half of all marriages end in divorce; a third of households are single-parent; both spouses work in almost two-thirds of two-parent households. This is what some deplore as the moral decay that cries out for remedy. Return to the way it used to be, they bemoan. In the "idyllic" 1950s, the good old days of growth and prosperity, these rates were thought to be much lower. At the same time racial persecution was sanctioned. No one talked about child or spousal abuse or molestation. Homosexuals were, if not invisible, then victimized.

And of course there are those who, even in constitutional democracies that encourage separation of church and state, feel that their own one right and true religion should become the country's official religion, and all citizens should adopt it. All these social issues challenge that delicate balance between what we imagine a good life should be and acknowledging historical inequities and exploitation. Just as we can't return in reality to *in illo tempore* as a fact, the beginning of human time, we can't and shouldn't return to a life imagined as an old-fashioned family sitcom, which hides a plethora of injustice. There are no easy answers, and imposing moralistic solutions based on any single religion is not the way forward. We live in a pluralistic society and so it must remain.

Yet in our secular society, the sacred aspect of religion is missing. Some institutions such as the Catholic Church lament the cultural slide into moral oblivion as ritual practices have fallen by the wayside. The Church deplores moral relativism, for instance, in which each individual is theoretically free to create her own ethical compass. Let's ignore for the moment the hypocrisy and turpitude that most major religions purvey and just focus on the virtuous ideals. Righteousness has been rewritten from the holy tomes into the laws of civil society, but without the priest, imam, or rabbi, there is only the president, prime minister, or despot to represent the moral leadership that was once owned by the clergy as spokesmen for the gods. But even without a spiritual aspect, people still act in religious ways, transferring their unconscious feelings to powerful rulers, cinematic heroes, rock stars, or otherworldly forces as a means to incarnate their internal processes into consciousness. The mortals in leadership or starring roles who receive and assume that responsibility are always fallible, which results in disappointing and inadequate moral assignment. The gods, for all their randy escapades and foibles, are above reproach. Transference, the ability to endow external things with our own feelings, is wired into us as a consequence of and compensation for our acquisition of consciousness and inability to accurately assign causation, so only the deities can safely bank our spiritual currency.

Joseph Campbell (1990) was concerned that modern religions were bereft of true sacredness. The efforts of many denominations to promulgate literal interpretations of scriptures robbed them of their hallowed, metaphorical meaning. Referring to Bastion's elementary ideas, precursors to Jung's archetypes, Campbell wrote,

> Poetry and art, whether "academic" or "moderate," are simply dead unless informed by elementary ideas: ideas, not as clear abstractions held in the mind, but as cognized, or rather re-cognized, vital factors of the subject's own being. Though it is true that such living ideas become manifest only in the terms and style of some specific historical moment, the force nevertheless lies not in what meets the eye but in what dilates the heart, and this force, precisely, is the essential trait. Hence, since mythology is a compendium of such ideas, the historian or anthropologist keeping only his objective eye is gelded of the organ that would have made it possible for him to distinguish his materials. He may note and classify circumstances, but can no more speak authoritatively of mythology than a man without taste buds of taste. (p. 48)

Campbell omits mention of religion, but the point applies just the same. The significance and impact of intrinsic religion is felt, not thought, and feeling the sacred aspect is what is lacking in our secularist society. That doesn't mean, however, that deeply religious people, who perceive their divinities as external entities, are immune from this disconnect from the sacred. Some very spiritual people realize that it isn't the outward deities that matter. In *A History of God*, Karen Armstrong (1993) describes Sufi mystics who realize,

> God was discovered to be mysteriously identified with the inmost self. The systematic destruction of the ego

led to a sense of absorption in a larger ineffable reality...God was not a separate, external reality and judge but somehow one with the ground of each person's being. (pp. 226-7)

Religion emanates from the personal sense of the sacred; it is an integral human trait. Externalizing religion can prevent a person from owning the sacred in its intrinsic essence.

Spirituality and intrinsic religion are innate and therefore must be expressed. The implication then is that the loss of the sacred aspect in society is detrimental to one's psychic and physical health, which raises uncomfortable questions. Humans are predisposed to practice religious behaviors in many different ways, but for those of us who lack faith, are stuck in uncertainty, or are suspicious of organized religion, how are we to honor our inner religious nature? Are we to revert from our science-based, logical moorings and join a religious institution or new-age cult just to have access to the numinous? If religion is innate, must we honor it at all costs? Can I just give up my way of life, my way of thinking about the world and force myself to believe in spiritual intangibles?

Faith has to live in the heart in order to touch the divine core. Deciding to believe does nothing. The challenge of modern faith for the disbeliever is the necessity to temporarily abandon consciousness in order to feel the transcendent without the spirit seeker becoming vulnerable to those who would prey on or manipulate sincere belief for their own aggrandizement. This is not a trivial problem, and pervades every religion and every culture. (I'm not sure about Buddhists.) Rare is the leader who doesn't use his exalted position of political or holy office to gain preferential access to wealth, sex, and power, which always comes at a cost to the devout minions. In the spiritual quest an important goal for the skeptic is to identify creeds that are leader-light as opposed to leader-heavy, while still providing the environment where consciousness can be set aside temporarily. It's an almost impossible situation.

And yet, there may a way out of this dilemma. The Split Hypothesis offers a new definition of intrinsic, personal religion: the spectrum of ritual behaviors that suppress higher-order consciousness and elicit emotions. Music, dance, art, mythology, and prayer are common ritual behaviors of religion that continue to be widely practiced. Being the amazing and adaptable creatures that we are, we have forged ahead with modified rituals that, without realizing it, tap our emotions similarly, if not identically, as they did when we lived in tribes. The new sacraments are only modernized, profane versions of what were once the sanctified customs. Where once the religious behaviors were the common heritage of a tribe, today they are delivered to us, often for a nominal price. Music, perhaps the most popular and pervasive modern evidence of secularized ritual behavior, is owned as property and sold to the consumer. Buy an LP, a cassette tape, a CD, or download a song. Our relationship to music has changed, but we still sway or tap our feet to the rhythm and revere the musicians, who are sometimes deified. They move us emotionally, personally. We feel the music, but we have no larger religious context for it.

The same immanent association happens in our modern mythologies. Originally passed verbally from elders, the tales have transformed into literature, films, and TV. Like pop musicians, film and TV stars are idolized, not because of who they are as real people, but because of who they represent—the heroes and villains in the universal myths. The stories they tell or the songs they perform come alive, touch us and profoundly inspire us in a deep-seated, unconscious way, and we can't help but transfer our feelings back to the deliverer just as we do with the spirits, ancestors, and gods. However, every few minutes you must endure advertising, the creators of which spend millions of dollars determining what will entice you to buy their products—a devil's bargain to feed the desire for myth. Otherwise you may spend twenty dollars or hundreds to see your favorite musician in concert or a quality theater production. This is radically different from the tribal rituals in which every person was expected to play a role in the rites simply by belonging. All the people participated or at least attended and observed when it was prescribed to do so, and the shaman was just another member of the tribe just like a doctor or priest is today. And yet, regardless of the commercialization of mythologies, we rapaciously consume them, bolstering our innate desire to exercise our empathic emotions.

Many modern movements have sprung up to fulfill the spiritual hole. Most are rejuvenations of existing religions: Christian fundamentalism, Neopaganism, the Western adoption of Eastern traditions like Buddhism and Hinduism. Cults derive from all these religious philosophies and have reaped followers looking for some kind of sacred message or psychic fulfillment. Countless self-help books and related media offer panaceas for contemporary angst. Many people have found yoga or meditation to be an effective practice for exercising conscious-less spirituality.

The Split Hypothesis offers a new definition of intrinsic, personal religion. Religion is the spectrum of ritual behaviors that suppress higher-order consciousness and elicit emotions. Art, music, and dance therapies are beneficial, ritually-based substitutes for faith and borrow credible components of intrinsic religious behaviors. These modern incarnations of religious rituals are a step towards preserving the human requirement for sacred space, but they may falter as a complete three-step ritual process. Employing rituals to feed the need for the sacred bears further exploration but the full complement of a rite—separation, transition (liminality), and incorporation—may be the most difficult aspect to achieve to recreate the modern, non-institutional religious experience.

Is there a detrimental consequence for ignoring ritual participation? Some people seem to do fine with minimal ritual practice, but others feel an emptiness and suffer because they are unable to find spiritual satisfaction, whatever that may be for them. They search for meaning to fulfill that need, but choosing requires faith and heart, not so much conscious consideration.

Like all aspects of human nature, there is no black and white, only gradients of grays. The time we spend in the sacred waters is precious, and meanwhile, we must maintain a conscious circumspection in between holy periods. Consciousness has its place, and we must use it to watch out for hacks and hucksters. Does the religious hierarchy seem unreasonably concerned about getting your money? How much tithing is enough for the service of providing the sacred space? Is access to the transcendent dependent on how much you pay? Does the hierarchy demand strict obedience? Do they ask you to believe in things that have nothing to do with the divine? The spiritual mentors should focus on the inward journey and ask little towards outward action. However we manage to find that balance, we attend to the inner, innate voice of the divine one way or another.

## Future of religion and human evolution

Because humans fell from grace by having acquired higher-order consciousness, we have knowledge of polarities: good and evil, love and hate, I and thou. The world presents too many choices, and we have little conscious ability to differentiate among them. We easily become overwhelmed, quickly reverting to safe, reliable cognitive biases. We are aware of ourselves as individual entities separate from the other, so we feel that we own our own feelings and thoughts and, because we have a theory of mind, project them onto others as well. Every animal wants to avoid dying, but, except for the human animal, doesn't *know* it is going to die. Besides humans, no animal asks why it exists or where it came from. We can only do that because we have consciousness (and language), which curses us with these questions and terrors. Yes, religion helps us face our fear of death and explains mythologically how the world came to be and our part in it, but that is secondary. Our fears and anxieties reveal themselves as intrusive thoughts that arise because consciousness enables us to think, remember, and consider our predicament. It also gives us the illusion that we are more powerful and cognizant than we really are. Religion acts to elicit emotions while also suppressing consciousness. Yet consciousness gives us fabulous culture, the ability to modify our surroundings in our lifetime and pass this knowledge to our progeny, which has led to incredible technologies as well as the ability to eradicate our own species from the planet—human auto-extinction. From evolution's point of view, it's just another notch on evolution's belt like dinosaurs and trilobites. "Chalk up that experiment and back to the drawing board." Yes, we have the might to destroy ourselves, but what is the take-home for consciousness in our own destruction? Consciousness is ultimately more of a problem than a solution.

Despite the conscious desires of many who want to eliminate violence and promote cooperation and even love, humans continue to behave as they always have. The majority of the time they hunt, gather, farm, and otherwise work to ensure their survival and the survival of their offspring. They engage in internecine warfare, often at a great cost. However, the rewards for the winners are usually enough to justify the losses in manpower and wealth. Murder, once thought to be the sole proprietorship of humans, is now known to be unexceptional among many animal species. The evolutionary benefits are uncomfortably obvious—the survivor faces less competition from conspecifics and is likelier to thrive. Despite civilized objections to the barbarity of war, sadly it remains a popular and commonplace occurrence, regardless of the sophistication of the society or form of government. Consciousness has ultimately led to more complex weapons systems. The more technologically advanced a society is, the more effective and deadly its war machine. The combination of our innate aggression and our consciousness-enabled machinations puts us in a very tenuous situation.

Religion, the effort to rein in consciousness and put the organism in touch with emotions, works its magic regardless of cultural or technological changes. Religion is part of the human genetic makeup, and, despite the knowledge and advancements wrought by modern civilization, continues to exert itself. For those who want the happy ending, you will not find it here, but neither is this a tragedy. Simply, it is an observation of the human animal and its fallen condition *in illo tempore*, at the beginning and realization of human time.

The hominid lineage that includes modern humans is in the midst of a multi-million year period of rapid evolution, hence the wide variety of morphologies (body characteristics and races) and cognitive variations including disorders like dyslexia, and others that are deemed mental illnesses. The human brain is a marvelous experiment in which various brain modules and interconnections developed to try out new cognitive strategies, but evolution is a series of compromises. Some of these brain changes precipitate autism, schizophrenia, bipolar disorder, or OCD in which emotional regulation or theory of mind are weakened or dysfunctional. Yes, the ruthless hand of evolution throws the dice, slapdash, which leaves a rather robust set of anomalies at the edges of the bell curve. So, too, does it take measure of the ongoing concessions between consciousness and religion.

The impervious forces of natural selection cooked up a remarkable animal several million years ago in East Africa. Trodding the same steps as Habilis, Erectus, Neanderthal, and others yet to be discovered, we moderns arrived to dominate the earth. Evolution, the blind watchmaker, gave us our genetic heritage which girds us based on the accumulated adaptations of these predecessors. Neither the adaptations of higher-order consciousness that enabled our fabulous creation of culture and modified our planet's environment, nor religion are our demise or our salvation. Blessed by our ability to reflect on our own existence, we remain a fascinating study, and the universe spins on regardless.

# BIBLIOGRAPHY

**American Dance Therapy Association,** Healing through movement. Accessed 2012, November 13.
Retrieved from http://www.adta.org

**Abramov,** Israel, et al. (2012a). Sex and vision I: Spatio-temporal resolution. *Biology of Sex Differences, 3*(20). doi:10.1186/2042-6410-3-20

**Abramov,** Israel, et al. (2012b). Sex and vision II: Color appearance of monochromatic lights. *Biology of Sex Differences, 3*(21). doi:10.1186/2042-6410-3-21

**Ader,** Robert. (2003). Conditioned immunomodulation: Research needs and directions. *Brain, Behavior, and Immunity, 17,* S51–S57.

**Alpert,** P. T., et al. (2009). The effect of modified jazz dance on balance, cognition, and mood in older adults. *Journal of the American Academy of Nurse Practitioners, 21*(2), 108–115.

**Ariely,** Dan. (2008). *Predictably irrational: The hidden forces that shape our decisions.* New York: HarperCollins.

**Armstrong,** Karen. (1993). *The history of god.* New York: Ballantine Books.

**Atran,** Scott and Norenzayan, Ara. (2004). Religion's evolutionary landscape: Counterintuition, commitment, compassion, communion. *Behavioral and Brain Sciences, 27,* 713–770.

**Bachner-Melman,** Rachel, et al. (2005). AVPR1a and SLC6A4 gene polymorphisms are associated with creative dance performance. *PLoS Genetics, 1*(3), e42.

**Bargh,** J. A. (2006). What have we been priming all these years? On the development, mechanisms, and ecology of nonconscious social behavior. *European Journal of Social Psychology, 36,* 147–168.

**Bargh,** J A. and Chartrand, T. L. (1999). The unbearable automaticity of being. *American Psychologist, 54*(7), 462–479.

**Bargh,** J. A., Chen, M., and Burrows, L. (1996). Automaticity of social behavior: Direct effects of trait construct and stereotype activation on action. *Journal of Personality and Social Psychology, 71*(2), 230–244.

**Barrett,** Justin L. and Keil, Frank C. (1996). Conceptualizing a non-natural entity: Anthropomorphism in god concepts. *Cognitive Psychology, 31*(17), 219–247.

**Baumeister,** Roy F. and Masicampo, E. J. (2010). Conscious thought is for facilitating social and cultural interactions: How mental simulations serve the animal-culture interface. *Psychological Review, 117*(3), 945–971.

**Benedetti,** Fabrizio, et al. (2005). Neurobiological mechanisms of the placebo effect. *Journal Of Neuroscience, 25*(45), 10390–10402.

**Bernardi,** Luciano, et al. (2001). Effect of rosary prayer and yoga mantras on autonomic cardiovascular rhythms: Comparative study. *British Medical Journal, 323,* 1446–1449.

**Berrol,** Cynthia F., et al. (1997). Dance/movement therapy with older adults who have sustained neurological insult: A demonstration project. *American Journal Of Dance Therapy, 19*(2), 135–160.

**Block,** Ned. (1995). On a confusion about a function of consciousness. *The Behavioral and Brain Sciences, 18*(2), 227–287.

**Blood,** Anne J. and Zatorre, Robert J. (2001). Intensely pleasurable responses to music correlate with activity in brain regions implicated in reward and emotion. *PNAS, 98*(20), 11818–11823.

**Blood,** Anne J., et al. (1999). Emotional responses to pleasant and Unpleasant Music Correlate with Activity in Paralimbic Brain Regions. *Nature Neuroscience, 2*(4), 382–387.

**Boecker,** Henning, et al. (2008). The runner's high: Opioidergic mechanisms in the human brain. *Cerebral Cortex, 18*(11), 2523–2531.

**Bourguignon,** Erika. (1973). *Religion, altered states of consciousness, and social change.* Ohio State University Press.

**Boyer,** Pascal. (2004). Why is religion natural? *Skeptical Inquirer, 28*(2), 25–31.

**Boyer,** Pascal and Liénard, Pierre. (2006). Why ritualized behavior? Precaution systems and action parsing in development, pathological and cultural rituals. *Behavioral and Brain Sciences, 29,* 595–650.

**Bradt,** J. and Dileo, C. (2009). Music for stress and anxiety reduction in coronary heart disease patients. *Cochrane Database Syst Rev,*(2). doi:10.1002/14651858.CD006577.pub2

**Brasil-Neto,** Joaquim P., et al. (1992). Focal transcranial magnetic stimulation and response bias in a forced-choice task. *Journal Of Neurology, Neurosurgery, and Psychiatry, 55,* 964–966.

**Breeden,** Robert L., Ed. (1973). *Primitive worlds: People lost in time.* National Geographic Society.

**Brown,** Steve, Götell, Eva, and Ekman, Sirkka-Liisa. (2001). 'Music-therapeutic caregiving': The necessity of active music-making in clinical care. *Arts In Psychotherapy, 28,* 125–135.

**Brown,** Steven. (2003). Biomusicology, and three biological paradoxes about music. *Bulletin Of Psychology and The Arts, 4,* 15-17. Accessed 2012, September 07.

http://www.loc.gov/podcasts/musicandthebrain/
podcast_stevebrown.html

**Brown,** Steven. (2008, July). The neuroscience of dance. *Scientific American.* 78–83.

**Burton,** Robert A. (2008). *On being certain: Believing you are right even when you're not.* St. Martin's Press.

**Buss,** David M., et al. (1998). Adaptations, exaptations, and spandrels. *American Psychologist, 53*(5), 533–548.

**Cabanac,** Michel and Bonniot-Cabanac, Marie-Claude. (2007). Decision making: Rational or hedonic? *Behavioral and Brain Functions, 3*(45). doi:10.1186/1744-9081-3-45

**Call,** J. and Tomasello, M. (1998). Distinguishing intentional from accidental actions in orangutans (Pongo pygmaeus), chimpanzees (Pan troglodytes), and human children (Homo sapiens). *Journal of Comparative Psychology, 112*(2), 192–206.

**Campbell,** Virginia. (2008). Brain Science Podcast. Accessed 2011, July 13. http://docartemis.com/Transcripts/49-brainscience-Milner.pdf

**Campbell,** Joseph. (1973). *Hero with a thousand faces.* Princeton University Press.

**Campbell,** Joseph. (1988). *Myths to live by.* Bantam Book.

**Campbell,** Joseph. (1990). *The flight of the wild gander.* HarperPerennial.

**Campbell,** Joseph. (2001). *Thou art that.* New World Library.

**Carroll,** Joseph. (2008). An evolutionary paradigm for literary study. *Style, 42*(2 & 3), 103–135.

**Cohen,** Gillian and Shamus, Eric. (2009). Depressed, low self-esteem: What can exercise do for you? *Internet Journal Of Allied Health Sciences and Practice, 7*(2). doi:10.1155/2014/456483

**Cole,** Jonathan. (1995). *Pride and a daily marathon.* MIT Press.

**Coolidge,** Frederick L. and Wynn, Thomas. (2005). Working memory, its executive functions, and the emergence of modern thinking. *Cambridge Archaeological Journal, 15*(1), 5–26.

**Cosmides,** Leda and Tooby, John. (1997, January 13). *Evolutionary psychology: A primer.* Center for Evolutionary Psychology. University of California, Santa Barbara. January 13, 1997. Accessed 2012, November 14. Retrieved from http://www.cep.ucsb.edu/primer.html

**Cosmides,** Leda and Tooby, John. (2000a). Consider the source: The evolution of adaptations for decoupling and metarepresentations. In Dan Sperber, (Ed.), *Metarepresentations: A multidisciplinary approach* (pp. 53-115). Vancouver Studies in Cognitive Science. New York: Oxford University Press.

**Cosmides,** Leda and Tooby, John. (2000b). Evolutionary psychology and the emotions. In M. Lewis and J. M. Haviland-Jones (Eds.), *Handbook of Emotions, 2nd Edition* (pp. 91-115). New York: Guilford.

**Csikszentmihalyi,** Mihaly. (1975). Play and intrinsic rewards. *Journal Of Humanistic Psychology, 15*(3), 41–63.

**Dale,** J. A., Hyatt, J., and Hollerman, J. (2007). The neuroscience of dance and the dance of neuroscience: Defining a path of inquiry. *Journal Of Aesthetic Education, 41*(3), 89–110.

**Damasio,** Antonio. (1994). *Descartes' error: Emotion, reason and the human brain.* Quill-HarperCollins.

**Damasio,** Antonio. (2000). *The feeling of what happens: Body and emotion in the making of consciousness.* Harcourt Brace.

**Damasio,** Antonio. (2003). *Looking for Spinoza: Joy, sorrow, and the feeling brain.* Harcourt Inc.

**Dawkins,** Richard. (2006). *The god delusion.* New York: Houghton Mifflin.

**de la Fuente-Fernández,** Raúl, et al. (2001). Expectation and dopamine release: Mechanism of the placebo effect in parkinson's disease. *Science, 293*(5532), 1164–1166.

**Dennett,** Daniel. (2006). *Breaking the spell: Religion as a natural phenomena.* New York: Viking Penguin.

**Dissanayake,** Ellen. (1982). Aesthetic experience and human evolution. *Journal Of Aesthetics and Art Criticism, 41*(2), 145–155.

**Dissanayake,** Ellen. (2000). *Art and intimacy: How the arts began.* University Of Washington Press.

**Dissanayake,** Ellen. (2003). Retrospective on homo aestheticus. *Journal Of The Canadian Association For Curriculum Studies, 1*(2), 7–11. Accessed 2013, March 26. Retrieved from http://pi.library.yorku.ca/ojs/index.php/jcacs/article/viewFile/16855/15661

**Dissanayake,** Ellen. (2006). Ritual and ritualization: Musical means of conveying and shaping emotion in humans and other animals. In Steven Brown and Ulrich Voglsten (Eds.), *Music and manipulation: On the social uses and social control of music* (pp. 31-56). New York: Berghahn Books.

**Dissanayake,** Ellen. (2008a). If music is the food of love, what about survival and reproductive success? *Musicae Scientiae, 12*(1) 169–195. doi:10.1177/1029864908012001081

**Dissanayake,** Ellen. (2008b). The arts after Darwin: Does art have an origin and adaptive function? In Zijlmans, K. and Van Damme, W. (Eds.), *World art studies: Exploring concepts and approaches* (pp. 241–263). Amsterdam: Valiz.

**Dissanayake,** Ellen. (2011, August 16). What is the (adaptive) value of art? *Blog of the National Endowment for the Arts.* Accessed 2013, April 03. Retrieved from http://arts.gov/artworks/2011/what-adaptive-value-art

**Dosamantes-Beaudry,** Irma. (1998). Regression-reintegration: Central psychodynamic principle in rituals of transition. *Arts In Psychotherapy,* 25(2), 79–84.

**Durkheim,** Émile (1994). The elementary forms of the religious life: The totemic system in Australia. In W. S. F. Pickering (Ed.), *Durkheim on religion.* (pp. 102–166) Scholars Press.

**Dutton,** Denis. (2009). *The Art Instinct.* New York: Bloomsbury Press.

**Earhart,** Gammon. (2009). Dance as therapy for individuals with Parkinson disease. *European Journal Of Physical and Rehabilitation Medicine,* 45(2), 231–238.

**Eccles,** John and Robinson, Daniel. (1985). *Wonder of being human.* New Science Library.

**Edelman,** Gerald. (2004). *Wider than the sky: The phenomenal gift of consciousness.* New Haven: Yale University Press.

**Ekman,** Paul. (2003). *Emotions revealed.* Holt.

**Eliade,** Mircea. (1975). *Myths, dreams, and mysteries.* New York: Harper Colophon Books.

**Eliade,** Mircea. (1964). *Shamanism: Archaic techniques of ecstasy.* Princeton University Press.

**Feierman,** Jay R. (2009). The evolutionary history of religious behavior. In Feierman, Jay R. (Ed.), *The biology of religious behavior: The evolutionary origins of faith and religion* (pp. 71-86). Santa Barbara: Praeger.

**Fetchenhauer,** Detlef. (2009). Evolutionary perspectives on religion — what they can and what they cannot explain (yet). In Eckart Voland and Wulf Schiefenhövel (Eds.), *The biological evolution of religious mind and behavior* (pp. 275–291). Series: The Frontiers Collection. Berlin: Springer.

**Fosha,** D., Siegel, D. J., and Solomon, M. F. (Eds.) (2009). *The healing power of emotion.* New York: W. W. Norton & Co.

**Francis,** L. J. and Evans, T. E. (1995). The psychology of Christian prayer: A review of empirical research. *Religion, 25,* 371–388.

**Fromm,** Erich. (1969). *Escape from freedom.* New York: Henry Holt & Co.

**Gazzaniga,** Michael S. (2000). Cerebral specialization and inter-hemispheric communication: Does the corpus callosum enable the human condition? *Brain, 123*(7), 1293–1326.

**Gazzaniga,** Michael S. (1998a). *The mind's past.* Berkeley: University of California Press.

**Gazzaniga,** Michael S. (1998b). The split brain revisited. *Scientific American, 279*(1), 50–55.

**Glausiusz,** Josie. (2003, October). Discover dialogue: Anthropologist Scott Atran. *Discover Magazine.* Accessed 2011, February 7. Retrieved from http://discovermagazine.com/2003/oct/featdialogue

**Goethals,** G. R. and Reckman, R. F. (1973). The perception of consistency in attitudes. *Journal Of Experimental Social Psychology, 9*(6), 491–501.

**Goleman,** Daniel. (1995). *Emotional intelligence.* Bantam.

**Guthrie,** Stewart, et al. (1980). A cognitive theory of religion. *Current Anthropology, 21*(2), 181–203.

**Hagendoorn,** Ivar. (2003). The dancing brain. *Cerebrum: The Dana Forum On Brain Science, 5*(2), 19–34.

**Hare,** Brian and Tomasello, Michael. (2005). Human-like social skills in dogs? *Trends In Cognitive Sciences, 99*(9), 439–444.

**Hsee,** C., Fang Y., Jiao Z., and Yao Z. (2003). Medium maximization. *Journal Of Consumer Research, 30.*

**Huxley,** Thomas Henry. (1894). *Method and results; essays.* London: Macmillan and Co.

**Iyengar,** Sheena and Lepper, Mark. (2000). When choice is demotivating: Can one desire too much of a good thing? *Journal of Personality and Social Psychology, 79*(6), 995–1006.

**Johnson,** David Read. (1998). On the therapeutic action of the creative arts therapies: The psychodynamic model. *Arts In Psychotherapy, 25*(2), 85–99.

**Johnson,** David Read. (1995). The therapeutic use of ritual and ceremony in the treatment of post-traumatic stress disorder. *Arts in Psychotherapy, 82*(2), 283–298.

**Jung,** Carl. (1933). *Modern man in search of a soul.* New York: Harcourt, Brace & Co.

**Jung,** Carl. (1964). *Man and his symbols.* J. G. Ferguson Publishing.

**Jung,** Carl. (1990). *The archetypes and the collective unconscious.* New York: Princeton/Bollingen.

**Juslin,** Patrik N. and Sloboda, John A. (2001). *Music and emotion: Theory and research.* Oxford University Press.

**Koenig,** Harold G., M.D. Religion, Spirituality and Public Health: Research, Applications, and Recommendations. Testimony by Harold G. Koenig, M.D., to Subcommittee on Research and Science Education of the U.S. House of Representatives on September 18, 2008. Accessed 17 April 2013. Retrieved from http://archives.democrats.science.house.gov/Media/File/ Commdocs/hearings/2008/Research/18sept/ Koenig_Testimony.pdf

**Kornfield,** Jack. (1993). *A path with heart.* Bantam Books.

**Krumhansl,** Carol. (2002). Music: A link between cognition and emotion. *Current Directions in Psychological Science, 11*(2), 45–50.

**Kuran,** Timur and Sunstein, Cass R. (1999). Availability cascades and risk regulation. *Stanford Law Review, 51*(4), 683–768.

**Lakoff,** George and Johnson, Mark. (1999). *Philosophy in the flesh.* Basic Books.

**Lamme,** Victor. (2003). Why visual attention and awareness are different. *Trends In Cognitive Sciences, 7*(1), 12–18.

**Ledoux,** Joseph. (1996). *Emotional brain: The mysterious underpinnings of emotional life.* Simon & Schuster.

**Lenhoff,** H. M., Wang, P. P., Greenberg, F., and Bellugi, U. (2006). Williams syndrome and the brain. *Scientific American, 31,* 11–15.

**Lewicki,** P., Hill T., and Bizot E. (1988). Acquisition of procedural knowledge about a pattern of stimuli that cannot be articulated. *Cognitive Psychology, 20,* 24–37.

**Liddon,** Sim C. (1989). *The dual brain, religion, and the unconscious.* Prometheus Books.

**Lorenz,** Konrad. (1967). *On aggression.* Bantam Books.

**Ludwig,** Arnold M. (1972). Altered states of consciousness. In Charles T. Tart, (Ed.), *Altered States Of Consciousness* (pp. 11–24). Doubleday Anchor.

**McGuffin,** P., Riley, B. P., and Plomin, R. (2001). Genomics and behavior: Toward behavioral genomics. *Science, 291*(5507), 1232–1233.

**Meadow,** Mary Jo and Kahn, Richard D. (1984). *Psychology of religion: Religion in individual lives.* Harper & Row.

**Miall,** David S. and Dissanayake, Ellen. (2003). The poetics of babytalk. *Human Nature, 14*(4), 337–364.

**Miller,** Joanne and Krosnick, Jon. (1998). The impact of candidate name order on election outcomes. *Public Opinion Quarterly, 62*(3), 291–330.

**Nainis,** Nancy, et al. (2006). Relieving symptoms in cancer: Innovative use of art therapy. *Journal of Pain and Symptom Management, 31*(2), 162–169.

**Needham,** Rodney. (1972). *Belief, language, and experience.* University Of Chicago Press.

**Newberg,** Andrew and Waldman, Mark. (2006). *Why we believe what we believe: Uncovering our biological need for meaning.* Free Press.

**Newberg,** Andrew, D'Aquili, Eugene, and Rause, Vince. (2002). *Why god won't go away: Brain science and the biology of belief.* New York: Random House.

**Nilsson,** Ulrica. (2004). Music and health: How to use music in surgical care. In Alan Dilani (Ed.), *Design & Health III - Health Promotion Through Environmental Design* (pp. 103–110). Stockholm: Design and Health. Accessed 2012, January 31. Retrieved from http://designandhealth.com/upl/files/113522

**Nisbett,** Richard E. and Wilson, Timothy D. (1977). Telling more than we can know: Verbal reports on mental processes. *Psychological Review, 84*(3), 231–259.

**Ornstein,** Robert. (1992). *Evolution of consciousness.* Simon & Schuster.

**Ornstein,** Robert. (1997). *The right mind: Making sense of the hemispheres.* Harcourt, Brace & Company.

**Oviedo,** Lluis. (2009). Is religious behavior "internally guided" by religious feelings and needs? In Jay R. Feierman (Ed.), *The Biology Of Religious Behavior: The Evolutionary Origins Of Faith and Religion* (pp. 141–156). Santa Barbara: Praeger

**Panksepp,** Jaak. (1995). The emotional sources of "chills" induced by music. *Music Perception, 13*(2), 171–207.

**Panksepp,** Jaak and Bernatzky, Günther (2002). Emotional sounds and the brain: The neuro-affective foundations of musical appreciation. *Behavioural Processes, 60,* 133–155.

**Panksepp,** Jaak and Panksepp, Jules. (2000). The seven sins of evolutionary psychology. *Evolution and Cognition, 6*(2), 108–131.

**Panksepp,** Jaak and Trevarthen, Colwyn (2008). The neuroscience of emotion in music. In S. Maloch and C. Trevarthen (Eds.), *Communicative Musicality: Exploring the Basis of Human Companionship* (pp. 105–146). Oxford University Press.

**Peretz,** Isabelle. (2001). Towards a neurobiology of musical emotions. In J. A. Sloboda and P. Juslin (Eds.), *Music and Emotion: Theory and Research* (pp. 99-126). Oxford: Oxford University Press.

**Pinker,** Steven. (2009). *How the mind works.* WW Norton & Company.

**Premack,** David and Woodruff, Guy. (1978). Does the chimpanzee have a theory of mind? *Behavioral and Brain Sciences, 1*(4), 515–526.

**Pulli,** K., et al. (2008). Genome-wide linkage scan for loci of musical aptitude in Finnish families: Evidence for a major locus at 4q22. *Journal Medical Genetics, 45*(7), 451–456. doi:10.1136/jmg.2007.056366

**Ramachandran,** V. S. (2004). *A brief tour of human consciousness.* New York: Pi Press.

**Ramachandran,** V. S. and Hirstein, W. (1999). The science of art. *Journal Of Consciousness Studies, 6*(67), 15–51.

**Rappaport,** Roy A. (1971). The sacred in human evolution. *Annual Review Of Ecology and Systematics, 2,* 23–44.

**Reeves,** Steve. (2010, January 7). Yoga helps vets find balance. *Official Home Page of the United States Army.* Accessed 2012, October 17. Retrieved from http://www.army.mil/article/32565/yoga-helps-vets-find-balance/

**Reiss,** Steven. (1980). Pavlovian conditioning and human fear: An expectancy model. *Behavior Therapy, 11*(3), 380–396.

**Rosenberg,** Karen R. and Trevathan, Wenda R. (2003). The evolution of human birth. *Scientific American, 13,* 80–85. doi:10.1038/scientificamerican0503-80sp

**Sandel,** S. L., et al. (2005). Dance and movement program improves quality-of-life measures in breast cancer survivors. *Cancer Nursing, 28*(4), 301–309.

**Saver,** J. and Rabin, J. (1997). The neural substrates of religious experience. *Journal Of Neuropsychiatry and Clinical Neurosciences, 9*(3), 498–510.

**Schiffer,** Fredric. (2000). Can the different cerebral hemispheres have distinct personalities? Evidence and its implications for theory and treatment of PTSD and other disorders. *Journal Of Trauma and Dissociation, 1*(2), 83–104.

**Schwartz,** Barry. (2000). Self-determination: The tyranny of freedom. *American Psychologist, 55*(1), 79–88.

**Seager,** William. (1999). *Theories of consciousness: An introduction and assessment.* Psychology Press.

**Severin,** Timothy. (1973). *Vanishing primitive man.* American Heritage Publishing Co.

**Silvia,** P. J. (2005). Emotional responses to art: From collation and arousal to cognition and emotion. *Review of General Psychology, 9*(4), 342–357. doi:10.1037/1089-2680.9.4.342

**Simons,** D. J. and Chabris, C. F. (1999). Gorillas in our midst: Sustained inattentional blindness for dynamic events. *Perception, 28*(9), 1059–1074.

**Sloan,** R.P., Bagiella, E., and Powell, T. (1999). Religion, spirituality, and medicine. *Lancet, 353*(9153), 664–667.

**Sosis,** Richard. (2009). The adaptationist-byproduct debate on the evolution of religion: Five misunderstandings of the adaptationist program. *Journal of Cognition and Culture, 9*(3), 315–332.

**Stevens,** Anthony. (1982). *Archetypes: A natural history of the self.* Quill.

**Stewart-Williams,** Steve and Podd, John. (2004). The placebo effect: Dissolving the expectancy versus conditioning debate. *Psychological Bulletin, 130*(2), 324–340.

**Suzuki,** D.T. (1994). *The training of the Zen Buddhist monk.* Charles E. Tuttle Co., Inc.

**Sylvan,** Robyn. (2002). *Traces of the spirit: The religious dimensions of popular music.* New York University Press.

**Sylvan,** Robyn. (2005). *Trance formation: The spiritual and religious dimensions of global rave culture.* Taylor & Francis Group, LLC.

**Teasdale,** Wayne. (2001). *The mystic heart: Discovering a universal spirituality in the world's religions.* Novato: New World Library.

**Thomason,** Timothy C. (2010). The role of altered states of consciousness in Native American healing. *Journal Of Rural Community Psychology, E13*(1), 1–19.

**Tooby,** John and Cosmides, Leda. (2001). Does beauty build adapted minds? Toward an evolutionary theory of aesthetics, fiction and the arts. *Substance: A Review Of Theory and Literary Criticism, 30*(1), 6–27.

**Trevarthen,** Colwyn. (2009). The functions of emotion in infancy: The regulation and communication of rhythm, sympathy, and meaning in human development. In D. Fosha, D. J. Siegel, and M. F. Solomon (Eds.), *The Healing Power Of Emotion* (pp. 55–85). New York: Norton & Co.

**Trigger,** Bruce G. (1987). *The children of Aataentsic: A history of the Huron people to 1660, volume 1.* Montreal: McGill-Queen's Press.

**Tversky,** Amos and Kahneman, Daniel. (1974). Judgment under uncertainty: Heuristics and biases. *Science, New Series, 185*(4157), 1124–1131.

**Tversky,** Amos and Kahneman, Daniel. (1981). The framing of decisions and the psychology of choice. *Science, New Series,* 211(4481), 453–458.

**Ukkola,** L. T., et al. (2009). Musical aptitude is associated with AVPR1A-haplotypes. *PLoS ONE, 4*(5), e5534. doi:10.1371/journal.pone.0005534

**Van Gennep,** Arnold. (1960). *Rites of passage.* University Of Chicago Press.

**Verghese,** Joe, et al. (2003). Leisure activities and the risk of dementia in the elderly. *New England Journal Of Medicine, 348,* 2508–2516. doi:10.1056/NEJMoa022252

**Wager,** Tor D. (2005a). The neural bases of placebo effects in anticipation and pain. *Seminars In Pain Medicine, 3,* 22–30.

**Wager,** Tor D. (2005b). The neural bases of placebo: Effects in pain. *Current Directions In Psychological Science, 14*(4), 175–179.

**Wager,** Tor D. (2007). Placebo effects on human μ-opioid activity during pain. *PNAS, 104*(26), 11056–11061.

**Wallace,** Anthony F. C. (1966). *Religion: An anthropological view.* Random House.

**Wegner,** Daniel. (2002). *The illusion of conscious will.* Cambridge: Bradford Books/MIT Press.

**Weisman,** Omri, et al. (2012). Oxytocin administration to parent enhances infant physiological and behavioral readiness for social engagement. *Biological Psychiatry, 72*(12), 982–989.

**Wilson,** E. O. (1998). *Consilience: The unity of knowledge.* New York: Alfred A. Knopf.

**Wilson,** Timothy D. (2002). *Strangers to ourselves: Discovering the adaptive unconscious.* Cambridge: Harvard University Press.

**Wilson,** Timothy and Kraft, Dolores. (1993). Why do I love thee? Effects of repeated introspections on attitudes towards relationships. *Personality and Social Psychology Bulletin, 19,* 409–418.

**Wise,** J. A. and Rosenberg, E. (1986). The effects of interior treatments on performance stress in three types of mental tasks. *Technical Report, Space Human Factors Office, NASA-ARC, Sunnyvale, CA.*

**Wyer,** R. S. Jr., (Ed.) (1997). *The automaticity of everyday life: Advances in social cognition.* Mahwah, NJ: Erlbaum.

# Index

CPSIA information can be obtained at www.ICGtesting.com
Printed in the USA
BVOW06s0946300116

434845BV00011B/208/P